Hallo liebe Leser,

es freut uns, dass ihr euch für das Kultliederbuch "DAS DING 2" entschieden habt.

Endlich ist unser Kultliederbuch "DAS DING 2" fertig. Wir danken allen, die dazu beigetragen haben. Besonders den kooperativen Musikverlagen und den vielen Freunden unserer Sammlung, die uns mit zahlreichen Zuschriften zu diesem zweiten Band motiviert haben. Schade, dass wir nicht von allen Liedern, die wir wollten, die Abdruckgenehmigungen bekommen haben. Vielleicht klappt das bei einem weiteren Band.

Schickt uns bitte weiterhin Wünsche und Kommentare an:

## www.kultliederbuch.de

Sollten euch Schreibfehler auffallen oder seid ihr mit den Akkorden oder den Texten nicht ganz einverstanden, dann besucht uns im Internet und teilt uns eure Verbesserungsvorschläge mit. Freuen würden wir uns auch über Lieder, die bisher in den Liederbüchern noch fehlen und eurer Meinung nach unbedingt hinein müssten.

Im Internet erfahrt ihr auch, wie ihr am schnellsten an ein eigenes "DING" kommt. Zusätzlich gibt es dort Neuigkeiten über alle Bände.

Die Texte und Melodien sind Eigentum der jeweiligen Verlage, Textdichter und Komponisten. Sie sind urheberrechtlich geschützt. Unerlaubtes Vervielfältigen ist verboten.
Ein herzliches Dankeschön geht an Fabian Ritter für die Gestaltung des Titelbildes.
Leider haben wir bei dieser verbesserten Neuauflage nicht alle Abdruckrechte erhalten und mussten einige wenige Titel ersetzen. Wir hoffen, dass viele Menschen mit der Musik und unserem Liederbuch Freude haben.

© 2005 by Edition DUX, Manching
D 77
ISMN 979-0-50017-028-0
ISBN 978-3-934958-77-7
A Bosworth production exclusively distributed by Edition DUX.
www.dux-verlag.de

Viel Spaß beim Singen wünschen euch

Andy Lutz                                                                                         Bernhard Bitzel

# INHALTSVERZEICHNIS

HIER FINDET IHR ALLE IN DIESEM BUCH ENTHALTENEN TITEL. ZUSÄTZLICH SIND NOCH BEKANNTE LIED- UND REFRAINANFÄNGE IN *KURSIVER SCHRIFT* VERZEICHNET.

```
A HARD DAY'S NIGHT ................................................... 232
A HARD RAIN'S GONNA FALL ............................................. 376
A KIND OF MAGIC ...................................................... 235
A LA LA LA LA LONG ................................................... 32
A SPACEMAN CAME TRAVELLING ........................................... 176
AB IN DEN SÜDEN ...................................................... 81
ACHY BREAKY HEART .................................................... 76
ADESSO TU ............................................................ 38
ADIEU, MEIN KLEINER GARDEOFFIZIER .................................... 181
AFRICA ............................................................... 14
AGAIN ................................................................ 323
AGAINST ALL ODDS ..................................................... 60
ALBATROS ............................................................. 248
ALINE ................................................................ 55
ALKOHOL .............................................................. 8
ALL I NEED IS THE RHYTHM DIVINE ...................................... 182
ALL I NEEDED WAS THE LOVE YOU GAVE ................................... 111
ALL MY LOVING ........................................................ 334
ALL OF MY LIFE WHERE HAVE YOU BEEN ................................... 323
ALL WE HEAR IS RADIO GA GA ........................................... 56
ALL YOU NEED IS LOVE ................................................. 204
ALLES WIRD SICH ÄNDERN ............................................... 101
ALONE ................................................................ 155
ALONG COMES MARY ..................................................... 349
ALWAYS LOOK ON THE BRIGHT SIDE OF LIFE ............................... 355
ALWAYS ON MY MIND .................................................... 244
AMADEUS .............................................................. 148
AMAZING GRACE ........................................................ 282
AN DER NORDSEEKÜSTE .................................................. 230
AN ENGLISHMAN IN NEW YORK ............................................ 274
AND THE OPERATOR SAYS „40 CENTS MORE ................................. 210
AND THE WIND CRIES MARY .............................................. 17
AND THROUGH IT ALL SHE OFFERS ME PROTECTION .......................... 146
ANGEL OF HARLEM ...................................................... 65
ANGELS ............................................................... 146
ANOTHER DAY IN PARADISE .............................................. 120
ARE YOU LONESOME TONIGHT? ............................................ 33
AROUND THE WORLD ..................................................... 310
AT THE AGE OF 37 ..................................................... 277
ATLANTIS ............................................................. 252
AUX CHAMPS-ELYSEES ................................................... 67

BA-BA-BANKÜBERFALL ................................................... 40
BABICKA .............................................................. 207
BACARDI FEELING ...................................................... 44
BAILA ME ............................................................. 18
BALLAD ............................................................... 287
BALLROOM BLITZ ....................................................... 371
BAMBOLEO ............................................................. 78
BANANA BOAT SONG ..................................................... 189
BATTLES .............................................................. 52
```

```
BECAUSE I GOT HIGH ................................................. 228
BEDS ARE BURNING ................................................... 381
BEHIND BLUE EYES .................................................... 11
BELFAST CHILD ....................................................... 87
BELIEVER ........................................................... 338
BELLA CIAO ......................................................... 301
BIENE MAJA ......................................................... 200
BIG IN JAPAN ....................................................... 365
BLAUE AUGEN ........................................................ 117
BLUE, BLUE, BLUE, JOHNNY BLUE ....................................... 20
BOCHUM ............................................................... 4
BOYS DON'T CRY ..................................................... 326
BREATHLESS ......................................................... 194
BROKEN WINGS ....................................................... 279
BROTHERS IN ARMS .................................................... 72
BROWN GIRL IN THE RING ............................................. 387
BY THE RIVERS OF BABYLON ............................................. 5


C'EST LA VIE SAY THE OLD FOLKS ..................................... 213
CALIFORNIA GIRLS ................................................... 143
CAN'T STOP THINKING OF YOU ......................................... 385
CAN'T HELP FALLING IN LOVE .......................................... 98
CARBONARA .......................................................... 198
CARRIE ............................................................. 103
CATCH ME ........................................................... 125
CAUSE I'M YOUR LADY ................................................. 45
CECILIA ............................................................ 319
CENTERFOLD ......................................................... 258
CHAMPS ELYSÉES ...................................................... 67
CHILD IN TIME ....................................................... 62
CITY OF NEW ORLEANS ................................................. 28
CLAIRE ............................................................. 126
CLOSE YOUR EYES AND I'LL KISS YOU .................................. 334
CODO ............................................................... 331
COME ON OVER HAVE SOME FUN .......................................... 44
COME TO SIN ........................................................ 152
COME TOGETHER ...................................................... 289
COME, MISSA TALLYMAN ............................................... 189
COSE DELLA VITA - CAN'T STOP THINKING OF YOU ...................... 385
COULD YOU BE LOVED ................................................. 294
COUNTRY HOUSE ...................................................... 265
CRYING IN THE RAIN ................................................. 179
CUANDO SEI MARIA DOLORES ............................................ 18


DA NAHM ER SEINE GITARRE ........................................... 158
DANCING QUEEN ...................................................... 138
DAS KUFSTEINER LIED (DIE PERLE TIROLS) ............................. 149
DAVE DUDLEY ........................................................ 391
DAYLIGHT IN YOUR EYES ................................................ 1
DAY-O (BANANA BOAT SONG) ........................................... 189
DEIN IST MEIN GANZES HERZ ........................................... 48
DEINE BLAUEN AUGEN ................................................. 117
DEINE SPUREN IM SAND ............................................... 325
DER ALBATROS ....................................................... 248
DER TEUFEL UND DER JUNGE MANN ...................................... 305
DER WILDE, WILDE WESTEN ............................................. 57
DESERT ROSE ........................................................ 108
```

| | |
|---|---|
| DESPERADO | 133 |
| *DEVIL IN DISGUISE* | *379* |
| DICH ZU LIEBEN | 353 |
| DIE AFFEN RASEN DURCH DEN WALD | 351 |
| DIE GLOCKEN VON ROM | 112 |
| DIE KARAWANE ZIEHT WEITER | 291 |
| DIE WEISSEN TAUBEN SIND MÜDE | 114 |
| DIRTY OLD TOWN | 89 |
| DISCO 2000 | 83 |
| DO WAH DIDDY DIDDY | 362 |
| DON'T LOOK BACK IN ANGER | 42 |
| DON'T THINK TWICE, IT'S ALL RIGHT | 186 |
| DON'T WORRY, BE HAPPY | 163 |
| DREAM ON | 285 |
| 13 TAGE | 303 |
| DSCHINGIS KHAN | 22 |
| DU HATTEST KEINE TRÄNEN MEHR | 327 |
| | |
| EASY | 240 |
| EASY DAY | 216 |
| EIN BISSCHEN FRIEDEN | 238 |
| EIN BISSCHEN SPASS MUSS SEIN | 313 |
| EIN GUTER TAG ZUM STERBEN | 160 |
| *EIN SCHÖNER TAG* | *47* |
| EL CONDOR PASA | 184 |
| EL LUTE | 64 |
| ER HAT EIN KNALLROTES GUMMIBOOT | 374 |
| *ER HAT NIE DAS LICHT DER SONNE GESEHEN* | *64* |
| ES GEHT UM MEHR | 2 |
| *ES IST VORBEI, BYE BYE JUNIMOND* | *7* |
| *ET J'AI CRIE, CRIE ALINE* | *55* |
| EYE OF THE TIGER | 50 |
| | |
| FALLEN ANGEL | 400 |
| FALLING IN LOVE AGAIN | 31 |
| FIELDS OF GOLD | 128 |
| 50 WAYS TO LEAVE YOUR LOVER | 59 |
| FIGHT FOR YOUR RIGHT | 170 |
| FIRE WATER BURN | 281 |
| FIRST WE TAKE MANHATTAN | 295 |
| FLUGZEUGE IM BAUCH | 110 |
| FOREVER YOUNG | 208 |
| FREUDE SCHÖNER GÖTTERFUNKEN | 369 |
| FROM A DISTANCE | 94 |
| FROM SARAH WITH LOVE | 405 |
| FUN FUN FUN | 333 |
| | |
| GANZ ODER GAR NICHT | 113 |
| GAUDEAMUS IGITUR | 106 |
| *GIB MIR MEIN HERZ ZURÜCK* | *110* |
| GIRL, YOU'LL BE A WOMAN SOON | 345 |
| GIRLS JUST WANT TO HAVE FUN | 178 |
| *GIVE ME A TICKET FOR AN AEROPLANE* | *23* |
| GO DOWN MOSES | 372 |
| GOD SHUFFLED HIS FEET | 246 |
| *GOOD MORNING AMERICA, HOW ARE YOU?* | *28* |

```
GOOD VIBRATIONS ................................................... 321
GRACELAND ......................................................... 317
GREENSLEEVES ........................................................ 3
GROSSVATER ......................................................... 70


HALLELUJAH ....................................................... 249
HARD DAY'S NIGHT ................................................. 232
HARD HEADED WOMAN ................................................ 122
HASTA MANANA, ALWAYS BE MINE ..................................... 354
HE LIVES IN A HOUSE, A VERY BIG HOUSE IN THE COUNTRY ............. 265
HEARTACHE TONIGHT ................................................. 12
HEDONISM ......................................................... 191
HELLO (TURN YOUR RADIO ON) ....................................... 347
HELLO AGAIN ...................................................... 329
HELLO ............................................................ 141
HELP ME RHONDA ................................................... 154
HELP ............................................................. 259
HELTER SKELTER ................................................... 364
HERE I GO AGAIN ................................................... 54
HEUT' IST EIN GUTER TAG ZUM STERBEN .............................. 160
HEY, HEY WICKIE .................................................. 342
HIGHWAY TO HELL .................................................. 308
HOMEWARD BOUND ................................................... 284
HORIZONT ......................................................... 180
HOW LONG? HOW LONG MUST WE SING THIS SONG? ...................... 193
HURRICANE ......................................................... 36


I AM A ROCK ....................................................... 85
I BEG YOUR PARDON ................................................ 183
I BELIEVE I CAN FLY .............................................. 150
I CAN SEE IT IN YOUR EYES ........................................ 141
I CAN'T BELIEVE THE NEWS TODAY ................................... 193
I CAN'T HELP FALLING IN LOVE ...................................... 98
I DREAM OF RAIN, ELAY ELAY ....................................... 108
I FEEL LONELY .................................................... 174
I GOT MY FIRST REAL SIX STRING ................................... 337
I GUESS THAT'S WHY THEY CALL IT THE BLUES ....................... 383
I HEAR THE DRUMS ECHOING TONIGHT .................................. 14
I HEARD IT THROUGH THE GRAPEVINE ................................. 269
I HOPE YOU'RE FEELING HAPPY NOW .................................. 191
I JUST CALLED TO SAY I LOVE YOU .................................. 119
(I JUST) DIED IN YOUR ARMS TONIGHT ............................... 298
I LIKE THE LOVE AND I LIKE THE PEACEFUL ......................... 241
I NEVER PROMISED YOU A ROSE GARDEN ............................... 183
I SAVED THE WORLD TODAY .......................................... 145
I STILL HAVEN'T FOUND WHAT I'M LOOKING FOR ...................... 250
I TURN TO YOU ..................................................... 99
I WANT IT THAT WAY ............................................... 104
I WANT TO KNOW WHAT LOVE IS ....................................... 16
I WANT TO STAND WITH YOU ON A MOUNTAIN .......................... 212
I WILL BE WITH YOU AGAIN ......................................... 348
I WILL LOVE AGAIN ................................................ 195
I WISH THEY ALL COULD BE CALIFORNIA GIRLS ....................... 143
I'D LOVE YOU TO WANT ME .......................................... 378
I'D RATHER BE A SPARROW THAN A SNAIL ............................ 184
I'LL MEET YOU AT MIDNIGHT ......................................... 97
```

VII

| Title | Page |
|---|---|
| *I'LL NEVER LET YOU SEE* | *179* |
| *I'M AN ALIEN, I'M A LEGAL ALIEN* | *274* |
| I'M OUTTA LOVE | 223 |
| I'M STILL STANDING | 350 |
| (I'VE HAD) THE TIME OF MY LIFE | 396 |
| *ICH BRAUCHE KEINE MILLIONEN* | *142* |
| ICH HAB DAS FRÄUL'N HELEN BADEN SEH'N | 92 |
| ICH HAB MEIN HERZ IN HEIDELBERG VERLOREN | 315 |
| *ICH HAB' HEUTE NICHTS VERSÄUMT* | *169* |
| *ICH MÖCHT SO GERN DAVE DUDLEY HÖRN'* | *391* |
| ICH VERMISS DICH... (WIE DIE HÖLLE) | 398 |
| ICH WILL SPASS | 69 |
| ICH WOLLT ICH WÄR EIN HUHN | 271 |
| IF YOU COULD READ MY MIND | 220 |
| IM OSTEN | 214 |
| IMAGINE | 166 |
| IMMORTALITY | 164 |
| *IN EINEM UNBEKANNTEN LAND* | *200* |
| IN THE AIR TONIGHT | 6 |
| IN THE SHADOWS | 90 |
| IN THE YEAR 2525 | 26 |
| IN THESE ARMS | 165 |
| INDIANER | 254 |
| *IRGENDWANN BLEIB' I DANN DORT* | *131* |
| IS THIS LOVE | 340 |
| IT'S A HEARTACHE | 367 |
| IT'S ALL COMING BACK TO ME NOW | 242 |
| IT'S ALL OVER NOW, BABY BLUE | 280 |
| *IT'S BEEN A HARD DAY'S NIGHT* | *232* |
| *IT'S BEEN SEVEN HOURS AND FIFTEEN DAYS* | *53* |
| *IT'S MY LIFE* | *343* |
| *IT'S NINE O'CLOCK ON A SATURDAY* | *312* |
| IT'S NOW OR NEVER | 187 |
| *IT'S ONLY WORDS* | *30* |
| IT'S RAINING MEN | 306 |
| *ITSY BITSY TEENIE WEENIE HONULULU-STRAND-BIKINI* | *318* |
| | |
| JACK AND DIANE | 75 |
| *JAWOHL, MEINE HERR'N* | *370* |
| *JET SET* | *215* |
| JOE, NOCH EINEN | 100 |
| JOHNNY BLUE | 20 |
| JUKE BOX HERO | 395 |
| *JUNIMOND* | *7* |
| *JUST BECAUSE YOU FEEL GOOD* | *191* |
| JUST LIKE A WOMAN | 124 |
| | |
| KALKUTTA LIEGT AM GANGES | 157 |
| *KENNST DU DIE PERLE* | *149* |
| KING OF THE ROAD | 307 |
| KISS FROM A ROSE | 80 |
| *KNALLROTES GUMMIBOOT* | *374* |
| KNOWING ME, KNOWING YOU | 263 |
| KREUZBERGER NÄCHTE SIND LANG | 406 |
| *KRIMINAL TANGO* | *175* |
| KUMBAYA | 211 |

| | |
|---|---:|
| LA CUCARACHA | 218 |
| LADY D'ARBANVILLE | 397 |
| LADY MADONNA | 237 |
| LASS UNS SCHMUTZIG LIEBE MACHEN | 357 |
| LAURA NON C'È | 63 |
| LEAN ON ME | 115 |
| LENINGRAD | 234 |
| LESSONS IN LOVE | 358 |
| (LET ME BE YOUR) TEDDY BEAR | 332 |
| *LET ME GO FROM THIS LONELY LAND* | *52* |
| *LET MY PEOPLE GO* | *372* |
| LET'S TWIST AGAIN | 127 |
| LIEBFICKEN | 41 |
| *LIEBLING, LASS UNS TANZEN* | *173* |
| LIES | 231 |
| LIFE FOR RENT | 224 |
| *LOOK MY EYES ARE JUST HOLOGRAMS* | *29* |
| *LOOKING FROM A WINDOW ABOVE* | *111* |
| LOSER | 74 |
| LOVE ME TENDER | 361 |
| LUCILLE | 278 |
| LUCKY MAN | 121 |
| LUCKY | 79 |
| LUKA | 261 |
| | |
| MA BAKER | 205 |
| MÄDCHEN | 390 |
| MAMMA MIA | 297 |
| *MAN KANN ES NICHT HÖR'N, MAN KANN ES NICHT SEH'N* | *305* |
| MANCHMAL MÖCHTE ICH SCHON MIT DIR | 403 |
| MANIC MONDAY | 167 |
| MÄRCHENPRINZ | 304 |
| MARIA | 336 |
| MASSACHUSETTS | 25 |
| *MEIN MASERATI FÄHRT 210* | *69* |
| MICHAEL ROW THE BOAT ASHORE | 197 |
| MICHELLE | 10 |
| MIT PFEFFERMINZ BIN ICH DEIN PRINZ | 173 |
| MONDAY MONDAY | 34 |
| MONEY FOR NOTHING | 116 |
| MORE THAN A FEELING | 192 |
| MOSKAU | 171 |
| MUSIK NUR WENN SIE LAUT IST | 407 |
| MUSIK, MUSIK, MUSIK(ICH BRAUCHE KEINE MILLIONEN) | 142 |
| *MY BLOOD RUNS COLD, MY MEMORY HAS JUST BEEN SOLD* | *258* |
| MY LOVE IS YOUR LOVE | 77 |
| *MY TEA'S GONE COLD, I'M WONDERING WHY* | *239* |
| | |
| NARCOTIC | 359 |
| NEVER BE THE SAME AGAIN | 392 |
| NEW YEAR'S DAY | 348 |
| NIEMALS GEHT MAN SO GANZ | 233 |
| NIKITA | 147 |
| *NO ONE KNOWS WHAT IT'S LIKE* | *11* |
| NO SON OF MINE | 201 |
| *NO YEAR'S DAY TO CELEBRATE* | *119* |
| NON, JE NE REGRETTE RIEN | 302 |

```
NOTHING COMPARES 2 U .................................................... 53
NOWHERE MAN .............................................................. 283
NUR GETRÄUMT ............................................................. 169


OB-LA-DI, OB-LA-DA ....................................................... 46
ODE TO MY FAMILY ......................................................... 226
OH BABY BABY IT'S A WILD WORLD ........................................... 21
OH CHAMPS-ELYSEES ........................................................ 67
OH PRETTY WOMAN .......................................................... 107
OHNE DICH (SCHLAF ICH HEUT NACHT NICHT EIN) .............................. 384
OHNE DICH ................................................................ 43
OLD TIME ROCK AND ROLL ................................................... 366
ON THE ROAD AGAIN ........................................................ 300
ONE DAY WE'LL RETURN HERE ................................................ 87
ONE MORE NIGHT ........................................................... 58
ONE OF US ................................................................ 188
ONE, TWO, THREE O'CLOCK, FOUR O'CLOCK ROCK ............................... 19
ONLY TIME ................................................................ 118
ONLY YOU ................................................................. 111


PAPERBACK WRITER ......................................................... 168
PASSENGER ................................................................ 256
PENNY LANE ............................................................... 177
PIANO MAN ................................................................ 312
PIECE OF MY HEART ........................................................ 140
PINBALL WIZARD ........................................................... 109
PLEASE FORGIVE ME ........................................................ 172
PLEASE MRS. AVERY ........................................................ 210
PRETTY WOMAN ............................................................. 107
PRIVATE DANCER ........................................................... 96


RADIO GA GA .............................................................. 56
RAMONA ................................................................... 217
RASPUTIN ................................................................. 153
RAWHIDE .................................................................. 15
RED, RED WINE ............................................................ 356
RETURN TO SENDER ......................................................... 401
RHYTHM DIVINE ............................................................ 182
RIDIN' ON THE CITY OF NEW ORLEANS ........................................ 28
RIVERS OF BABYLON ........................................................ 5
ROCK AROUND THE CLOCK .................................................... 19
ROCK ME AMADEUS .......................................................... 148
ROLLING ROLLING ROLLING .................................................. 15
ROSE GARDEN .............................................................. 183
RUBY, DON'T TAKE YOUR LOVE TO TOWN ....................................... 288
RUNAWAY .................................................................. 135
RUSSIANS ................................................................. 257


S.O.S. ................................................................... 71
SAD LISA ................................................................. 225
SAG MAL WEINST DU ........................................................ 299
SANTA MARIA .............................................................. 82
SAVE TONIGHT ............................................................. 314
SAY YOU SAY ME ........................................................... 260
SCHOOL'S OUT ............................................................. 389
```

| | |
|---|---|
| SEE YOU LATER ALLIGATOR | 185 |
| SEHNSUCHT | 344 |
| SEX BOMB | 267 |
| *SHE CALLS OUT TO THE MAN ON THE STREET* | *120* |
| SHE LOVES YOU | 102 |
| SHE'S ALWAYS A WOMAN TO ME | 144 |
| SIEBEN FÄSSER WEIN | 196 |
| *SING WITH ME, SING FOR THE YEARS* | *285* |
| SING | 9 |
| *SINGEN, KOCHEN, TANZEN, LACHEN, GLÜCKLICH MACHEN* | *207* |
| SMOOTH | 51 |
| SO LONELY | 402 |
| *SO LONG, THIS LOVE WON'T LET ME GO* | *65* |
| *SO SALLY CAN WAIT* | *42* |
| SO SCHMECKT DER SOMMER | 159 |
| *SO THIS IS WHO I AM* | *164* |
| *SO WHEN YOU'RE NEAR ME, DARLING* | *71* |
| SOMETHING STUPID | 86 |
| SON OF A PREACHER MAN | 360 |
| SOUNDS LIKE A MELODY | 268 |
| SPANISH TRAIN | 136 |
| SPICKS AND SPECKS | 352 |
| STAN | 202 |
| STAND BY ME | 309 |
| STAY | 292 |
| STRANGERS IN THE NIGHT | 375 |
| SUMMER DREAMING (BACARDI FEELING) | 44 |
| SUMMER IN BERLIN | 88 |
| SUMMER MOVED ON | 346 |
| SUMMER OF '69 | 337 |
| SUMMER SON | 276 |
| SUNDAY BLOODY SUNDAY | 193 |
| SUPERGIRL | 229 |
| SUPREME | 247 |
| SUSPICIOUS MINDS | 35 |
| SUZANNE | 388 |
| SWEAT (A LA LA LA LA LONG) | 32 |
| SWEET CAROLINE | 105 |
| *SWEET CHILD IN TIME* | *62* |
| SWEET DREAMS | 227 |
| SYLVIA'S MOTHER | 210 |
| (TAKE A LITTLE) PIECE OF MY HEART | 140 |
| *TAKE A LOOK AT ME NOW* | *60* |
| TAKE GOOD CARE OF MY BABY | 408 |
| TAKE MY BREATH AWAY | 221 |
| TAKE ON ME | 296 |
| *TEDDY BEAR* | *332* |
| TEENAGE DIRTBAG | 363 |
| THANK YOU FOR THE MUSIC | 129 |
| THANK YOU | 239 |
| THE BAD TOUCH | 190 |
| THE BALLAD OF CHASEY LAIN | 253 |
| THE BALLAD OF LUCY JORDAN | 277 |
| THE BOYS OF SUMMER | 162 |
| THE CARPET CRAWLERS | 328 |
| THE DAY BEFORE YOU CAME | 66 |
| THE FINAL COUNTDOWN | 394 |

| | |
|---|---|
| THE GAMBLER | 68 |
| THE JET SET | 215 |
| THE LAST UNICORN | 272 |
| THE LETTER | 23 |
| THE MAN WHO SOLD THE WORLD | 91 |
| THE NIGHT CHICAGO DIED | 335 |
| *THE ONLY ONE WHO COULD EVER REACH ME* | *360* |
| THE POWER OF LOVE | 45 |
| *THE ROOF, THE ROOF, THE ROOF IS ON FIRE* | *281* |
| *THE TIME OF MY LIFE* | *396* |
| THE TIMES THEY ARE A-CHANGING | 27 |
| THE UNFORGIVEN | 251 |
| THE WIND CRIES MARY | 17 |
| *THERE SHE WAS, JUST-A WALKING DOWN THE STREET* | *362* |
| *THERE'S GONNA BE A HEARTACHE TONIGHT* | *12* |
| THESE BOOTS ARE MADE FOR WALKING | 311 |
| THESE DAYS | 49 |
| *THESE MIST COVERED MOUNTAINS* | *72* |
| THIS IS WHERE I CAME IN | 382 |
| TOTAL ECLIPSE OF THE HEART | 324 |
| TRUE COLORS | 293 |
| TRULY MADLY DEEPLY | 212 |
| *TURN AROUND* | *324* |
| TWENTYFIRST CENTURY DIGITAL BOY | 266 |
| TWIST AND SHOUT | 245 |
| TWIST IN MY SOBRIETY | 29 |
| TWO PRINCES | 61 |
| | |
| ÜBERDOSIS GFÜHL | 368 |
| UNA FESTA SUI PRATI | 275 |
| UNCLE JOHN FROM JAMAICA | 123 |
| *UND ICH DÜSE, DÜSE, DÜSE, DÜSE IM SAUSESCHRITT* | *331* |
| *UND IRGENDWANN BLEIB I DANN DORT* | *131* |
| *UND SIE TANZEN EINEN TANGO* | *175* |
| UPTOWN GIRL | 316 |
| | |
| VIDEO KILLED THE RADIO STAR | 339 |
| VIENNA | 151 |
| VIVA FOREVER | 354 |
| | |
| WALK OF LIFE | 341 |
| WANNABE | 270 |
| WANTED DEAD OR ALIVE | 236 |
| WAS SOLL DAS | 39 |
| WATERLOO | 13 |
| *WAY DOWN BELOW THE OCEAN* | *252* |
| WE DON'T NEED ANOTHER HERO | 134 |
| WE SHALL OVERCOME | 286 |
| *WE'RE CAUGHT IN A TRAP* | *35* |
| *WEIL ICH 'N MÄDCHEN BIN* | *390* |
| *WEINST DU* | *299* |
| WEISS DER GEIER | 273 |
| WEISSE ROSEN AUS ATHEN | 373 |
| WELCH EIN TAG | 47 |
| WELCOME TO HEARTLIGHT | 241 |

| | |
|---|---:|
| WELL, SOMEONE TOLD ME YESTERDAY | *402* |
| WEM | 156 |
| WER HAT DIE KOKOSNUSS GEKLAUT | *351* |
| WE'RE NOT GONNA TAKE IT | 399 |
| WHANG I SING WHILE THE OTHERS SWING | 152 |
| WHAT I'VE FELT, WHAT I'VE KNOWN | 251 |
| WHAT WOULD YOU DO IF I SANG OUT OF TUNE | 264 |
| WHAT'S LOVE GOT TO DO WITH IT | 386 |
| WHEN I COME AROUND | 209 |
| WHEN I GET OLDER, LOSING MY HAIR | *84* |
| WHEN I WAS YOUNG | 262 |
| WHEN I'M SIXTY-FOUR | 84 |
| WHEN ISRAEL WAS IN EGYPT'S LAND | *372* |
| WHEN SUSANNAH CRIES | 161 |
| WHENEVER, WHEREVER | 380 |
| WHERE HAVE ALL THE COWBOYS GONE? | 73 |
| WHERE THE STREETS HAVE NO NAME | 130 |
| WHO BY FIRE | 330 |
| WHY DOES IT ALWAYS RAIN ON ME? | 322 |
| WHY WORRY | 290 |
| WICKIE | *342* |
| WIEDER ALLES IM GRIFF | 139 |
| WILD WORLD | 21 |
| WISE MEN SAY | *98* |
| WITH A LITTLE HELP FROM MY FRIENDS | 264 |
| WITH OR WITHOUT YOU | 199 |
| WO SIND ALL DIE INDIANER HIN | *254* |
| WOMIT HAB ICH DAS VERDIENT | *39* |
| WONDERFUL LIFE | 320 |
| WONDERWALL | 255 |
| WORDS | 206 |
| WORDS | 30 |
| | |
| YOU | 24 |
| YOU ARE MY FIRE | *104* |
| YOU LOOK LIKE AN ANGEL | *379* |
| YOU NEVER CAN TELL | 213 |
| YOU SANG TO ME | 132 |
| YOU WERE ALWAYS ON MY MIND | *244* |
| YOU'LL REMEMBER ME WHEN THE WEST WIND MOVES | *128* |
| YOUR LATEST TRICK | 404 |
| YOU'RE THE DEVIL IN DISGUISE | 379 |
| YOU'RE THE ONE THAT I WANT | 222 |
| YUMMY, YUMMY, YUMMY | 95 |
| | |
| ZEHN NACKTE FRISEUSEN | 93 |

- Die wichtigsten Themengebiete im Bereich der Musik
- Übersichtlich auf 6 Seiten
- Cellophanierte, stabile Klappkarte
- Für alle Schüler, Studenten und Musikinteressierte

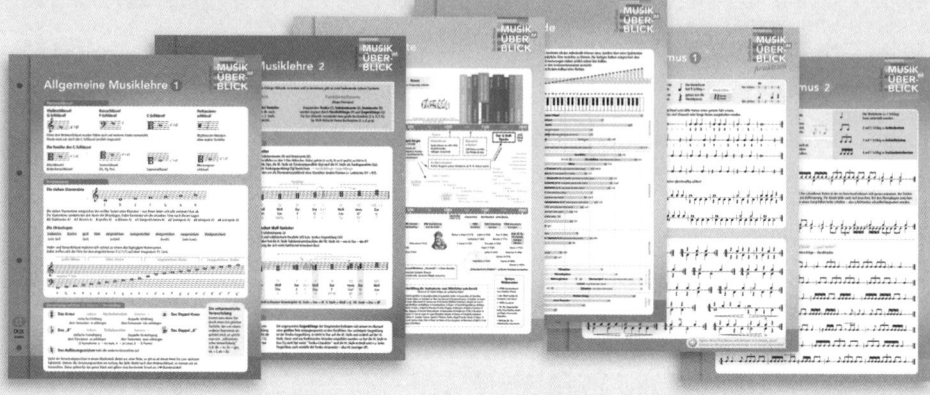

## Allgemeine Musiklehre 1

- Basiswissen zur Allgemeinen Musiklehre
- Notenschlüssel, Notennamen und Oktavlagen
- Intervalle und Skalen / Kirchentonarten
- Quintenzirkel mit allen Dur und Molltonarten
- Akkorde mit Umkehrungen
- Notenwerte und Taktarten

D 1093/ISBN 978-3-86849-311-5

## Allgemeine Musiklehre 2

- Stufenlehre und Funktionstheorie, Leitereigene Akkorde in Dur und Moll, Medianten
- Parallel- und Gegenklänge, Akkordsymbole
- Grundkenntnisse der Harmonielehre – 4-sti. Satz, einfache und erweiterte Kadenzen, Zwischendominanten, Generalbass, Auflösung von Dissonanzen
- 2-seitiges Lexikon der musikal. Fachbegriffe, übersichtliche Tafeln u. a. für Schlussarten und Verzierungen

D 1094/ISBN 978-3-86849-312-2

## Musikgeschichte

- Geschichtstafeln der Epochen und ihrer bedeutendsten Komponisten
- Entwicklung der Gattungen, Instrumente und musiktheoretischen Neuerungen
- Informativer Begleittext mit aufschlussreichem Bezug zur Weltgeschichte

D 1095/ISBN 978-3-86849-313-9

## Spaß am Rhythmus 1

- Erste Einführung in den Rhythmus
- Einfache Taktarten und Notenwerte
- Zweistimmige Rhythmusübungen für Pianisten oder für den Gruppenunterricht
- Anschauliche Erklärungen rhythmischer Besonderheiten

D 1090/ISBN 978-3-86849-203-3

## Spaß am Rhythmus 2

- Pädagogisch wertvolle Fortsetzung des Rhythmuslehrgangs 1 mit ein- und zweistimmigen Übungen (Pianisten)
- Umfangreiches Training von Achteltriolen, Sechzehntelnoten und der kleinen Punktierung
- Erweiterung auf alle Taktarten; 32tel-Noten, 16tel-Triolen, Taktwechsel und Polyrhythmus (3 gegen 2, Duolen, Vierteltriolen)

D 1096/ISBN 978-3-86849-317-7

## Instrumentenkunde

- Tonumfang der wichtigsten Instrumente zum Arrangieren und Komponieren
- Alle Instrumente im Überblick
- Geschichtstafel der Instrumente
- Obertonreihe / Transponierende Instrumente
- Entwicklung des Orchesters

D 1091/ISBN 978-3-86849-204-0

# DAYLIGHT IN YOUR EYES

(NO ANGELS)

```
   E                      A                         E
1. Wanna know you better, wanna push you baby but never too far.
E                    A                           E
Wanna show you heaven, wanna feel like you just as strong as you are.
          A              C#m7           E              F#7
I wanna be daylight in your eyes, I wanna be sunlight only warmer.
          A              C#m7           E              F#7
I wanna be daylight in your eyes, I wanna be love only stronger.
          A
I wanna be daylight.

   E                  A                               E
2. Wanna live forever, wanna touch your hand and explode like a star.
E                 A                           E
Wanna stand beside you always be together wherever you are.
```

**Refrain:**
```
          A              C#m7           E              F#7
I wanna be daylight in your eyes, I wanna be sunlight only warmer.
          A              C#m7           E              F#7
I wanna be daylight in your eyes, I wanna be love only stronger.
          A              C#m7           E              F#7
I wanna be daylight in your eyes, I wanna be sunlight only warmer.
          A
I wanna be daylight.

   E                      A                         E
3. Wanna know you better, wanna push you baby but never too far.
E                  A                           E
Wanna live forever, wanna be like you just as weak as you are.

Refrain

C#m              A
Daylight, I see it in your eyes.
F#7            B7                              E
Daylight, I wanna be, just you and me warmer inside.

Daylight in your eyes, in your eyes, in your eyes.

Refrain
C#m        E       F#7         A
Daylight. I see it in your eyes.
```

M + T: Anthony Michael Bruno / Thomas V. Byrnes / Paul Mahos
© Wintrup Musikverlag, Detmold / Partitur Musikverlag, Berlin / Paul Mahos Songs administered by
WB Music Corp., Warner/Chappell North America Ltd, London. Reproduced by permission of Faber.
All Rights Reserved.

# ES GEHT UM MEHR

(HOWARD CARPENDALE)

```
       A                        Bm
1. Die Stadt ist leer der Wind weht kalt, nun ist die Nacht zu Ende bald
       E                              A            E
   und ich geh' ganz alleine durch die Straßen ohne Ziel.
   A                           Bm
   Wir haben einen Punkt erreicht, an dem ein Tag dem andern gleicht,
       E                                      A              E
   nun kann es sein, dass alles bricht und doch: wir wollen das nicht.
```

**Refrain:**
```
            A
Es geht um mehr als um flüchtige Stunden.
            Bm
Es geht um mehr als wir beide gedacht.
              D
Ich hab' dich nicht erst gestern gefunden
              A
wir haben viel Zeit miteinander verbracht.

            A
Es geht um mehr als bei wem ich nachts liege.
        Bm
Eine Nacht ist so schnell vorbei.
        D
Meine Zukunft trägt deine Züge,
            A
es geht um mehr, es geht um uns zwei.

               A
Wenn du heute gehst. So viele tun es.
          Bm
Einfach so gehst. Wie sinnlos das ist.
        D
Bin ich allein. Sie geh'n auseinander.
            A   E   A   E
Statt einen Weg zu finden.

               A
Wenn du heute gehst. Sie suchen nach Liebe.
          Bm
Einfach so gehst. Und haben sie schon.
        D
Bin ich allein. Sie geh'n dann vorüber.
            A   E   A   E   A
Statt einen Weg zu suchen.
```

```
2. Der Morgen fängt zu dämmern an, wo geh' ich hin, was mach' ich dann?
   Ob du wohl jetzt zuhause bist und nachdenkst so wie ich?
   Der Schlüssel da zu deiner Tür, der scheint zu sagen: geh zu ihr.
   Und wenn ich es nicht wirklich tu, wozu das Ganze? Wozu?
```

Refrain

M + T: Howard Carpendale / Joachim Horn-Berngs / Fred Jay
© 1980 Musikverlag Intersong GmbH & Co KG,
Warner/Chappell Overseas Holdings Ltd, London. Reproduced by permission of Faber Music Limited.
All Rights Reserved.

# GREENSLEEVES

```
    Em              D              C              B7
1. Alas, my love, you do me wrong to cast me off discourteously;
Em              D              C          B7      Em
And I have loved you so long delighting in your company.
```

**Refrain:**
```
G               D              C              B7
Greensleeves was my delight, Greensleeves my heart of gold.
G               D              C            B7    Em
Greensleeves was my heart of joy and who but my lady Greensleeves.
```

```
    Em              D              C              B7
2. I have been ready at your hand to grant whatever thou would'st crave;
Em              D              C          B7      Em
I have waged both life and land your love and goodwill for to have.
```

Refrain

```
    Em              D              C              B7
3. Thy petticoat of sandle white with gold embroidered gorgeously;
Em              D              C          B7      Em
Thy petticoat of silk and white and these I bought gladly.
```

Refrain

Traditionell
© 2005 by Edition DUX, Manching

# BOCHUM

(HERBERT GRÖNEMEYER)
[TRANSP. +3]

```
A        E                      A
Tief im Westen, wo die Sonne verstaubt,
         E                      A/C#    D E
ist es besser, viel besser als man glaubt.
      F#m    D F#m D       A      E F#m D
Tief im Westen.        Tief im Westen.

   Bm      A          D      Bm     A          D
1. Du bist keine Schönheit, vor Arbeit ganz grau,
Bm  A/C#          D       F              Em
du liebst dich ohne Schminke, bist ne ehrliche Haut,
F        Em           F        G           C    Bm
leider total verbaut, aber grade das macht dich aus.

   Bm       A         D     Bm      A        D
2. Du hast'n Pulsschlag aus Stahl, man hört ihn laut in der Nacht,
Bm        A/C#      D        F            Em
du bist einfach zu bescheiden, dein Grubengold
F        Em           F          E7
hat uns wieder hochgeholt, du Blume im Revier.
```

**Refrain:**
```
Am  F       C       G     Am  F       C       G
Bochum, ich komm aus dir, Bochum, ich häng an dir.
Am     F    C  G       Bm
Ah, ah Glück auf: Bochum.

   Bm      A         D      Bm     A            D
3. Du bist keine Weltstadt, auf deiner Königsallee
Bm    A        D         F             Em
finden keine Modenschau'n statt, hier, wo das Herz noch zählt,
F        Em          F                       E7
nicht das große Geld, wer wohnt schon in Düsseldorf?
```

Refrain

```
   Bm      A         D          Bm    A         D
4. Du bist das Himmelbett für Tauben und ständig auf Koks,
Bm       A             D      F              Em
hast im Schrebergarten deine Laube, machst mit dem Doppelpass
F      Em         F           E7
jeden Gegner nass, du und dein VfL.
```

Refrain 2x

M + T: Herbert Grönemeyer
© Copyright Grönland Musikverlag
All Rights Reserved. International Copyright Secured.

# RIVERS OF BABYLON

(BONEY M.)

**Refrain:**
```
               C
By the rivers of Babylon there we sat down,
         G                           C
ye-eah we wept when we remembered Zion.
               C
By the rivers of Babylon, there we sat down,
         G                           C
ye-eah we wept when we remembered Zion.

               C                         F                  C
When the wicked carried us away in captivity required from us a song.
                                             G           C
Now how shall we sing the Lord's song in a strange land?
               C                         F                  C
When the wicked carried us away in captivity requiring of us a song.
                                             G           C
Now how shall we sing the Lord's song in a strange land?

            C         G            C                G
Let the words of our mouth and the meditation of our heart
     C            G7         C
be acceptable in thy sight here tonight.

            C         G            C                G
Let the words of our mouth and the meditation of our heart
     C            G7         C
be acceptable in thy sight here tonight.
```

Refrain

By the rivers of Babylon, (Dark tears of Babylon)
there we sat down, (You got to sing a song)
ye-eah we wept (Sing a song of love)
when we remembered Zion. (Yeah yeah yeah yeah yeah)

By the rivers of Babylon, (Rough bits of Babylon)
there we sat down, (You hear the people cry)
ye-eah we wept (They need that song)
when we remembered Zion. (Ooh, have the power)

M + T: James McNaughton / Frank Farian / George Reyam / Brent Dowe
© Blue Mountain Music Limited / Far Musikverlag GmbH. Mit freundlicher
Genehmigung von Far Musikverlag GmbH & Co. KG. All Rights Reserved.
International Copyright Secured.

# IN THE AIR TONIGHT

(PHIL COLLINS)

**Intro:** Dm C Bb C (2x)
**Refrain:**
```
Dm           C/D              Bb/D     C/D
I can feel it coming in the air tonight, oh Lord.
Dm               C/D              Bb/D     C/D
I've been waiting for this moment for all my life, oh Lord.
Dm             C/D              Bb/D      C/D
Can you feel it coming in the air tonight, oh Lord?
    Dm
Oh Lord.
```

```
           Dm                       Am/D
1. Well when you told me you were drowning I would not lend a hand.
       Bb/D
I've seen your face before my friend
          F/D
but I don't know if you know who I am.
       Dm                               Am/D
But I was there and I saw what you did, saw it with my own two eyes.
          Bb/D
So you can wipe off that grin, I know where you've been.
       F/D
It's all been a pack of lies.
```

Refrain

```
              Dm
2. Well I remember, I remember, don't worry.
Am/D
How could I ever forget?
         Bb/D                          F
It's the first time and the last time we ever met.
         Dm
But I know the reason why you keep this silence up.
Am/D                      Bb/D
No, you don't fool me for the hurt doesn't show,
                        F
but the pain still grows some stranger to you and me.
```

```
Dm         C                 Bb        C
I can feel it coming in the air tonight, oh Lord.
Dm             C                 Bb        C
I've been waiting for this moment for all my life, oh Lord.
Dm         C                 Bb        C
I can feel it coming in the air tonight, oh Lord.

Dm         C                 Bb        C
I can feel it coming in the air tonight, oh Lord.
Dm             C                 Bb        C
I've been waiting for this moment for all my life, oh Lord.
Dm         C                 Bb        C
I can feel it coming in the air tonight, oh Lord.
    Dm
Oh Lord.
```

M + T: Phil Collins
© Copyright 1981 Philip Collins Limited.
Imagem Music.
All Rights Reserved. International Copyright Secured.

## JUNIMOND

(RIO REISER)

`Intro: E E/D C D Em D/F# G F C/E D  (2x)`

```
             G         C        D
1. Die Welt schaut rauf zu meinem Fenster,
           G          C          D
mit müden Augen ganz staubig und scheu.
         G       C          D
Ich bin hier oben auf meiner Wolke,
        G              C           Bm
ich seh dich kommen, aber du gehst vorbei.
                    Em    C                      Em    A
Doch jetzt tut's nicht mehr weh, nee, jetzt tut's nicht mehr weh.
      D                       A                          B
Und alles bleibt stumm und kein Sturm kommt auf, wenn ich dich seh.
       E    E/D    C      D       Em  D/F# G
Es ist vorbei, bye bye Junimond, es ist vorbei,
       F    C/E D
es ist vorbei, bye bye.


              G         C        D
2. Zweitausend Stunden hab ich gewartet,
          G         C        D
ich hab sie alle gezählt und verflucht.
         G         C        D
Ich hab getrunken, geraucht und gebetet,
         G              C              Bm
hab dich flussauf- und flussabwärts gesucht.
                    Em    C                      Em    A
Doch jetzt tut's nicht mehr weh, nee, jetzt tut's nicht mehr weh,
      D                       A                          B
Und alles bleibt stumm und kein Sturm kommt auf, wenn ich dich seh.
       E    E/D    C      D       Em  D G
Es ist vorbei, bye bye Junimond, es ist vorbei,
       F    C/E D
es ist vorbei, bye bye.
```

M: Martin Hartmann
T: Rio Reiser
© SMPG Publishing (Germany) GmbH. Mit freundlicher Genehmigung von SMPG Publishing (Germany) GmbH.

# ALKOHOL

(HERBERT GRÖNEMEYER)

```
Intro: Em C Em C Em C Em C
       Em               C
1. Wir haben wieder die Nacht zum Tag gemacht,
   Em                      C
   ich nehm' mein Frühstück abends um acht.
   Em                  C
   Gedanken fließen zäh wie Kaugummi,
   Em                          C                 Em C Em C
   mein Kopf ist schwer wie Blei, mir zittern die Knie.

      Em                C              Em                  C
2. Gelallte Schwüre in rotblauem Licht, vierzigprozentiges Gleichgewicht
   Em              C              Em                    C
   graue Zellen in weicher Explosion, Sonnenaufgangs- und untergangsvision.
   D            C      D                                    C
   Was ist los, was ist passiert? Ich hab' bloß meine Nerven massiert.
```

**Refrain:**
```
      Em             C         A
   Alkohol ist dein Sanitäter in der Not,
      Em             C                   A
   Alkohol ist dein Fallschirm und dein Rettungsboot.
      Em            C           A
   Alkohol ist das Drahtseil, auf dem du stehst,
      Em        C   Em9
   Alkohol, Alkohol.
```

```
      Em                         C
3. Die Nobelszene träumt vom Kokain
   Em                           C
   und auf dem Schulklo riecht's nach Gras.
   Em                    C
   Der Apotheker nimmt Valium und Speed,
   Em                        C
   und wenn es dunkel wird, greifen sie zum Glas.
   D            C      D
   Was ist los, was ist passiert?
   D                          C
   Ich hab' bloß meine Nerven massiert.
```

Refrain
```
      Em                   C            A
   Alkohol ist das Schiff mit dem du untergehst.
      Em             C         A
   Alkohol ist dein Sanitäter in der Not,
      Em             C                   A
   Alkohol ist dein Fallschirm und dein Rettungsboot.
      Em            C            A
   Alkohol ist das Dressing für deinen Kopfsalat.
      Em        C   Em9
   Alkohol, Alkohol.
```

M + T: Herbert Grönemeyer
© Copyright Grönland Musikverlag.
All Rights Reserved. International Copyright Secured.

# SING

(TRAVIS)
[TRANSP. +2]

**Intro:** Em Am7 Am7 Em (2x)

```
      Em                        Am7
1. Baby, you've been going so crazy.
Am7                      Em
Lately, nothing seems to be going right.
Em                        Am7
Solo, why do you have to get so low?
Am7                              Em
You're so. You've been waiting in the sun too long.

              G     D     Am                   G
But if you sing, sing, sing, sing, sing, sing.
              G      D         Am
For the love you bring won't mean a thing.
            Am             G
Unless you sing, sing, sing, sing.

      Em                   Am7
2. Colder, crying on your shoulder.
Am7                                  Em
Hold her, and tell her everythings gonna be fine.
Em                         Am7
Surely, you've been going to early.
Am7                         Em
Hurry, cause no one's gonna be stopped, no, no, no, no.
```

**Refrain:**
```
             G     D     Am                   G
Not if you sing, sing, sing, sing, sing, sing.
              G      D         Am
For the love you bring won't mean a thing.
            Am             G               G D
Unless you sing, sing, sing, sing, sing, sing, sing.

Am Am7   G      D Am Am7  G
Ooooh... Aaaah... Ooooh...

      Em                              Am7
3. Baby, there's something going on today.
Am7          Em
But I say nothing, nothing, nothing,
Em               Am7                Em
nothing, nothing, nothing, nothing...so no, no, no.
```

Refrain

```
           G     D     Am                   G
Oh baby, sing, sing sing, sing, sing, sing.
              G      D         Am
For the love you bring won't mean a thing.
            Am             G
Unless you sing, sing, sing, sing.
```

M + T: Fran Healy
© Copyright 2001 Sony/ATV Music Publishing.
All Rights Reserved. International Copyright Secured.

# MICHELLE

(THE BEATLES)

**Refrain:**
```
F           Bbm7        Eb6              D°           C      G7b9 C
Michelle, ma belle, these are words that go together well, my Michelle
F           Bbm7        Eb6              D°         G7b9    C
Michelle, ma belle, sont les mots qui vont tres bien ensemble,
G7b9          C
tres bien ensemble.

   Fm                                 Ab7              Db
I love you, I love you, I love you, that's all I want to say.
C7           Fm              FmMaj7 Fm7      Fm6       Bbm/F
Until I find a way I will say the only words I know that you'll
     C
understand.

Refrain

   Fm                                 Ab7              Db
I need you, I need you, I need you, I need to make you see
C7                  Fm          FmMaj7 Fm7     Fm6      Bbm/F  C
oh what you mean to me until I do I'm hoping you will know what I mean.

Refrain

   Fm                                 Ab7              Db
I want you, I want you, I want you, I think you know by now
C7             Fm              FmMaj7 Fm7   Fm6    Bbm/F         C
I'll get to you somehow until I do I'm telling you so you'll understand.

F           Bbm7        Eb6              D°         G7b9    C
Michelle, ma belle sont les mots qui vont tres bien ensemble,
G7b9          C
tres bien ensemble
         Db            Fm/C              Bbm7       C              F
I will say the only words I know that you'll understand, my Michelle.
```

M + T: John Lennon & Paul McCartney
© Copyright 1965 Sony/ATV Music Publishing.
All Rights Reserved. International Copyright Secured.

# BEHIND BLUE EYES

(LIMP BIZKIT)
(THE WHO)

```
        Em7                 G6              Dsus2
1. No one knows what it's like, to be the bad man,
         Cadd9          Asus2
to be the sad man, behind blue eyes.
   Em7                G6            Dsus2
No one knows what it's like to be hated,
       Cadd9              Asus2
to be fated, to telling only lies.
```

**Refrain:**
```
         C   D              G            C          D         Em
But my dreams, they aren't as empty, as my conscience seems to be.
        Bm          C                 D                    A
I have hours, only lonely. My love is vengeance that's never free.
```

```
        Em7                 G6                    Dsus2
2. No one knows what it's like to feel these feelings
         Cadd9          Asus2
like I do, and I blame you.
   Em7                G6              Dsus2
No one bites back as hard on their anger,
             Cadd9                Asus2
none of my pain and woe, can show through.
```

Refrain

```
           Em7    G6     Dsus2
Discover    l.  i.  m.  p.  say it.
         Cadd9          Asus2
Discover    l.  i.  m.  p.  say it.
           Em7    G6     Dsus2
Discover    l.  i.  m.  p.  say it.
         Cadd9          Asus2
Discover    l.  i.  m.  p.  say it.
```

```
        Em7                 G6              Dsus2
3. No one knows what its like to be mistreated,
         Cadd9      Asus2
to be defeated, behind blue eyes.
      Em7                 G6                  Dsus2
And no one knows how to say that they're sorry
             Cadd9          Asus2
and don't worry I'm not telling lies.
```

Refrain

```
Em7                 G6              Dsus2
No one knows what it's like, to be the bad man,
         Cadd9          Asus2
to be the sad man, behind blue eyes.
```

M + T: Pete Townshend
© Fabulous Music Ltd.

# HEARTACHE TONIGHT

(EAGLES)

**Intro:** Bb F  F C  C G

```
        G                      Em              G                       Em
1. Somebody's gonna hurt someone before the night is through.
   G                        C                  G                     D
   Somebody's gonna come undone, there's nothing we can do.
   G                  Em              G                  Em
   Everybody wants to touch somebody if it takes all night.
   G                        C                      G                     D
   Everybody wants to take a little chance and make it come out right.
```

**Refrain:**
```
                         C                                            G
There's gonna be a heartache tonight, a heartache tonight, I know.
                         C                                            A
There's gonna be a heartache tonight, a heartache tonight, I know,
         D
Lord, I know.
```

2. Some people like to stay out late some folks can't hold out that long
   But nobody wants to go home now, there's too much going on.
   This night is gonna last forever, last all, last all summer long.
   Sometimes before the sun comes up, the radio is gonna play that song.

Refrain

```
                          G                          G7
There's gonna be a heartache tonight, the moon's shining bright,
         C                        C#°
so turn out the light and we'll get it right.
                          G                    D                       G
There's gonna be a heartache tonight, a heartache tonight, I know.
```

1. Strophe

Refrain

```
                    G                              G7
We can beat around the bushes, we can get down to the bone.
         C                        C#°
We can leave it in the parking lot but either way
                         G                    D                       G    C
there's gonna be a heartache tonight, a heartache tonight, I know.
                         G                    D                       G
There's gonna be a heartache tonight, a heartache tonight, I know.
```

**Outro:** Bb F  F C  C G  (4x)

M + T: Glenn Frey, Don Henley, Bob Seger and John Souther
© 1980 GEAR PUBL./ Woody Creek Music / Red Cloud Music / EMI Blackwood Music Inc. Warner/Chappell North America Ltd, London / Universal Music Publishing GmbH. Reproduced by permission of Faber Music Ltd and International Music Publications Ltd (a trading name of Faber Music Ltd). All Rights Reserved. Abdruck erfolgt mit freundlicher Genehmigung von MELODIE DER WELT, J. Michel GmbH & Co. KG, Frankfurt/Main.

# WATERLOO

(ABBA)

```
      D        E/D           A/C#    G/B       A
1. My my, at Waterloo Napoleon did surrender.
      D        E/D           A/C# G/B   D/A     A        Bm
Oh yeah, and I have met my destiny in quite a similar way.
                                E7              A    G D/F# A/E
The history book on the shelf is always repeating itself.
```

**Refrain:**
```
D                                 G
Waterloo. I was defeated, you won the war.
A                             D       A
Waterloo. Promise to love you for ever more.
D                                 G
Waterloo. Couldn't escape if I wanted to.
A                             D
Waterloo. Knowing my fate is to be with you.
            A                 D
Wa Wa Wa Wa Waterloo. Finally facing my Waterloo.
```

```
      D        E/D           A/C#    G/B       A
2. My my, I tried to hold you back but you were stronger.
      D        E/D           A/C# G/B   D/A     A        Bm
Oh yeah, and now it seems my only chance is giving up the fight.
                                E7              A
And how could I ever refuse, I feel like I win when I lose.
```

Refrain

```
    Bm                      E7                  A
So how could I ever refuse, I feel like I win when I lose.
D                                 G
Waterloo. Couldn't escape if I wanted to.
A                             D
Waterloo. Knowing my fate is to be with you.
            A                 D
Wa Wa Wa Wa Waterloo. Finally facing my Waterloo.
A                             D
Waterloo. Knowing my fate is to be with you.
            A                 D
Wa Wa Wa Wa Waterloo. Finally facing my Waterloo.
```

M + T: Benny Andersson, Björn Ulvaeus & Stig Anderson
© Copyright 1974 Universal/Union Songs Musikforlag AB.
Universal Music Publishing Limited.
All Rights Reserved. International Copyright Secured.

# AFRICA

(TOTO)

**Intro:** F Em Am7 (4x)

```
       G              Bm7           Em7
1. I hear the drums echoing tonight.
   G/D         F/C           C/D           Em7   F Em Am7
   She hears only whispers of some quiet conversation.
   G              Bm7           Em7
   She's coming in, twelve-thirty flight.
   G/D         F/C  ·                C/D           Em7   F Em Am7
   Moonlit wings reflect the stars that guide me toward salvation.
   G              Bm7           Em7
   I stopped an old man along the way
   G/D         F/C           C/D           Em7 F Em Am7
   hoping to find some old forgotten words or ancient melodies.
   G              Bm7       Em7
   He turned to me as if to say:
                      F                     Em Am7
   Hurry boy, it's waiting there for you!
```

**Refrain:**
```
Dm              Bb              F         C
It's gonna take a lot to drag me away from you.
Dm              Bb          F              C
There's nothing that a hundred men or more could ever do.
Dm          Bb          F    C
I bless the rains down in Africa.
Dm              Bb          F           Am  C Dm C/E
Gonna take some time to do the things we never had.
```

F Em Am7 (2x)

```
       G              Bm7           Em7
2. The wild dogs cry out in the night,
   G/D         F/C           C/D           Em7   F Em Am7
   they grow restless longing for some solitary company.
   G              Bm7           Em7
   I know that I must do what's right,
   G/D         F/C           C/D           Em7   F Em Am7
   sure as Kilimanjaro rises like Olympus over the Serengeti.
   G              Bm7           Em7
   I seem to cure what's deep inside
                      F                     Em Am7
   frightened of this thing that I've become.
```

Refrain

M + T: David Paich & Jeff Porcaro
© Copyright 1982 Hudmar Publishing Company
Incorporated/Cowbella Music, USA.
Sony/ATV Music Publishing (UK) Limited.
All Rights Reserved. International Copyright Secured.

# **RAWHIDE**

(THE BLUES BROTHERS)

```
Am
Rolling rolling rolling
Rolling rolling rolling
Rolling rolling rolling
Rolling rolling rolling
E   Am
Rawhide.

   Am
1. Rolling rolling rolling, though the streams are swollen,
C
keep them doggies rolling, Rawhide!
Am                      Dm     G         Am
Rain and wind and weather, hell bent for leather,
G       F            E
wishing my girl was by my side.
Am                            Dm        G       Am
All the things I'm missing, good fiddles, love and kissing,
   Dm         Am  G      Am
are waiting at the end of my ride.
```

**Refrain:**
```
        Am                       E
Move em' on, head em' up, head em' up, move em' on,
                              E
move em' on, head em' up, Rawhide.
        Am                       E
Cut em' out,  ride em' in, ride em' in, cut em' out,
                     F   E  Am
cut em' out, ride em' in, Rawhide.

        Am
2. Keep moving, moving, moving, though they're disapproving,
C
keep them doggies moving, Rawhide.
       Am               Dm     G         Am
Don't try to understand them, just rope, throw and brand em',
G       F            E
soon we'll be living high and wide.
Am                      Dm       G       Am
My heart's calculating, my true love will be waiting,
   Dm         Am  G      Am
be waiting at the end of my ride.
```

Refrain

```
Am
Rolling rolling rolling
Rolling rolling rolling
Rolling rolling rolling
Rolling rolling rolling
E   Am
Rawhide.
```

M + T: Ned Washington / Dimitry Tiomkin
© Copyright 1958 Patti Washington Music, USA/Volta Music Corporation, USA/Hinen Catharine.
Universal/MCA Music Limited/Universal Music Publishing MGB Limited/Shapiro Bernstein & Company Incorporated.
All Rights Reserved. International Copyright Secured.

# I WANT TO KNOW WHAT LOVE IS

(FOREIGNER)
[TRANSP. +1]

**Intro:** Dm   C   F   Bb   Dm
```
             C               F
1. I've got take a little time,
         Bb                  Dm
a little time to think things over.
                   C           F
I'd better read between the lines
           Bb              Dm    C   Dm
in case I need it when I'm older, oh.

                 C           F
2. Now this mountain I must climb
         Bb              Dm
feels like the world upon my shoulders.
                   C          F
Through the clouds I see love shine,
            Bb                  Dm
it keeps me warm as life grows colder.
```

**Bridge:**
```
Bb      Gm7   Gm          C/G            Gm
In my life there's been heartache and pain.
Gm7         Gm            C/G         Gm
I don't know if I can face it again.
Gm7         Gm            C/G         Gm
Can't stop now I've traveled so far
     Bb    F/A   Gm   F   Bb/C
to change this lonely life.
```

**Refrain:**
```
F                     Dm    C
I want to know what love is.
Gm          Dm  C
I want you to show me.
F                     Dm    C
I want to feel what love is.
Gm          Dm    C          Dm
I know you can show me, oh.

                 C          F
3. I'm gonna take a little time,
         Bb              Dm
a little time to look around me.
                 C       F
I've got nowhere left to hide,
              Bb               Dm
it looks like love has finally found me.
```

Bridge

Refrain 4x

M + T: Mick Jones
© Copyright 1984 Somerset Songs Publishing. This arrangement
© 2011 Somerset Songs Publishing, Incorporated. International
Copyright Secured. All Rights Reserved. Reprinted by permission
of Cherry Lane Music Company.

# THE WIND CRIES MARY

(JIMI HENDRIX)

**Intro:** Eb E F (4x)

```
   C           Bb                F
1. After all the jacks are in their boxes
   C           Bb              F
and the clowns have all gone to bed
   C           Bb              F
you can hear happiness staggering on down the street,
G       Bb          Eb E F
footsteps dressed in red.
        G    Bb       Eb E F   Eb E F
And the wind whispers Mary.

   C           Bb        F
2. A broom is drearily sweeping
   C         Bb              F
up the broken pieces of yesterdays life.
C           Bb         F
Somewhere a queen is weeping,
G           Bb          Eb E F
somewhere a king has no wife.
        G    Bb       Eb E F   Eb E F
And the wind, it cries Mary.

   C              Bb                 F
3. The traffic lights, they turn, uh, blue tomorrow
   C           Bb                F
and shine their emptiness down on my bed.
   C           Bb    F
The tiny island sags down stream
          G       Bb          Eb E F
cause the life that lived is, is dead.
        G    Bb       Eb E F   Eb E F
And the wind screams Mary.

   C              Bb          F
4. Uh, will the wind ever remember
        C         Bb              F
the names it has blown in the past?
              C              Bb             F
And with this crutch, its old age, and its wisdom
           G    Bb          Eb E F
it whispers no, this will be the last.
        G    Bb       Eb E F   Eb E F
And the wind cries Mary.
```

M + T: Jimi Hendrix
© Copyright 1967 Experience Hendrix L.L.C. (ASCAP).
All Rights Reserved. International Copyright Secured.

# BAILA ME

(GIPSY KINGS)

```
         G                              D
1. Cuando sei maria dolores, cuando sei quei mal d'amore,
              D7                              G
   cuando sei quei mal a su vera, cuando sei me va al dottore.
                                              D
   Cuando sei maria dolores, cuando sei quei mal d'amore,
              D7                              G
   cuando sei quei mal a su vera, cuando sei me va al dottore.
```

**Refrain:**
```
   G                              D
   Baila baila baila baila, baila baila baila me,
              D7                     G
   este rumba a ta guitara que yo siempre cantare.
                                                D
   Pero yo siempre cantare, pero yo siempre cantare,
              D7                     G
   este rumba a ta gitana, que yo siempre cantare.
```

1. Strophe

Refrain

```
            G            C      C7              G
Bridge: Que solo vivo enamora te, que solo vivo enamora te.
                       D                        G
   Me enamore de esta guitara, que ya se ponga a bailando.
```

Refrain

1. Strophe

Refrain

```
   G                                          D
   Pero yo siempre cantare, pero yo siempre cantare,
              D7                     G
   este rumba a ta gitana, que yo siempre cantare.
   G                                          D
   Pero yo siempre cantare, pero yo siempre cantare,
              D7                     G
   este rumba a ta gitana, que yo siempre cantare.
   G                                          D
   Pero yo siempre cantare, pero yo siempre cantare,
              D7                     G
   este rumba a ta gitana, que yo siempre cantare.
   G                                          D
   Pero yo siempre cantare, pero yo siempre cantare,
              D7                     G
   este rumba a ta gitana, que yo siempre cantare.
```

M + T: Andre Reyes, Nicolas Reyes, Canut Reyes,
Maurice Baliardo, Tonino Baliardo & Jacques Baliardo
© Copyright 1991 Sony/ATV Music Publishing (UK) Limited.
All Rights Reserved. International Copyright Secured.

# ROCK AROUND THE CLOCK

(BILL HALEY)
[TRANSP. +1]

```
G
One, two, three o'clock, four o'clock rock.
G
Five, six, seven o'clock, eight o'clock rock.
G
Nine, ten, eleven o'clock, twelve o'clock rock.
         D7
We gonna rock around the clock tonight.

           G                            G
1. Put your glad rags on, join me hon we'll have some fun
           G7
when the clock strikes one.
```

**Refrain:**
```
         C7
We gonna rock around the clock tonight,
          G
we gonna rock, rock, rock till the broad daylight,
         D7            C7              G        D7
we gonna rock, gonna rock around the clock tonight.

             G
2. When the clock strikes two and three and four
   G                   G7
if the band slows down, we'll yell for more.
```
Refrain

```
              G
3. When the chimes ring five and six and seven
   G                   G7
we'll be rocking up till the seventh heaven.
```
Refrain

```
                G
4. When it's eight, nine, ten, eleven too
   G               G7
I'll be going strong and so will you.
```
Refrain

```
                G
5. When the clock strikes twelve, we cool off again,
   G                   G7
start rocking around the clock again.
```
Refrain

```
         D7             C7              G
We gonna rock, gonna rock around the clock tonight.
```

M + T: Max C. Freedman, Jimmy de Knight
© 1952 by Myers Music Limited / Edition Ed Kassner Musikverlag.

# JOHNNY BLUE

(LENA VALAITIS)

**Intro:** Dm A F Gm A Dm

```
   Dm    A      F                  Gm        A    Dm     A
   Blue, blue, blue, Johnny blue, alle singen deine Lieder.
   Dm    A      F                  Gm        A         Dm
   Blue, blue, blue, Johnny blue, und die ganze Welt hört zu.
```

```
         F            C              Eb             Bb
   1. Er wuchs auf ohne Freunde, denn keiner wollt' spielen
         A                    Dm
   mit einem, der blind war, wie er.
         F         C             Eb            Bb
   Und er saß meist zu Hause. Die Jungen dort draußen,
         A                      Dm
   die riefen bloß hinter ihm her. Sie riefen:
```

```
   Dm    A      F                  Gm        A     Dm    A
   Blue, blue, blue, Johnny blue, welche Farbe hat die Sonne?
   Dm    A      F                  Gm        A        Dm
   Blue, blue, blue, Johnny blue, Kinder können grausam sein.
```

```
           F          C              Eb          Bb
   2. Auf der alten Gitarre, die ihm jemand schenkte,
         A                    Dm
   da spielte er, sie war sein Freund.
         F           C              Eb             Bb
   Seine Lieder, die klangen nach Hoffnung und Freude
         Dm             Bb         A
   und manchmal als ob jemand weint. Und er sang:
```

```
   Ebm   Bb     Gb                 Abm       Bb    Ebm    Bb
   Blue, blue, blue, Johnny blue, welche Farbe hat die Sonne?
   Ebm   Bb     Gb                 Abm         Bb       Ebm
   Blue, blue, blue, Johnny blue, und die Kinder hörten zu.
```

```
                Bb       Gb
   Und bald spielte keiner so wie er.
   Abm     Bb           Ebm
   Seine Lieder, die gingen den Menschen ans Herz.
            Bb         Gb            Abm        Bb      Ebm
   Und er malte Farben aus Musik und vergaß all seinen Schmerz.
```

```
            Gb          Db           E              B
   3. Und bald kamen zehntausend zu seinen Konzerten,
         Bb                Ebm
   denn er schenkte ihnen die Kraft
         Gb         Db          E              B
   an die Zukunft zu glauben im Dunkel des Lebens.
         Ebm      B       Bb
   Er hatte es selber geschafft.
```

```
   Oh, Johnny blue, blue, blue, Johnny blue, und sie kamen immer wieder,
   Blue, blue, blue, Johnny blue, keiner spielt so schön, wie du.
   Blue, blue, blue, Johnny blue, alle singen deine Lieder.
   blue, blue, blue, Johnny blue, und die ganze Welt hört zu.
```

M + T: Ralph Siegel, Bernd Meinunger
© Copyright 1982 Edition Meridian Ralph Siegel KG, Germany.
Warner/Chappell Overseas Holdings Limited, London.
Reproduced by permission of Faber Music Limited.
All Rights Reserved.

# WILD WORLD

(CAT STEVENS)

```
      Am            D7                 G
1. Now that I've lost every thing to you,
            Cmaj7               F
you say you wanna start something new
         Dm              E
and it's breaking my heart you're leaving.

Baby, I'm grieving.
 Am                   D7               G
But if you want to leave, take good care,
              Cmaj7                F
hope you have a lot of nice things to wear
           Dm                 E       G7
but then a lot of nice things turn bad out there.
```

**Refrain:**
```
C   G              F
Oh, baby, baby it's a wild world.
G           F            C
It's hard to get by just upon a smile.
C   G              F
Oh, baby, baby it's a wild world.
G          F             C          D E
I'll always remember you like a child, girl.
```

```
      Am               D7                      G
2. You know I've seen a lot of what the world can do
         Cmaj7              F
and it's breaking my heart in two
         Dm                   E
because I never want to see you sad girl.

Don't be a bad girl.
 Am                   D7               G
But if you want to leave, take good care,
              Cmaj7                     F
hope you make a lot of nice friends out there
           Dm                  E       G7
but just remember there's a lot of bad everywhere.
```
**Refrain:**
```
C   G              F
Oh, baby, baby it's a wild world.
G           F            C
It's hard to get by just upon a smile.
C   G              F
Oh, baby, baby it's a wild world.
G          F             C          D E   Am D7 G Cmaj7 F Dm E
I'll always remember you like a child, girl.   la, la, la...
E          Am
Baby I love you.
    Am                D7               G
3. But if you want to leave, take good care,
              Cmaj7                     F
hope you make a lot of nice friends out there
           Dm                  E       G7
but just remember theres a lot of bad everywhere.    Refrain
```

M + T: Cat Stevens
© Copyright 1970 Salafa Limited. BMG Rights Management (UK) Limited.
All Rights Reserved. International Copyright Secured.

# DSCHINGIS KHAN

(DSCHINGIS KHAN)

     Em                                            G
1. Sie ritten um die Wette mit dem Steppenwind, tausend Mann. Ha Hu Ha!
   Em                                       G
Und einer ritt voran, dem folgten alle blind, Dschingis Khan. Ha Hu Ha!
  Am
Die Hufe ihrer Pferde durchpeitschten den Sand,
    Em
sie trugen Angst und Schrecken in jedes Land,
    Am          F#/A#        B7
und weder Blitz noch Donner hielt sie auf. Hu Ha!

**Refrain:**
Em
Dsching, Dsching, Dschingis Khan!
G
He, Reiter! Ho, Reiter! He, Reiter! Immer weiter!
Em
Dsching, Dsching, Dschingis Khan!
G
Auf, Brüder! Sauft, Brüder! Rauft, Brüder! Immer wieder!
Am                                       Em
Lasst noch Wodka holen, hohoho! Denn wir sind Mongolen, hahahaha!
Am          F#/A#       B7
Und der Teufel kriegt uns früh genug!
Em
Dsching, Dsching, Dschingis Khan!
G
He, Reiter! Ho, Reiter! He, Reiter! Immer weiter!
Em
Dsching, Dsching, Dschingis Khan!
G
He, Männer! Ho, Männer! Tanzt, Männer, so wie immer!
Am                                 Em
Und man hört ihn lachen, hohohoho! Immer lauter lachen, hahahaha!
Am         B7         Em
Und er leert den Krug in einem Zug.

      Em
2. Und jedes Weib, das ihm gefiel,
                  G
das nahm er sich in sein Zelt. Ha Hu Ha!
  Em
Es hieß, die Frau, die ihn nicht liebte,
               G
gab es nicht auf der Welt. Ha Hu Ha!
  Am
Er zeugte sieben Kinder in einer Nacht,
    Em
und über seine Feinde hat er nur gelacht,
    Am          F#/A#     B7
denn seiner Kraft konnt keiner widerstehn. Hu Ha!

Refrain

M + T: Ralph Siegel, Bernd Meinunger
© 1979 Edition Meridian Ralph Siegel KG, Germany.
Warner/Chappell Overseas Holdings Limited, London. Reproduced by permission of Faber Music Limited.
All Rights Reserved.

# THE LETTER

(BOX TOPS)

```
Am                       F
Give me a ticket for an aeroplane,
G               D7
ain't got time to take the fastest train.
Am                  F
Lonely days are gone, I'm agoing home,
   E7              Am
my baby just wrote me a letter.

Am                            F
I don't care how much money I gotta spend,
G               D7
got to get back to my baby again.
Am                  F
Lonely days are gone, I'm agoing home,
   E7              Am
my baby just wrote me a letter.

            C        G              F      C       G
Well she wrote me a letter, said she couldn't live without me no more.
C           G          F          C
Listen mister, can't you see I got to get back
      G            E7
to my baby once more. Anyway.

Am                       F
Give me a ticket for an aeroplane,
G               D7
ain't got time to take the fastest train.
Am                  F
Lonely days are gone, I'm agoing home,
   E7              Am
my baby just wrote me a letter.

            C        G              F      C       G
Well she wrote me a letter, said she couldn't live without me no more.
C           G          F          C
Listen mister, can't you see I got to get back
      G            E7
to my baby once more. Anyway.

Am                       F
Give me a ticket for an aeroplane,
G               D7
ain't got time to take the fastest train.
Am                  F
Lonely days are gone, I'm agoing home,
   E7              Am
my baby just wrote me a letter.
   E7              Am
My baby just wrote me a letter.
```

M + T: Carson, Wayne
© 1967 Budde Songs, Inc.
Rechte für D/A/CH: Rolf Budde Musikverlag GmbH.

## YOU

(TEN SHARP)

```
Intro: Bm7 E/B G/B G/A D F#/A#
    Bm7              E           G/E G/A        D      F#/A#
1. It's alright with me as long as you are by my side,
Bm7              E              G/E      G/A          D     F#/A#
talk or just say nothing, I don't mind your looks never lie.

Bm    Bm/A        G  G/F# Em7        G/A D           F#/A#
I was always on the run,      finding out    what I was looking for and
Bm    Bm/A        G  G/F# Em7 G/A        D      F#/A#
I was always insecure,    just    until I found

      Bm7                  E
2. Words often don't come easy,
       G/E      G/A              D           F#/A#
I never learned to show you the inside of me, oh no, my baby but
Bm7            E                G/E G/A          D     F#/A#
you were always patient, dragging out what I tried to hide.

Bm    Bm/A        G  G/F# Em7        G/A D           F#/A#
I was always on the run,      finding out    what I was looking for and
Bm    Bm/A        G  G/F# Em7 G/A        D      F#/A#
I was always insecure,    just    until I found, oho.


Refrain:
D                             Gmaj7 Em7   G/A            D
You, you were always on my mind, you, you're the one I'm living for.
D                             Gmaj7 Em/C# A/F# Bm7
You, you're my everlasting fire,
        Gm/Bb
you're my always shining star.

Intro

      Bm7                E
3. The night's always a good friend,
         G/E  G/A              D    F#/A#
a glass of wine and the lights down low.
Bm7       E               G/E G/A         D     F#/A#
You lying beside me, me full of love and filled with hope.

Bm    Bm/A        G  G/F# Em7        G/A D           F#/A#
I was always on the run,      finding out    what I was looking for and
Bm    Bm/A        G  G/F# Em7 G/A        D      F#/A#
I was always insecure,    just    until I found, oho.

Refrain

Intro
```

M + T: Nicolaas Hermes & Teunes Groen
© Copyright 1991 Sony/ATV Music Publishing (UK) Limited.
All Rights Reserved. International Copyright Secured.

# MASSACHUSETTS

(BEE GEES)

```
   G              Am       C     G
1. Feel I'm going back to Massachusetts.
G                  Am      C     G
Something's telling me I must go home.
                                     C
And the lights all went out in Massachusetts.
            G          D7            G   Am D7
The day I left her standing on her own.

   G              Am       C     G
2. Tried to hitch a ride to San Francisco.
G            Am        C     G
Gotta do the things I wanna do.
                                     C
And the lights all went out in Massachusetts.
            G          D7            G   Am D7
They brought me back to see my way with you.

   G              Am       C     G
3. Talk about the life in Massachusetts.
G                  Am      C     G
Speak about the people I have seen.
                                     C
And the lights all went out in Massachusetts.
            G          D7            G   Am D7
And Massachusetts is one place I have seen.

          Am      C    G
I will remember Massachusetts.
          Am      C    G
I will remember Massachusetts.
```

M + T: Barry Gibb, Maurice Gibb, Robin Gibb
© Crompton Songs / Universal Music Publishing International MGB Limited. Warner/Chappell Music Limited, London / Universal Music Publishing MGB Limited. Reproduced by permission of Faber Music Limited. All Rights Reserved. International Copyright Secured.

# IN THE YEAR 2525

(ZAGER & EVANS)

```
Em                                   D
In the year twentyfive twentyfive, if man is still alive,
C                              B7
if woman can survive, they may find.
Em
In the year thirtyfive thirtyfive,
D
ain't gonna need to tell the truth, tell no lies,
C                              B7
ev'rything you think, do and say is in the pill you took today.
```

In the year 4545, you ain't gonna need your teeth, won't need your eyes
You won't find a thing to chew, nobody's gonna look at you.

In the year 5555, your arm's hangin' limp at your sides, your legs got
nothin' to do, some machine is doin' that for you.

In the year 6565, you won't need your husband, won't need no wife,
you'll pick your son, pick your daughter too, from the bottom of a long
glass tube.

In the year 7575, if God's a comin' He oughta' make it by then, maybe
he'll look around himself and say, guess it's time for the judgement
day.

In the year 8585, God is gonna shake his mighty head, he'll either say
I'm pleased where man has been. Or tear it down and start again.

In the year 9595, I'm kinda wonderin' if man is gonna be alive. He's
taken ev'rything this old earth can give and he ain't put back nothin'.

Now it's been 10.000 years, man has cried a billion tears, for what, he
never know, now man's reign is through.

But through eternal night, the twickling of starlight so very far away,
maybe it's only yesterday.

M + T: Richard Evans
© Chelsea Music Publishing Co. Ltd. Rechte für D/A/CH: Edition
Nordton. Mit freundlicher Genehmigung der Rolf Budde
Musikverlag GmbH, Berlin.

# THE TIMES THEY ARE A-CHANGING

(BOB DYLAN)

```
       G            Em         C          G
1. Come gather around people wherever you roam
       G           Am         C              D
and admit that the waters around you have grown
       G              Em             C              G
and accept it that soon you'll be drenched to the bone
            G       Am          D
if your time to you is worth saving.
           D          G                              D
Then you better start swimming or you'll sink like a stone
       G                  C  D  G
for the times they are a-changing.
```

2. Come writers and critics, who prophecies with your pen
and keep your eyes wide the change won't come again
and don't speak too soon for the wheel's still in spin
and there's no telling who that is naming.
For the loser now will be later to win
for the times they are a-changing.

3. Come senators, congress-men, please heed the call,
don't stand in the doorway, don't block up the hall
for he that gets hurt will be he who has stalled.
There's a battle outside and it's raging,
it'll soon shake your windows and rattle your walls
for the times they are a-changing.

4. Come mothers and fathers throughout the land
and don't criticize what you can't understand.
Your sons and your daughters are beyond your command,
your old road is rapidly again.
Please get out of the new one if you can't lend your hand
for the times they are a-changing.

5. The line it is drawn the curse it is cast,
the slow one now will later be fast.
As the present now will later be past
the order is rapidly fading.
And the first one now will later be last
for the times they are a-changing.

M + T: Bob Dylan
© Copyright 1963, 1964 Warner Brothers Incorporated.
© Copyright Renewed 1991, 1992 Special Rider Music.
All Rights Reserved. International Copyright Secured.

# CITY OF NEW ORLEANS

(STEVE GOODMAN)
(WILLIE NELSON)

```
        D            A           D
1. Ridin' on the City of New Orleans,
   Bm           G            D    A
   Illinois Central monday mornin' rail.
   D               A              D
   Fifteen cars and fifteen restless riders,
   Bm              A               D
   three conductors and twentyfive sacks of mail.
       Bm
   All along the southbound Odyssey,
       F#m                         A
   the train pull out Of Kankakee and rolls along
                         E       Bm
   the houses, farms and fields, passin' towns that have no name
       F#m
   and freight yards full of old black men,
         A            A7            D
   and the grave yards of the rusted auto mobiles.

              G         A         D
   Refrain: Good morning America, how are you?
         Bm              G         D    A7
   Say, don't you know me, I'm your native son.
         D             A          Bm
   I'm the train they call the City of New Orleans.
           G            A               D
   I'll be gone five hundred miles when the day is done.
```

2. Dealin' card games with the old man in the club car.
Penny a point and noone keeping score.
Pass the paper back, that holds the bottle,
feel the wheels, rumblin' neath the floor.
And the sons of Foreman Harders and the sons of engineers
ride their father's magic carpets made of steel.
Mothers sweep their babies to sleep rocking on the gentle beat
and the rhythm of the rails is all they feel.

3. Night time on the City of New Orleans,
changing cars in Memphis, Tennessee.
Half way home we will be there by morning,
through the Mississippi darkness, rolling down to the sea.
But all the towns and people seem to fade into a bad dream,
and the steel rail still ain't heard the news.
The conducter sings his song again,
the passengers will please refrain.
This train got to disappear in the railroad blues.

M + T: Steve Goodman
© Copyright 1973 Jurisdad Music & Turnpike Tom Music, USA.
Sony/ATV Music Publishing (UK) Limited.
All Rights Reserved. International Copyright Secured.

## TWIST IN MY SOBRIETY

(TANITA TIKARAM)

```
   Fm                        Bbm
1. All god's children need travelling shoes
C                       Fm
Drive your problem from here
Fm                      Bbm
All good people read good books
C                           Fm
Now your conscience is clear I hear you talk girl
C                          Fm
Now your conscience is clear
```

```
   Fm                       Bbm
2. In the morning when I wipe my brow
C                  Fm
Wipe the miles away
Fm                     Bbm
I like to think I can be so willed
C                              Fm
And never do what you say I'll never hear you
C                          Fm
And never do what you say
```

**Refrain:**
```
Fm       C                Fm
Look my eyes are just holograms
            C                     Fm
Look your love has drawn red from my hands
       Bbm                    Fm
From my hands you know you'll never be
                 C            Fm
More than twist in my sobriety
                 C            Fm
More than twist in my sobriety
                 C            Fm   Fm Bbm C Fm
More than twist in my sobriety
```

```
   Fm                      Bbm
3. We just poked a little pie
C                      Fm
For the fun the people had at night
Fm                       Bbm
Late at night don't need hostility
C                         Fm
The timid smile and pause to free
```

```
   Fm                       Bbm
4. I don't care about their different thoughts
C                        Fm
Different thoughts are good for me
Fm            Bbm
Up in arms and chaste the whole
C                      Fm
All god's children took their toll
```

Refrain

M + T: Tanita Tikaram
© 1988 by BROGUE MUSIC
Warner/Chappell Music Limited, London.
Reproduced by permission of Faber Music Limited.
All Rights Reserved.

## WORDS

(BEE GEES)

```
   G                                             A
1. Smile an everlasting smile, a smile can bring you near to me.
      D                                          C    . G
Don't ever let me find you gone, cause that would bring a tear to me.
   Bb
This world has lost it's glory,
                               F
let's start a brand new story now, my love.
   G                                        A        D
Right now, there'll be no other time, and I can show you how, my love.

   G                                      A
2. Talk in everlasting words and dedicate them all to me.
      D                                      C       G
And I will give you all my life, I'm here if you should call to me.
   Bb                                     D
You think that I don't even mean a single word I say.

D           G                      D                     G
It's only words, and words are all I have to take your heart away.
D           G                      D                     G
It's only words, and words are all I have to take your heart away.
D           G                      D                     G
It's only words, and words are all I have to take your heart away.
```

M + T: Maurice Gibb, Robin Gibb, Barry Alan Gibb
© Universal Music Publishing MGB International Limited, Crompton Songs, Gibb Brothers Music. Warner/Chappell Music Ltd, London. Reproduced by permission of Faber Music Ltd. International Copyright Secured. All Rights Reserved.

# FALLING IN LOVE AGAIN

(EAGLE EYE CHERRY)

**Intro:** Am C G G Am C G G

```
           Am      C   G                        Am      C        G
1. I'm so tired of falling in love, finding it easier to fall out.
           Am      C   G                        Am      C        G
I can't deny it, I feel it inside, I'll keep its fire you can't hide.
```

**Refrain:**
```
              Am           C       G
I'm falling in love again, ain't nothing I can do.
              Am         C G
Falling in love again this time it's with you.
           Am    C   G
When I fall it's always the same
                  Am     C          G
and I'm so tired of playing this game.
```

```
           Am        C       G
2. It's so long now since I gave up my heart.
                     Am            C      G
I've kept the light down, I don't wanna get it hard.
           Am          C      G
So let me tell you now, I just wanna be sure
                  Am       C       G
that you won't hurt me. Can you promise me that?
```

Refrain

```
         Am                  C
Got to tell me if you're gonna break my heart
      G
If you don't wanna take the chance.
      Am                     C             G
And if it ain't true, all it's gonna be is nothing but a poor romance.
      F                         C                    G
So, give me that promise to hold on now, I'll never let you go.
      F                  C       F       G
I've got to have something on, oh then you know now.
```

Refrain

```
G        Am         C G
Falling in love again.
Falling in love again.
Falling in love again.
```

M + T: Eagle-Eye Cherry
© Published by Kobalt Music Publishing Ltd.

# SWEAT (A LA LA LA LA LONG)

(INNER CIRCLE)

```
I've been watching you.
C             Am                  Dm                    G
A la la la la long, a la la la la long long li long long long. Come on!
C             Am                  Dm                    G
A la la la la long, a la la la la long long li long long long. Hey!


      C           Am          Dm          G
1. Standing across the room I saw you smile.
C             Am            Dm          G
Said I want to talk to you for a little while.
C           Am            Dm7                    G
But before I make my move my emotions start running wild.
C             Am          Dm        G
My tongue gets tied, and that's no lie,
                    C     Am Dm
looking in your eyes,
G                           C             Am
looking in your big brown eyes.  Ooh yeah
           Dm                G
And I've got this to say to you. Hey!
```

**Refrain:**
```
C             Am                Dm                    G
Girl, I want to make you sweat, sweat till you can't sweat no more.
C             Am         Dm                        G
And if you cry out, I'm gonna push it some more, more, more.
C             Am                Dm                    G
Girl, I want to make you sweat, sweat till you can't sweat no more.
C             Am         Dm              G                    C
And if you cry out, I'm gonna push it, push it, push it some more.

              Am                  Dm                    G
A la la la la long, a la la la la long long li long long long. Come on!
C             Am                  Dm                    G
A la la la la long, a la la la la long long li long long long. Hey!


2. So I said to myself, "If she loves me or not?"
But the dreads don't know, that love is his to get.
With a little bit of this, and a little bit of that,
my lyric goes on the attack.
My tongue gets tied, and that's no lie,
looking in your eyes,
looking in your big brown eyes, oh girl.
And I've got this to say to you. Hey!

Refrain

              Am                  Dm                    G
A la la la la long, a la la la la long long li long long long. Come on!
C             Am                  Dm                    G
A la la la la long, a la la la la long long li long long long. Hey!
```

M + T: Ian Lewis
© Copyright 1992 Rock Pop Music.
EMI Music Publishing Limited, London, W8 5SW.
Reproduced by permission of Faber Music Limited a trading name of Faber Music Ltd)
All Rights Reserved.

## ARE YOU LONESOME TONIGHT?

(ELVIS PRESLEY)

**Intro:** C  Dm  G  C  G7

```
      C           Em             Am
Are you lonesome tonight, do you miss me tonight?
      C          C7        F
Are you sorry we drifted apart?
            G                G7
Does your memory stray to a brighter sunny day,
       G              G7           C
when I kissed you and called you sweetheart?
      C7                           F
Do the chairs in your parlor seem empty and bare?
       D7                          G          G7
Do you gaze at your doorstep and picture me there?
        C              Em           D
Is your heart filled with pain, shall I come back again?
         Dm        G7          C       G7
Tell me dear are you lonesome tonight.
```

Gesprochen:
```
C          Em        Am
I wonder if you are lonesome tonight.
                                           C
You know someone said that the world is a stage,
                   C7
and you must play a part.
                                   F
Fate had me playing in love with you as my sweetheart.
                                     G
Act one was when I met you, I loved you at first glance.
G7                                      G
You read your line so cleverly and never missed a cue.
              G7
Then came act 2, you seemed to change and you acted strange,
    C             C7
and why I'll never know.
                              F
Honey, you lied when you said you loved me,
                          D
and I had no cause to doubt you.
                                G
But I'd rather go on hearing your lies,
          G7               C
than go on living without you.
                Em                  D7
Now the stage is bare and I'm standing there
                   Dm
with emptiness all around.
                G7
And if you won't come back to me,
          C                     G7
then they can bring the curtain down.
```

```
        C              Em           D
Is your heart filled with pain, shall I come back again?
         Dm        G7          C
Tell me dear are you lovesome tonight.
```

M + T: Roy Turk & Lou Handman
© Copyright 1926 Redwood Music Limited.
All Rights Reserved. International Copyright Secured.

# MONDAY MONDAY

(THE MAMAS & THE PAPAS)
[TRANSP. -1]

```
G  C/G G    C/G   G  C/G G    C/G   G  C/G G
Ba da, ba da da da, ba da, ba da da da, ba da, ba da

     C/G    G    C/G G C/G    G    C/G G
1. Monday, Monday, so good to me,
C/G    G        C/G      G                    F
Monday morning, it was all I hoped it would be.
         Bb                                   D
Oh Monday morning, Monday morning couldn't guarantee,
                G              C/G                 G
that Monday evening you would still be here with me.

     C/G    G           C/G       G
2. Monday, Monday, can't trust that day,
C/G   G         C/G         G                 F
Monday, Monday, sometimes it just turns out that way.
         Bb                                           D
Oh Monday morning you gave me no warning of what was to be,
             G                    F/G                  G
oh Monday, Monday, how could you leave and not take me.

Ab
Every other day, every other day,
                                F
every other day of the week is fine, yeah!
Ab
But whenever Monday comes, but whenever Monday comes,
                G              E7
you can find me crying all of the time.

        A    D/A A  D/A    A   D/A A
1. Monday, Monday, so good to me,
D/A    A        D/A      A                    G
Monday morning, it was all I hoped it would be.
         C                                    E
But Monday morning, Monday morning couldn't guarantee,
                A              G/A                 A
that Monday evening you would still be here with me.

Bb
Every other day, every other day,
                                G
every other day of the week is fine, yeah!
Bb
But whenever Monday comes, but whenever Monday comes,
                E7             A     G
you can find me crying all of the time.

        A    D/A A    D/A      A   D/A A
3. Monday, Monday, can't trust that day,
D/A    A     D/A A      D/A        A   D/A A
Monday, Monday, it just turns out that way.
     D/A    A     D/A  A   D/A  A    D/A A
Oh, Monday, Monday, won't go away,
D/A    A     D/A A    D/A      A   D/A A
Monday, Monday, it's here to stay.
```

M + T: John Phillips
© Copyright 1966 Trousdale Music Publishers Incorporated.
Universal/MCA Music Limited. All Rights Reserved.
International Copyright Secured.

# SUSPICIOUS MINDS

(ELVIS PRESLEY)

```
      G                       C
1. We're caught in a trap, I can't walk out
   D         C             G     C
because I love you too much baby.
   G                    C
Why can't you see what you're doing to me
   D                  C          D C  Bm D7
when you don't believe a word I say?

C           G            Bm         C      D
We can't go on together with suspicious minds
Em          Bm           C          D
and we can't build our dreams on suspicious minds.

      G                            C
2. So, if an old friend I know drops by to say hello,
   D             C         G          C
would I still see suspicion in your eyes?
   G                  C
Here we go again asking where I've been,
   D              C             D C    Bm D7
you can't see these tears are real I'm crying.

C           G            Bm         C      D
We can't go on together with suspicious minds
Em          Bm           C          B7
and we can't build our dreams on suspicious minds

Em           Bm          C        D
Oh let our love survive or dry the tears from your eyes.
Em                  Bm
Let's, don't let a good thing die
C              D                G
when honey, you know I've never lied to you.
C   G     D7   C
Mmm yeah, yeah.

      G                       C
1. We're caught in a trap, I can't walk out
   D         C             G     C
because I love you too much baby.
   G                    C
Why can't you see what you're doing to me
   D                  C          D C  Bm D7
when you don't believe a word I say?
```

M + T: Francis Zambon
© Copyright 1969 Sony/ATV Songs LLC, USA.
Sony/ATV Music Publishing.
All Rights Reserved. International Copyright Secured.

# HURRICANE

(BOB DYLAN)

**Intro:** Am    F    Am    F

```
    Am                            F
1. Pistol shots ring out in the barroom night,
Am                       F
enter Patty Valentine from the upper hall.
Am                       F
She sees the bartender in a pool of blood,
Am                   F
cries out "My God they killed them all!"
C                      F
Here comes the story of the Hurricane,
C                    F
the man the authorities came to blame
Dm              C
for something that he never done.
Dm                    C         Em            Am
Put in a prison cell but one time he could have been
    F         C     G  Am  F  Am  F
the champion of the world.
```

2. Three bodied lying there does Patty see
and another man named Bello moving mysteriously.
"I didn't do it", he says and he throws up his hands.
"I was only robbin the register, I hope you understand
I saw them leavin", he says and he stops.
One of us had better call the cops,
so Patty calls the cops
and they arrive on the scene with their red lights flashin
in the hot New Jersey night
3. Meanwhile somewhere in another part of town
Rubin Carter and a couple of friends are driving around
number one contender for the middleweight crown
had no idea what kind of shit was about to go down
when a cop pulled him over on the side of the road
just like the time before and the time before that
in Paterson that just the ways things go.
If you're black you might as well not show up on the streets,
less you wanna draw the heat.
4. Alfred Bello had a partner and he had a rap for the cops.
Him and Arthur Dexter Bradley were just out prowlin around.
He said "I saw two men runnin out, they looked like middleweights,
they jumped into a white car with out of state plates".
And Miss Patty Valentine just nodded her head.
Cop said "Wait a minute boys, this one's not dead",
so they took him to the infirmary
and although this man could hardly see,
they told him that he could identify the guilty men.
5. Four in the morning and they haul Rubin in.
Take him to the hospital and bring him upstairs
the wounded man looks up though his one dying eye
says "why'd you bring him here for? he ain't the guy!"
Yes, here's the story of the Hurricane.
The man the authorities came to blame
for something that he never done,
put in a prison cell but one time he could've been
the champion of the world.
6. Four months later the ghetto's in flame.
Rubin's in South America fightin for his name

while Arthur Dexter Bradley's still in the robbery game
and the cops are puttin the screw to him looking for somebody to blame.
"Remember that murder that happened in a bar?"
"Remember you said you saw the getaway car?"
"You think you'd like to play ball with the law?"
"Think it might have been that fighter that you saw running that night?"
"Don't forget that you are white".
**7.** Arthur Dexter Bradley said "I'm really not sure".
Cops said "A poor boy like you could really use a break.
We got you for the motel job and were talking to your friend Bello.
Now you don't want to have to go back to jail, be a nice fellow.
You'll be doin' society a favor.
That son of a bitch is brave and getting braver.
We want to put his ass in the stir.
We want to pin this trip murder on him.
He ain't no Gentleman Jim".
**8.** Rubin could take a man out with just one punch,
he never did like to talk about it all that much.
It's my work he'd say, I do it for pay
and when it's over I'd just as soon go on my way
up to some paradise
where the trout streams flow and the air is nice
and ride a horse along a trail
but then they took him to the jail house
where they try to make a man into a mouse.
**9.** All of Rubin's card were marked in advance.
The trial was a pig-circus, he never had a chance,
the judge made Rubin's witnesses drunkards from the slums
to the white folks who watched he was a revolutionary bum
but to the black folks he was a crazy nigger,
no one doubted that he pulled the trigger
and though they could not produce the gun,
the D.A. said he was the one who did the deed.
And the all-white jury agreed
**10.** Rubin Carter was falsely tried
the crime was murder "one", guess who testified?
Bello and Bradley and the both badly lied
and the newspapers all went along for the ride
how can the life of such a man
be in the palm of some fool's hand?
To see him obviously framed
couldn't help but be ashamed to live in a land
where justice is a game.
**11.** Now all the criminals in their coats and their ties
are free to drink martinis and watch the sun rise
while Rubin sits like Buddha in a ten foot cell
an innocent man in a living hell.
That's the story of the Hurricane
but it won't be over till they clear his name
and give him back the time he's done,
put in a prison cell but one time he could've been
the champion of the world.

M + T: Bob Dylan & Jacques Levy
© Copyright 1975 Ram's Horn Music. All Rights Reserved.
International Copyright Secured.

# ADESSO TU

(EROS RAMAZZOTTI)

**Intro:** Fm Db

```
Fm            Db           Fm Db Fm         Db           Bbm
Nato ai bordi di periferia    dove i tram non vanno avanti più
                          Fm
dove l'aria è popolare è più facile sognare
Db            C           Fm
che guardare in faccia la realtà.

Fm                                                    Bbm
Quanta gente giovane va via a cercare più di quel che ha

forse perchè i pugni presi
Fm                    Db                  C7        Fm
a nessuno li ha mai resi e dentro fanno male ancor di più.

       Bbm          Eb          Ab           Fm
Ed ho imparato che nella vita nessuno mai ci da di più
        Bbm         Cm7         Db             Eb
ma quanto fiato quanta salita andare avanti senza voltarsi mai.
```

**Refrain:**
```
Eb   Ab  Ab/G  Fm  Fm/Eb
E ci sei adesso tu
        Db                     Bbm        Eb
a dare un senso ai giorni miei va tutto bene dal momento
     Ab  Ab/G  Fm Fm/Eb
che ci sei adesso tu
       Db              Bbm         Eb              Ab
ma non dimentico tutti gli amici miei che sono ancora là.

         Bbm         Eb         Ab   Ab/G    Fm
E ci si trova sempre più soli a questa età non sai non sai.
Ab         Bbm          Cm7         Db             Eb
Ma quante corse ma quanti voli andare avanti senz'arrivare mai.
```

**Refrain:**
```
Eb   Ab  Ab/G  Fm  Fm/Eb
E ci sei adesso tu
         Db                   Bbm           Eb
al centro dei pensieri miei la parte interna dei respiri tu
   Ab  Ab/G   Fm Fm/Eb       Db              Bbm        Eb        Ab  E7
sarai la volontà che non si limita tu che per me sei già una rivincita.
```
**Solo:** A A/G# F#m F#m/E D

```
       Bm7         E7         A          G#7
Adesso sai chi è quell' uomo che c'è in me.
F#m                                                     Bm
Nato ai bordi di periferia dove non ci torno quasi più
                         F#m
resta il vento che ho lasciato come un treno già passato
D          C#
oggi che mi sei accanto,
D          C#           D         C#           F#m
oggi che ci sei soltanto, oggi che ci sei adesso tu.
```

M + T: Pierangelo Cassano / Eros Ramazzotti / Adelio Cogliati
© Errebiemme Ed. Musicali Srl., Universal Music Publishing Ricordi SRL.
Universal Music Publishing Limited. All Rights Reserved. International Copyright Secured.

# WAS SOLL DAS

(HERBERT GRÖNEMEYER)

```
         A
1. Sein Pyjama liegt in meinem Bett, sein Kamm in meiner Bürste steckt.
   F#m
Was soll das? Was soll das?
         A
Seine Schuhe stehn in Reih und Glied, ein Anblick den man gerne sieht.
   F#m
Was soll das? Was soll das?
   C#m                                       E
Sein Aftershave klebt in der Luft, warum hat er nicht gleich meins
benutzt.
   A
Was soll das? Was soll das?

2. Du sagst, er wohnt ab jetzt bei dir, und zeigst nur stumm auf die
Ausgangstür.
Was soll das? Was soll das?
Du kochst gerade sein Leibgericht, meine Faust will unbedingt in sein
Gesicht.
Und darf nicht! Und darf nicht!
Von Verlegenheit überhaupt keine Spur, er ist nun mal eine Frohnatur.
Er grinst nur! Er grinst nur!
```

**Refrain:**
```
A       D    E                    A         D
Womit hab ich das verdient, daß der mich so blöde angrient?
    A             E            A
Warum hast du mich nicht wenigstens gewarnt? Oh.
      D    E                         A         D
Zu einer betrognen Nacht hätt ich vielleicht nichts gesagt,
          A             E                   A        D
hätt mich zwar schockiert, wahrscheinlich hätt ich's noch kapiert.
     A         E                      A
Aber du hast ja, uh, gleich auf Liebe gemacht!

3. Sein Kopf stützt sich auf sein Doppelkinn, seit wann zieht's dich zu
Fetten hin?
Los, sag was. Los, sag was.
Wie man an einen solchen Schwamm sein Herz einfach verschleudern kann?!
Los, sag was. Los, sag was.
Ich laß dich viel zu oft allein, aber der muß es doch nun wirklich nicht
sein!
Was soll das? Was soll das?
Refrain

D               B              D                B
Ihr glotzt mit euren Unschuldsmienen wie zwei, die einander verdienen,
D                    A       E
Spielt verliebt, doch ihr lacht zu laut.
D              B               D              B
Hat dich, beim Wühlen in den Kissen, denn nie dein Gewissen gebissen?
D              A        E              B     F#   B
Seit wann bist du so abgebrüht, hast mich so schnell abgeliebt? Oh!

Refrain 2x (ein Ton höher)
```

M + T: Herbert Grönemeyer
© Copyright Grönland Musikverlag/EMI KICK Musikverlag
All Rights Reserved. International Copyright Secured

# BA-BA-BANKÜBERFALL

(EAV)

**Intro:** A A A A A A E/A

```
      A                          E/A A
1. Der Kühlschrank ist leer, das Sparschwein auch,
                                     E/A A
   ich habe seit Wochen kein Schnitzel mehr im Bauch.
                                 E   A
   Der letzte Scheck ist weg, ich bin nicht liquid,
                                 E F#m E F#m E
   auf der Bank krieg' ich sowieso keinen Kredit.

   A                                   E/A A
   Gestern enterbt mich auch noch meine Mutter,
                                 E/A A
   und vor der Tür steht der Exekutor.
                                          A
   Mit einem Wort, die Lage ist fatal, da hilft nur eins:
      A
   Ein Banküberfall!
```

**Refrain:**
```
A                    E          A
Ba-Ba- Banküberfall, Ba-Ba- Banküberfall,
     D                 E                        A
Ba-Ba- Banküberfall, das Böse ist immer und überall.
A                    E          A
Ba-Ba- Banküberfall, Ba-Ba- Banküberfall,
     D                 E                        A
Ba-Ba- Banküberfall, das Böse ist immer und überall.
```

2. Auf meinem Kopf einen Strumpf von Palmers,
steh ich vor der Bank und sage: Überfall!
Mach's mit dem Finger im Mantel statt einer Puffn,
ich kann kein Blut seh'n, darum muss ich bluffen.

Ich schrei: Hände hoch, das ist ein Überfall,
und seid ihr nicht willig, dann gibt's an Krawall!
Eine Oma dreht sich um und sagt: "Junger Mann,
stell'n Sie sich gefälligst hinten an!"

Refrain

3. Nach einer halben Stund' bin ich endlich an der Reih',
mein Finger ist schon steif von der blöden Warterei.
Ich sag: Jetzt, oder nie, her mit der Marie!
Der Kassierer schaut mich an und fragt: Was haben Sie?

Ich sag: An Hunger und an Durscht und keinen Plärrer,
ich bin der böse Kassenentleerer!
Der Kassierer sagt: Nein, was fällt Ihnen ein?
Na gut, sag ich, dann zahl' ich halt was ein!

Refrain

The evil is always and everywhere!
Ba-ba- bank robbery ba-ba- bank robbery,...

M: Thomas Spitzer / Günter Schönberger / Nino Holm /Klaus Eberhartinger / Gerhard Breit
T: Thomas Spitzer
© Wintrup Musikverlag, Detmold / Blanko Musikverlag, München.

# LIEBFICKEN

(SOFAPLANET)

```
C
Ein gutes Gespräch ist kaum zu ersetzen.
All meine Freunde können dies schätzen.
Doch als ich eben aus dem Fenster sah,
wurde mir eines sofort klar:
         Bb                              C
Wärst Du jetzt hier und nicht so weit fort,
         Bb                           G
dann gingen wir raus und sagten sicher kein Wort.
```

**Refrain:**
```
                      C                      G
Wir würden einfach lieb ficken, ficken für vier.
             C                 G
Du auf dem Rücken und ich über dir.
                     Am                     G
Mal schnell und mal langsam, und irgendwann
             F                        G
seh'n wir uns gemeinsam die Sterne an.

                      C       G           C       G
Wir würden einfach lieb ficken, einfach lieb ficken.
C
Was für ein Himmel, was für eine Nacht!?!
In der hätte ich so gern mit dir Liebe gemacht.
So warm und so klar, und Grillen die singen.
Doch leider muss ich die Nacht alleine verbringen.
          Bb                C
Wärst du jetzt hier, sicherlich
          Bb                       G
dächtest du dann genau das Gleiche wie ich.
Refrain
                      C       G           C       G
Wir würden einfach lieb ficken, einfach lieb ficken.
                     Am                     G
Mal schnell und mal langsam, und irgendwann
             F                        G
seh'n wir uns gemeinsam die Sterne an.
                      C       G           C     G G F# F
Wir würden einfach lieb ficken, einfach lieb ficken.

F                   G
Nun schlaf' ich ein und schon
        G#           Bb
träum' ich von der Penetration
    F                G               G#           G G# G G# G G# GG#G
im Glas und deiner Hand in meinem Haar. Wärst du doch da.

Refrain 2x
C    G             C    G
Ficken, ordentlich ficken.
                     Am                     G
Mal schnell und mal langsam, und irgendwann
             F                        G
seh'n wir uns gemeinsam die Sterne an.
                          C
Wir würden einfach lieb....Ficken.
```

M + T: Sven Rathke
© 2001 by George Glueck Publishing GmbH / Sony/ATV Music Publishing (Germany) GmbH / EMI Music Publishing Germany GmbH & Co. KG. Mit freundlicher Genehmigung der EMI Music Publishing Germany GmbH.

## DON'T LOOK BACK IN ANGER

(OASIS)

**Intro:** C F C F

```
C                G            Am
Slip inside the eye of your mind,
         E7           F    G              C     Am G
don't you know you might find a better place to play.
C                G            Am
You said that you'd never been
         E7             F    G            C     Am G
but all the things that you've seen slowly fade away.
```

**Bridge:**
```
F              Fm            C
So I start a revolution from my bed,
         F              Fm           C
cause you said the brains I have went to my head
F              Fm           C
step outside the summertime's in bloom.
G
Stand up besides the fireplace,
G#°
take that look from off your face
        Am            G          F        G
cause you ain't ever gonna burn my heart out.
```

**Refrain:**
```
C    G       Am        E7           F
So Sally can wait, she knows it's too late
         G       C    Am G
as we're walking on by.
     C     G      Am      E7               F          G
Her soul slides away, but don't look back in anger
              C   G Am E7 F G C Am G
I heard you say.

C              G             Am
Take me to the place where you go,
       E7     F    G            C    Am G
where nobody knows if it's night or day.
C                     G          Am
Please don't put your life in the hands
     E7       F    G                C    Am G
of a Rock'n'Roll band who'll throw it all away.
```

```
Bridge
Refrain
Bridge (Instrumental):F Fm C 3x - G G#°  Am G F G
Refrain 2x
              F
But don't look back in anger,
              Fm7                      C
but don't look back in anger I heard you say
G Am E7 F Fm         C
         please not today.
```

M + T: Noel Gallagher
© Copyright 1995 Creation Songs Limited/Oasis Music (GB).
Sony/ATV Music Publishing.
All Rights Reserved. International Copyright Secured.

# OHNE DICH

(SELIG)

**Intro:** C G/B C/Bb

```
   C                            G/B           C/Bb
1. Langeweile besäuft sich meilenweit ich zähl' die Ringe an meiner Hand
   C                             G/B
   Dort draußen, alles dreht sich still um nichts herum
C/Bb                    F
und ich male deine Schatten an jede Wand.

D                                                   Fm
Es kommt so anders als man denkt, Herz vergeben, Herz verschenkt, hmm.

   C                           G/B
2. Ich gab dir meine Liebe, gab dir Zeit, Geduld und Geld.
   C/Bb                F7
Ich legte mein Leben in deine kleine Welt.
              C
Wer auch immer dir jetzt den Regen schenkt,
   G/B
ich hoffe, es geht ihm schlecht.
         C/Bb                              F
Wer auch immer dich durch die Nacht bringt, bitte glaub ihm nicht.
```

**Refrain:**
```
D7                                                Fm
Es kommt so anders als man denkt, Herz vergeben, Herz verschenkt.
C             C+          F
Es ist so o ohne dich, es ist so widerlich, ich will das nicht,
D
denkst du vielleicht auch mal an mich.
      C       E             Am
Es ist so o ohne dich und wenn Du einsam bist,
                         D          Fm
denkst du vielleicht auch mal an mich.

   C                             G/B
3. Ich nähte mir ein Bettbezug aus der Zeit, die wir hatten
   C/Bb                  F/A
und trink mir alte Wunden an so tief und allein.
       C
Kein Berg, den ich nicht versetzt hab,
   G/B
zog jede Chance an den Haaren herbei
      C/Bb                    F/A
für ein Leben lang zu leben, so wild und so frei.
```

Refrain

M + T: Christian Neander, Jan Plewka
© SMPG Publishing (Germany) GmbH / EMI Music Publihsinh Germany GmbH. Edition Was ist Musik?
Mit freundlicher Genehmigung der EMI Music Publishing Germany GmbH.

# SUMMER DREAMING (BACARDI FEELING)

(KATE YANAI)

```
   C           Em/B         F              G
1. Come on over have some fun, dancing in the morning sun.
Em            A7           Dm              G
Looking to the brand new sky, come and let your spirit fly.
C              Em/B         F              G
Living it up this brand new day, summer sun it's time to play.
Em             A7           Dm             G
Doing things that feel so good. Get into the motion.
```

**Refrain:**
```
        Em7 Am7       Dm7        G
What I'm feeling. It's never been so easy.
        Em7 Am7    Dm          G              C Em/B F G
When I'm dreaming. Summer dreaming when you're with me.
```

```
   C           Em/B         F              G
2. Just another lucky day. No one makes me feel this way.
Em             A7           Dm             G
Watch the waves and feel the sand, kiss me now and take my hand.
C              Em/B          F                G
Hear all the laughter in the street. Smiling in the summer heat.
Em             A7           Dm             G
Cool touching your hand in mine. We can be together.
Refrain
```

```
C  Em/B  F           G
Dreaming, never been so easy.
C
All the people they turn as we walk on by.
```

```
      C           Em/B          F              G
3. Now loving you just feels so right, lighting up the darkest night.
Em            A7           Dm         G
Go turn up the radio. Don't ever let me go.
C              Em/B           Dm             G
All the tears I've cried before, they can't touch me anymore.
Em             A7           Dm             G
Now that you are by my side, it's all I need to know.
Refrain
```

```
   D            F#m/C#        G              A
4. Come on over have some fun, dancing in the morning sun
F#m           B7           Em             A
We can keep this dream alive, will you try
D             F#m/C#            G      A F#m B7
Hear all the laughter in the street. You smile
Em            A
All the people they turn as we walk on by
D           F#m/C#        G           A
Just another lucky day, living it up
D             F#m/C#        G           A
No one makes me feel this way. Living it up
```

```
Refrain 2x
(in D-Dur)    M: Olivier Bloch-Laine
              T: Joe Hamer / Kate Yanai / Chris Trulio
              © Copyright 1991 La Frette Studio. Universal Music Publishing MGB Limited.
              All Rights Reserved. International Copyright Secured.
```

# THE POWER OF LOVE

(JENNIFER RUSH)
[TRANSP. +1]

```
   D                      G                       Em
1. The whispers in the morning of lovers sleeping tight,
                    G                        D
are rolling by like thunder now, as I look in your eyes.
                     G                       Em
I hold on to your body and feel each move you make,
                       C              G         D
your voice is warm and tender, a love that I could not forsake.
```

**Refrain:**
```
             G                   C
Cause I'm your lady and you are my man,
   G/B     Am                         D7
whenever you reach for me, I'll do all that I can.
```

```
                    G                   Em
2. Lost is how I'm feeling, lying in your arms,
                          G
when the world outside's too numb to take
            D
that I lose when I love you.
                         G                   Em
Even though there may be times, it seems I'm far away,
                   C                 G              D
but never wonder where I am cause I am always by your side.
```

Refrain

```
     D              G
We're heading for some place,
                   C            G/B Am
somewhere I've never been, sometimes I am frightened
                D            C         G
but I'm ready to learn about the power of love.

C  D              G         C        D         Em D C
The sound of your heart beating, made it clear suddenly,
    D             G              C                D
the feeling that I can't go on is light-years away.
```

Refrain

```
     D              G
We're heading for some place,
                   C            G/B Am
somewhere I've never been, sometimes I am frightened
                D            C         G
but I'm ready to learn about the power of love.
     D              G
We're heading for some place,
                   C            G/B Am
somewhere I've never been, sometimes I am frightened
                D            C         G   D           G
but I'm ready to learn about the power of love. The power of love.
```

M: Candy DeRouge / Günther Mende
T: Jennifer Rush / Mary Susan Applegate
© Copyright 1984 by EMI Music Publishing GmbH & Co. KG.
Rechte für Deutschland, Österreich, Schweiz:
EMI Music Publishing Germany GmbH & Co. KG, Hamburg.
All Rights Reserved. International Copyright Secured.

# OB-LA-DI, OB-LA-DA

(THE BEATLES)

```
   Bb                              F
1. Desmond has a barrow in the market place,
                     Bb
Molly is a singer in the band.
                              Eb
Desmond says to Molly: Girl I like your face
         Bb             F              Bb
and Molly says this as she takes him by the hand.
```

**Refrain:**
```
Bb                     F   Gm    Bb       F         Bb
Ob la di, ob la da, life goes on, bra, la la how the life goes on.
Bb                     F   Gm    Bb       F         Bb
Ob la di, ob la da, life goes on, bra, la la how the life goes on.
```

```
   Bb                          F
2. Desmond takes a trolley to the juwelier's store,
                       Bb
buys a twenty carat golden ring,
                            Eb
takes it back to Molly waiting at the door
         Bb           F            Bb
and as he gives it to her she begins to sing.
```

Refrain

**Bridge:**
```
Eb                                            Bb
In a couple of years they have built a home, sweat home,
Eb
with a couple of kids running in the yard of
Bb/F            F
Desmond and Molly Jones.
```

```
   Bb                      F
3. Happy ever after in the market place,
                             Bb
Desmond lets the children lend a hand.
                              Eb
Molly stays at home and does her pretty face
         Bb            F                Bb
and in the evening she still sings it with the band.
```

Refrain

Bridge

```
4. Happy ever after in the market place
Molly lets the children lend a hand.
Desmond stays at home and does his pretty face
and in the evening she's a singer with the band.
```

```
          Gm           F         Bb
And if you want some fun take Obladiblada.
```

M + T: John Lennon & Paul McCartney
© Copyright 1968 Sony/ATV Music Publishing (UK) Limited.
All Rights Reserved. International Copyright Secured.

# WELCH EIN TAG

(MARIO JORDAN)

```
   C              G/B               Am7
1. Durch den Raum voll Rauch und Stimmen sah ich zu dir hin.
   F           C/E            Dm7            Gsus4  G
   Und dein Blick hielt meinen fest, ich fühlte, wer ich bin.
   C              G/B               Am7
   Ich wagte nicht dich anzusprechen, sah dich lächelnd gehn.
   F           C/E            Dm7            Gsus4  G
   War mir irgendwie ganz sicher, ich hab heut das Glück gesehn.
```

**Refrain:**
```
   C              G/B               Am
   Ein schöner Tag, die Welt steht still, ein schöner Tag.
       F              Dm7           Gsus4 G
   Komm Welt, lass dich umarmen, welch ein Tag.
       C              G/B           Am
   Denn du bist da und jeder Traum zum Greifen nah,
       F           G           C    C/Bb F/A Dm7 Fm
   das Glück hat einen Namen, welch ein Tag.
```

```
   C              G/B               Am7
2. Ein paar Ziffern hingekritzelt auf ein Stück Papier.
   F           C/E            Dm7            Gsus4  G
   Ich verstand die Botschaft, und sie führte mich zu dir.
   C              G/B               Am7
   Ein schneller Griff zum Telefon, als ich zu Hause war.
   F           C/E            Dm7            Gsus4  G
   Ich hörte deine Stimme und schon war alles klar.
```

Refrain

```
   Eb         Bb       Ab              Gsus4  G
   Gestern noch schien jeder Wunsch vergebens,
   Cm         Fm            Fm/D         Cm/G  G
   und schon heut beginnt der beste Teil des Lebens.
       C              G/B           Am
   Denn du bist da und jeder Traum zum Greifen nah,
       F           G           C    C/Bb F/A Dm7 Fm C
   das Glück hat einen Namen, welch ein Tag.
```

Refrain

T + M: Peter Schon/Jaap Eggermont/ Mario Killer/ Michael Kunze/ Evelyne Wenzel
© Forty Five Music / Chrysalis Music Holdings GmbH.
Für D/A/CH: Strengholt Musikverlag GmbH, Berlin.

# DEIN IST MEIN GANZES HERZ

(HEINZ RUDOLF KUNZE)
[TRANSP. +1]

**Intro:** F#m
```
            D                       E
1. Wir haben uns auf Teufel-komm-raus geliebt.
     F#m
Dann kam er, und wir wussten nicht mehr weiter.
         D                        E
Du machtest dich nicht gut als sterbender Schwan,
     F#m                       E/G#
ich hab versagt als finsterer Reiter.

         A
Statt Pech und Schwefel plötzlich nur noch
Bm
Gletscher und Geröll.
     A/C#                     D
Wir haben so viel Glück auf dem Gewissen.
    A                            F#m
Ich brauche jeden Morgen deinen Nachtgeruch
      B7                        E
und keine falschen Wimpern auf dem Kissen.
```

**Refrain:**
```
F#m             E/G#         Bm            A
Dein ist mein ganzes Herz. Du bist mein Reim auf Schmerz.
D        Bm            Esus4           E
Wir werden Riesen sein. Uns wird die Welt zu klein.
```

2. Was sind das bloß für Menschen, die "Beziehungen" haben?
Betrachten die sich denn als Staaten?
Die verführen sich nicht, die entführen sich höchstens.
Die enden wie Diplomaten.

Wo du nicht bist, kann ich nicht sein.
Ich möchte gar nichts andres ausprobieren.
Wir sind wie alle andern, denn wir möchten heim.
Es ist fast nie zu spät, das zu kapieren.

Refrain 2x

<small>M + T: Heiner Lürig, Heinz-Rudolf Kunze
© 1985 by Neue Welt Musikverlag GmbH Co KG/ SMV Schacht Musikverlage GmbH & Co. KG.
Warner/Chappell Overseas Holdings Limited, London / Musik Unserer Zeit Verlag GmbH. Reproduced by permission of Faber Music Limited. All Rights Reserved.</small>

# THESE DAYS

(BON JOVI)

**Intro:** |:C D Em :| 6x

```
       C                    D                       Em
1. I was walking around, just a face in the crowd, trying to keep myself
                   C                    D
out of the rain. Saw a vagabond king wear a styrofoam crown,
       Em
wondered if I might end up the same.
          C              D         Em                        C
There's a man out on the corner, singing old songs about change.
                    D                    G
Everybody got their cross to bear, these days.

2. She came looking for some shelter with a suitcase full of dreams
To a motel room on the boulevard, guess she's trying to be James Dean.
She's seen all the disciples an all the 'wanna be's'.
C              D               Em
No one wants to be themselves these days.
             C              D              G
Still there's nothing to hold on to but these days.
```

**Refrain:**
```
     C           D            Em
These days - the stars seem out of reach.
     C            D                 G
These days - there ain't a ladder from the streets oh no no.

     C            D           G                    C
These days are fast, love don't last in this graceless age.
                  D              G
There ain't nobody left but us these days.
```

Jimmy shoes busted both his legs, trying to learn to fly.
From a second story window, he just jumped and closed his eyes.
His momma said he was crazy - he said momma "I've got to try".
Don't you know that all my heroes died?
And I guess I'd rather die than fade away.

Refrain
These days are fast, nothing lasts it's a graceless age.
Even innocence has caught the midnight train.
There ain't nobody left but us these days.     C Am C Am

```
C     Am                    C        Am
I know Rome's still burning though the times have changed.
C     Am                D                                      C
This world keeps turning round and round and round and round these days.
```
Solo C G D (4x)

Refrain
These days are fast, nothing lasts it's a graceless age.
Even innocence has caught the midnight train.

Refrain
These days are fast, nothing lasts there ain't no time to waste.
There ain't nobody left to take the blame.
```
      C              D              G
|: There ain't nobody left but us these days. :|
```

M + T: Jon Bon Jovi & Richie Sambora
© Copyright 1995 Bon Jovi
Publishing/Aggressive Music, USA.
Sony/ATV Music Publishing (UK) Limited /
Kobalt Music Limited. All Rights Reserved.
International Copyright Secured.

## EYE OF THE TIGER

(SURVIVOR)

```
      Cm         Ab/C
1. Risin' up, back on the street,
Bb/C              Cm
did my time, took my chances.
 Cm              Ab/C
Went the distance, now I'm back on my feet,
      Bb/C              Cm
just a man and his will to survive.

      Cm              Ab
2. So many times, it happens too fast,
Bb                    Cm
you change your passion for glory.
Cm                    Ab
Don't lose your grip on the dreams of the past,
         Bb                  Cm
you must fight just to keep them alive.
```

**Refrain:**
```
Bb   Cm7 Fm              Eb/G          Bb
It's the eye of the tiger, it's the thrill of the fight
Bb Cm7 Fm                 Cm7 Bb
rising up to the challenge of our rival.
Bb   Cm7 Fm              Eb/G          Bb
And the last known survivor stalks his prey in the night
Bb   Cm7 Fm    Eb/G     Ab         Cm
and he's watching us all in the eye of the tiger.
```

```
      Cm         Ab/C
3. Face to face, out in the heat,
Bb/C              Cm
hanging tough, staying hungry.
 Cm                    Ab/C
They stack the odds till we take to the street
      Bb/C              Cm
for we kill with the skill to survive.
```

Refrain

```
      Cm         Ab/C
4. Rising up, straight to the top,
Bb/C              Cm
have the guts, got the glory.
 Cm              Ab/C
Went the distance, now I'm not gonna stop,
      Bb/C              Cm
just a man and his will to survive.
```

Refrain

```
      Ab         Cm
The eye of the tiger.
```

M + T: James Michael Peterik, Frank Michael Sullivan III
© Copyright 1982 Three Wise Boys Music LLC/W.B. Music Corporation/Easy Action Music, USA, Ensign Music Corp.
Warner/Chappell Music Limited, London. Sony/ATV Harmony (UK) Limited.
All Rights Reserved. International Copyright Secured.

# SMOOTH

(SANTANA)

**Intro:** Am E Am E Am E Am E

```
          Am                E                          Am
1. Man it's a hot one, like seven inches from the midday sun,
E                         Dm     Dm/C       Dm/B
I hear you whisper and the words melt everyone,
   E/G#          Am      E
but you stay so cool.
          Am          E                      Am
My Muñequita, my Spanish Harlem Mona Lisa,
E                         Dm   Dm/C Dm/B E/G#     E  Am
you're my reason for reason,   the   step in my groove.
```

**Refrain:**
```
E          Am                    E                  Am
And if you said this life ain't good enough, I would give
              E                     Am
my world to lift you up, I could change
              E           Dm Dm/C Dm/B           Bsus4   E7
my life to better suit your mood,      cause you're so smooth.
```

**Bridge:**
```
           Am              E
And it's like the ocean under the moon,
               Am                          E
well, that's the same as the emotion that I get from you.
     Am                          E
You got the kind of lovin' that could be so smooth,
Dm                       E7                           Am E Am E
give me your heart, make it real, or else forget about it.
```

```
                  Am        E                         Am       E
2. Well, I'll tell you one thing if you would leave it be a crying shame
                         Dm       Dm/C     Dm/B E/G#     E  Am    E
in every breath and every word, I hear your name calling me out.
           Am       E                         Am      E
Out from the barrio, you hear my rhythm on your radio,
                         Dm         Dm/C      Dm/B
you feel the turning of the world so soft and slow,
E/G#     E   Am                E
turning you round and round.
```

Refrain

Bridge 2x

```
Am                           E7
Give me your heart, make it real, or else forget about it!
Am    E                Am    E                    Am    E
Let's all forget about it, let's all forget about it!
```

M + T: Itaal Shur, Rob Thomas
© 1999 Itaal Shur Music, Warner-Tamerlane Publishing Corp / EMI Blackwood Music Inc / U Rule Music.
Warner/Chappell North America Ltd, London. Reproduced by permission of Faber Music Limited. All Rights Reserved.

## BATTLES

(AXE)

**Intro:** Dm C Bb C Dm

```
        Dm                              C
1. I often dream of nights I'd sit and watch the rising sun.
        Bb                         C
And I spoke to you of life and of the battles I had won.
        Dm                       C
A warm wind blowing memories makes me long for home.
        Bb                              C
But a cold wind blows much harder and makes me want to roam.
```

**Refrain:**
```
        Dm              C/D
Let me go from this lonely land
   Bb/D                           Dm
before my dreams all vanish like water in the sand.
        Dm              C/D
Let me run from this lonely place
   Bb/D                      Dm               Dm C Bb C Dm
before my dreams are shattered by love I can't erase.
```

```
        Dm                              C
2. I search to find the meaning of the path that I am on.
        Bb                            C
And I hope that my direction will not make me walk alone.
        Dm                          C
I stumble for the answers to the questions that remain.
        Bb                                    C
Around the world I've touched the sun, and now I'm back again.
```

**Refrain:**
```
        Dm              C
Let me go from this lonely land
   Gm                             Dm
Before my dreams all vanish like water in the sand.
        Dm              C
Let me run from this lonely place
   Gm                         Dm
Before my dreams are shattered by love I can't erase.
```

M + T: Bobby Barth
© NEH MUSIC.
Für D/A/CH - ROBA MUSIC VERLAG GMBH.

# NOTHING COMPARES 2 U

(SINEAD O'CONNOR)

```
   F                            C/E
1. It's been seven hours and fifteen days,
Dm                  F Gm/C
since you took your love away.
F                       C/E                Dm                  F Gm/C
I go out every night and sleep all day, since you took your love away.
F                                C/E
Since you been gone, I can do whatever I want,
Dm                       F Gm/C
I can see whomever I choose.
F                                C/E
I can eat my dinner in a fancy restaurant,
    Dm                                    A7
but nothing, I said, nothing, can take away these blues.
     Eb          Bb         Eb          Bb         C
Cause nothing compares, nothing compares 2 U.

   F                      C/E            Dm                    F Gm/C
2. It's been so lonely without you here, like a bird without a song.
F                            C/E
Nothing can stop these lonely tears from falling,
         Dm                Bb
tell me, baby, where did I go wrong?
F                               C/E
I could put my arms around every boy I see,
Dm                      F Gm/C
but they only remind me of you.
F                                       C/E
I went to the doctor and guess what he told me, guess what he told me.
          Dm                                               A7
He said, "Girl, you better try to have fun no matter what you do",
                      Eb         Bb        Dm       C
but he's a fool, cause nothing compares, nothing compares 2 U.

   F                                   C/E
3. All the flowers that you planted, mama, in the back yard,
Dm                  F Gm/C
all died when you went away.
F                                     C/E
I know that living with you, baby, was sometimes hard,
Dm                             A7
but I'm willing to give you another try.
 Eb       Bb        Dm         C
Nothing compares, nothing compares 2 U.
 Eb       Bb        Dm         C
Nothing compares, nothing compares 2 U.
 Eb       Bb        Dm         C
Nothing compares, nothing compares 2 U.
```

M + T: Prince Nelson Rodgers
© Copyright 1985 Controversy Music. Universal Music Publishing Limited.
All Rights Reserved. International Copyright Secured.

# HERE I GO AGAIN

(WHITESNAKE)

**Intro:** G D C   G D C

```
    G        D              C     D
1. I don't know where I'm going,
   G     D              C     D
but I sure know where I've been.
G           D/F#       C/E          C   G/B Am
Hanging on the promises in songs of yesterday.
                          D
And I've made up my mind.
Am                    D
I ain't wasting no more time,
        Em   Am  C
here I go again.
              G    Em Am C D
Here I go again.
```

```
    G             D            C     D
2. Though I keep searching for an answer,
   G       D                    C   D
I never seem to find what I'm looking for.
G          D/F#        C/E            C   G/B Am
Oh Lord I pray you give me strength to carry on,
                       D
cause I know what it means,
    Am                            D C D
to walk along, the lonely street of dreams.
```

**Refrain:**
```
       G         C        D   C D
And here I go again on my own,
         G            C        D    C D
going down the only road I've ever known.
           G          C         D    C G/B
Like a drifter I was born to walk alone.
Am7                  D
And I've made up my mind,
Am7                       D    C D
I ain't wasting no more time.
```

```
     G              D/G         C/C    D/G
3. I'm just another heart in need of rescue,
   G        D/G      C/G   D/G
waiting on love's sweet charity.
G          D/F#        C/E         C   G/B Am7
And I'm gonna hold on for the rest of my days,
                       D
cause I know what it means,
    Am7                           D    C D
to walk alone, the lonely street of dreams.
```

Refrain 2x

M + T: David Coverdale and Bernie Marsden
© 1982 Seabreeze Music Ltd and C.C. Songs Ltd. Warner/Chappell North America Ltd, London.
Reproduced by permission of Faber Music Limited. All Rights Reserved.

## **ALINE**

(CHRISTOPHE)

**Intro:** G B7 C D7

```
        G               B7              C              D7
1. J'avais dessiné sur le sable son doux visage qui me souriait.
        G               B7              C              D7
Puis il a plu sur cette plage, dans cet orage, elle a disparu.

              G        B7 C             D7
Et j'ai crié, crié Aline pour qu'elle revienne.
              G        B7    C          D7
Et j'ai pleuré, pleuré, oh! j'avais trop de peine.

                G                 B7              C               D7
2. Je me suis assis auprès de son âme, mais la belle dame s'était enfuie
             G                B7                 C               D7
Je l'ai cherchée sans plus y croire, et sans un espoir, pour me guider.

              G        B7 C             D7
Et j'ai crié, crié Aline pour qu'elle revienne.
              G        B7    C          D7
Et j'ai pleuré, pleuré, oh! j'avais trop de peine.

                 G              B7             C              D7
3. Je n'ai gardé que ce doux visage comme une épave sur le sable mouillé

              G        B7 C             D7
Et j'ai crié, crié Aline pour qu'elle revienne.
              G        B7    C          D7
Et j'ai pleuré, pleuré, oh! j'avais trop de peine.
              G        B7 C             D7
Et j'ai crié, crié Aline pour qu'elle revienne.
              G        B7    C          D7
Et j'ai pleuré, pleuré, oh! j'avais trop de peine.
```

M + T: Christophe
© 1965 by Editions Musicales Caravelle für D, A Nero Musikverlag GmbH & Co. Ohg.

# RADIO GA GA

(QUEEN)

**Intro:** F Gm Bb Gm Bb F

   F
1. I'd sit alone and watch your light,
  Gm
my only friend through teenage nights
    Bb
and everything I had to know
  Gm                Bb  F
I heard it on my radio.

2. You gave them all those old time stars
through wars of worlds invaded by Mars.
You made 'em laugh, you made 'em cry,
you made us feel like we could fly. Radio.

**Bridge 1:**
   F
So don't become some background noise,
  Ab°
a backdrop for the girls and boys
  Bb
who just don't know or just don't care
    G/B
and just complain when you're not there.
    F/C
You had your time, you had the power,
     C7sus4         C7          Bb  F
you've yet to have your finest hour: Radio.

**Refrain:**
F/Eb         Bb    F      Bb    F      Bb    F
All we hear is Radio ga ga, Radio goo goo, Radio ga ga.
F/Eb         Bb    F      Bb    F
All we hear is Radio ga ga, Radio blah blah.
Eb        Bb  C
Radio what's new?
Dm     F/C C    Bb/C  C7     F
Radio, someone still loves you!

3. We watch the shows, we watch the stars
on videos for hours and hours.
We hardly need to use our ears
how music changes through the years.

**Bridge 2:**
Let's hope you never leave old friend
like all good things on you we depend.
So stick around cause we might miss you
when we grow tired of all this visual.
You had your time, you had the power,
you've yet to have your finest hour: Radio.

Refrain

M + T: Roger Taylor
© Copyright 1983 Queen Music Limited, W8 5SW.
Reproduced by permission of International Music
Publications Limited (a trading name of Faber Music Ltd).
All Rights Reserved.

# DER WILDE, WILDE WESTEN

(TRUCK STOP)

```
          D
1. Die kleine Country Band, die heute jeder kennt,
               A
sie hat's nicht immer leicht gehabt.
    A7                        G            D
Sie spielte schon in Hamburg als es noch keine Panik gab.
          D
Ein Jazzer sagte mal, das ist mir zu banal,
            A
es gibt doch keine Cowboys hier.
        A7                    G              D
Wir sind doch nicht im Wilden Westen, er hat sich schwer geirrt.
```

**Refrain:**
```
     D                              A
Der wilde, wilde Westen fängt gleich hinter Hamburg an,
        A7                 G           D
in einem Studio in Maschen, gleich bei der Autobahn.
                D
Hier hört man Geige, Banjo, Steel guitar,
       A                    A7
hier sind sie gut gelaunt, die Cowboys von der Waterkant
G            D
mit ihrem Nashville Sound.
```

```
            D
2. Ob du aus Bayern kommst oder in Hamburg wohnst,
              A
das ist doch sowas yon egal,
      A7                      G            D
solang du denkst du bist in Honky Tonk und stehst im Bierlokal.
            D
Mit ein Paar Cowboyboots und einem Fernwehblues
           A
und einem kleinen Knacks im Herz,
  A7                        G           D
dein Kreislauf geht nach oben, wenn du die Cowboys singen hörst.
```

Refrain

M + T: Doll, Erich / Bach, Rainer
© Edition Joe Menke / Universal Music Publishing GmbH.

# ONE MORE NIGHT

(PHIL COLLINS)
[TRANSP. +1]

```
A       D     A  D    A         D      A     D
One more night,        one more night.

      G        D/F#         Em      D
1. I've been trying ooh so long to let you know.
   G        D/F#        Em
   Let you know how I feel.
   G        D/F#          Em         D
   And if I stumble if I fall, just help me back.
   G        D/F#     Em
   So I can make you see.
```

**Refrain:**
```
              A         D          A        D
Please give me one more night, give me one more night.
 A      D              Em          A
One more night cos I can't wait forever.
              A         D         A         D
Give me just one more night, oh just one more night.
    A        D            Em           A
Oh one more night cos I can't wait forever.
```

2. I've been sitting here so long,
wasting time, just staring at the phone.
And I was wondering should I call you,
then I thought maybe you're not alone.

**Refrain:**
Please give me one more night, give me just one more night.
Oh one more night, cos I can't wait forever.
Please give me one more night, ooh just one more night.
Oh one more night, cos I can't wait forever.
Give me one more night, give me just one more night.
Ooh one more night, cos I can't wait forever.

**Bridge:**
```
Bm7      D/C
Like a river to the sea
Bm7      C/D
I will always be with you.
Bm7 D/C
And if you sail away
Bm7      C/D
I will follow you.
```

Give me one more night, give me just one more night.
Oh one more night, cos I can't wait forever.

I know there'll never be a time you'll ever feel the same.
And I know it's only words,
but if you change your mind you know that I'll be here.
And maybe we both can learn.

Give me just one more night, give me just one more night.
Ooh one more night, cos I can't wait forever.
Give me just one more night, give me just one more night.
Ooh one more night, cos I can't wait forever.

M + T: Phil Collins
© Copyright 1984 Philip Collins Limited/Imagem CV
Imagem Music. All Rights Reserved. International Copyright Secured.

# 50 WAYS TO LEAVE YOUR LOVER

(PAUL SIMON)

```
      Em/G            D6              Cmaj7             B7b9  B7
1. "The problem is all inside your head", she said to me.
   Em         D#°          F#°            B+
   "The answer is easy if you take it logic'lly.
   Em           D6              Cmaj7              B7b9
   I'm here to help you if you're struggling to be free,
        B7      Em    Am7                  Em
   there must be fifty ways to leave your lover."

   Em/G            D6              Cmaj7          B7b9   B7
   She said, "It's really not my habit to intrude,
   Em         D#°          F#°             B+
   I hope my meaning won't be lost or misconstrued.
        Em           D6              Cmaj7            B7b9
   But I'll repeat myself at the risk of being crude,
        B7      Em    Am7                  Em
   there must be fifty ways to leave your lover."
   Em     Am7              Em
   Fifty ways to leave your lover.
```

**Refrain:**
```
                       G                         Bb6
Just slip out the back, Jack. Make a new plan, Stan.
                    C7                         G
You don't need to be coy, Roy, just get yourself free.
             G                         Bb6
Hop on the bus, Gus. You don't need to discuss much.
             C7                         G
Just drop off the key, Lee. And get yourself free.

                       G                         Bb6
Just slip out the back, Jack. Make a new plan, Stan.
                    C7                         G
You don't need to be coy, Roy, just listen to me.
             G                         Bb6
Hop on the bus, Gus. You don't need to discuss much.
             C7                         G
Just drop off the key, Lee. And get yourself free.
```

2. She said, "It grieves me now to see you in such pain.
I wish there was something I could do to make you smile again."
I said, "I appreciate that, and could you please explain about the
fifty ways?"

She said, "Why don't we both just sleep on it tonight;
I'm sure in the morning you'll begin to see the light."
And then she kissed me and I realized she probably was right,
there must be
fifty ways to leave your lover,
fifty ways to leave your lover.

Refrain

M + T: Paul Simon
© Copyright 1975 Paul Simon (BMI).
All Rights Reserved. International Copyright Secured.

# AGAINST ALL ODDS

(PHIL COLLINS)

**Intro:** Dm G Dm G

```
    Am                  Bm                    C                    Dm
1. How can I just let you walk away, just let you leave without a trace,
      F            G/F             Em         Am
when I stand here taking every breath with you, oooh.
          Dm         F                  G
You're the only one who really knew me at all.

    Am                  Bm                    C                      Dm
2. How can you just walk away from me, when all I can do is watch you
leave
          F               G/F             Em                     Am
cause we've shared the laughter and the pain, and even shared the tears.
          Dm         F              Gsus4 G
You're the only one who really knew me at all.
```

**Refrain:**
```
                  C/G                          D/G
So take a look at me now, cause there's just an empty space,
               Am              F
and there's nothing left here to remind me,
       Dm              Gsus4 G
just the memory of your face.
                  C/G                          D/G
oh, take a look at me now, cause there's just an empty space,
               Am              F
and you coming back to me is against the odds,
       Dm              Gsus4 G
and that's what I've got to face.

    Am                  Bm                    C                   Dm
3. I wish I could just make you turn around, turn around and see me cry,
        F            G/F             Em             Am
there's so much I need to say to you, so many reasons why.
          Dm         F              Gsus4 G
You're the only one who really knew me at all.
```

**Refrain:**
```
                  C/G                          D
So take a look at me now, cause there's just an empty space,
               Am              F
and there's nothing left here to remind me,
       Dm              Gsus4 G
just the memory of your face.
                  C/G                          D/G
Now, take a look at me now, cause there's just an empty space,
           Am                    F
but to wait for you, well that's all I can do,
       Dm              Gsus4 G
and that's what I've got to face.
                  C/G                          D/G
Take a good look at me now, 'cause I'll still be standing here,
               Am              F
and you coming back to me is against all odds,
       Dm              Gsus4 G Dm G Dm G
it's the chance I've got to take.
              Dm    Csus2 G/B F G
Take a look at me now.
```

M + T: Phil Collins
© 1984 Philip Collins Ltd. EMI GOLDEN TORCH MUSIC CORP. and Imagem Music. ALFRED MUSIC. All Rights Reserved. International Copyright Secured. Used by Permission.

# TWO PRINCES

(SPIN DOCTORS)

```
   D          Bm           A               G
1. One, two, princes kneel before you. (That's what I said, now)
   D          Bm           A             G
Princes, princes who adore you. (Just go ahead, now)
   D          Bm           A          G
One has diamonds in his pockets. (That's some bread, now)
   D          Bm              A             G
This one,he wants to buy you rockets. (Ain't in his head, now)

      D              Bm                 A              G
2. This one, he's got a prince new racket. (That's what I said, now)
   D            Bm           A              G
Got some big seal upon his jacket. (Ain't in his head, now)
   D            Bm              A          G
Marry him, your father will condone you. (How bout that, now)
   D            Bm              A          G
Marry me, your father will disown you. (He'll eat his hat now)
```

**Bridge:**
```
        G                       D
Aww, marry him or marry me, I'm the one

that loves you baby, can't you see?
            G
Ain't got no future or a family tree
  A
but I know what a prince and lover ought to be,
  A
I know what a prince and lover ought to be...

         D          Bm              A            G
3. Said if you want to call me baby. (Just go ahead, now)
       D          Bm            A           G
And if you want to tell me maybe. (Just go ahead, now)
   D          Bm          A           G
If you wanna buy me flowers. (Just go ahead, now)
       D          Bm            A            G
And if you want to talk for hours. (Just go ahead, now)
```

M + T: Chris Barron, Eric Schenkman, Mark White & Aaron Comess
© Copyright 1992 Mow B Jow Music Incorporated/Sony/ATV Songs LLC.
Sony/ATV Music Publishing (UK) Limited.
All Rights Reserved. International Copyright Secured.

# CHILD IN TIME

(DEEP PURPLE)

**Intro:** G G Am    G G Am    F F G    G G Am    G G Am

```
               G G Am               F F G
Sweet child in time      you'll see the line,
                  G G Am              G G Am
line that's drawn between    good and bad.
              G G Am               F F G
See the blind man      shooting at the world,
         G G Am             G G Am
bullets flying     taking toll.
              G G Am                   F F G
If you've been bad.    Oh Lord I bet you have.
            G G Am              G G Am
And you've not been hit,     oh by flying lead.
                     G G Am        F F G             G G Am
You'd better close your eyes     aahouh     bow your head.
              G G Am
Wait for the ricochet.
```

Ooh ooh ooh...

```
               G G Am               F F G
Sweet child in time      you'll see the line,
                  G G Am              G G Am
line that's drawn between    good and bad.
              G G Am               F F G
See the blind man      shooting at the world,
         G G Am             G G Am
bullets flying     taking toll.
              G G Am                   F F G
If you've been bad.    Oh Lord I bet you have.
            G G Am              G G Am
And you've not been hit,     oh by flying lead.
                     G G Am        F F G             G G Am
You'd better close your eyes,    aahouh,    bow your head.
              G G Am
Wait for the ricochet.
```

Ooh ooh ooh...

M + T: Jon Lord, Ritchie Blackmore, Ian Gillan, Roger Glover and Ian Paice
© 1972 B Feldman & Co Ltd trading as Hec Music, London, W8 5SW. reproduced by permission od International Music Publications Ltd
(a trading name of Faber Music Ltd). All Rights Reserved.

# LAURA NON C'È

(NEK)

```
         Am              Fmaj7          G            Em7
1. Laura non c'è, è andata via. Laura non è più cosa mia.
         Am                      Fmaj7
E te che sei qua, e mi chiedi perché.
      G         Em7     Fmaj7         G
L'amo se niente più mi dà. Mi manca da spezzare il fiato
   Am           Em7     Fmaj7         G
fa male e non lo sa che non mi è mai passata.
         Am              Fmaj7     G             Em7
2. Laura non c'è, capisco che è stupido cercarla in te.
          Am                    Fmaj7
Io sto da schifo credi e non lo vorrei
      G           Em7     Fmaj7         G
stare con te pensare a lei. Stasera voglio stare acceso
   Am           Em7    Fmaj7            G
andiamocene di là a forza di pensare ho fuso.
```

**Refrain:**
```
G                Am          C
Se vuoi ci amiamo adesso, se vuoi
       Dsus2           Fmaj7
però non è lo stesso, tra di noi.
            Am              C
Da solo non mi basto stai con me
                 Dsus2         Fmaj7      Am C Dsus2 Fmaj7
solo è strano che al suo posto ci sei te, ci sei te.
```

```
3. Laura dov'è, mi manca sai, magari c'è un altro accanto a lei
giuro non c'ho pensato mai, che succedesse proprio a noi
lei si muove dentro un altro abbraccio
su di un corpo che non è più il mio
e io cosí non ce la faccio.
```

Refrain

```
Dm    G    C       F C/E  Dm       G         Am G C Em7
Forse è difficile così       ma non so che cosa fare
Dm    E/G#   Am C/G     F                              E
Credo che sia logico, per quanto io provi a scappare lei c'è.

A                   B           C#m7           G#m
Non vorrei che tu fossi un emergenza, ma tra bene e amore c'è
    A               B                   C#m7         E
solo Laura e la mia coscienza.   Se vuoi ci amiamo adesso oh no
      F#              Amaj7                C#m7               E
peró non è lo stesso ora so. C'è ancora il suo riflesso tra me e te
         F#             Amaj7
mi dispiace ma non posso, Laura c'è.
       C#m7          E                      F#         Amaj7
Se vuoi ci amiamo adesso, oh no mi casca il mondo addosso ora so
          C#m7               E
c'è ancora il suo riflesso tra me e te
            F#            A Bsus4      C#m7 C#m7
mi dispiace ma non posso Laura c'è, Laura c'è.
```

M + T: Nek / Varini
© Don't Worry Ed Mus S.r.l.
Universal Music Publishing Limited.
All Rights Reserved. International Copyright Secured.

# EL LUTE

(MICHAEL HOLM)

```
D                                A
Dies ist die Geschichte von El Lute, einem Mann, der geboren wurde,
                                          E
um wie ein wildes Tier gejagt zu werden, weil er arm war und sich nicht
                                      A
wehren konnte. Aber er gab sich mit seinem Schicksal nicht zufrieden
```

und heute wurde seine Ehre wiederhergestellt.

A E D E A   E D A   E D A

```
        A
1. Er war neunzehn und arm und und verurteilt zum Tod.
                                          D     A Bm
Dabei wussten alle, der Schuldige war nicht El Lute.
```

Man begnadigte ihn, er bekam lebenslang.

```
                  E
Er träumte von Flucht und ließ nichts unversucht
A                        E                       A
bis er schließlich entkam, damit fing die Jagd an, nach El Lute.

                D                               A
Er hat nie das Licht der Sonne gesehen, sie nannten Ihn El Lute.
                   E
Was er wollte, war nur ein Zuhaus' und mehr Brot
          A
und ein Ende von Hunger und Not.
                D                                  A
Aber Spanien war damals kein Land für einen wie El Lute,
                      E
doch weil er für das Recht aller Rechtlosen stand,
         D    A
waren sie für El Lute.
```

A E D E A   E D A   E D A  Am

```
    Am                                         E
Und es sprach sich herum, dass es nicht um El Lute nur ging.
Dm                                            E                 Am
Hier war einer wie sie und er beugte sich nie, ihre Hoffnung, sie stieg.
     E                          A
Denn sein Sieg war ihr Sieg. Denn sein Sieg war ihr Sieg.
```

2. Auf und ab durch das Land ging die endlose Jagd,
wo immer er war, überall hing das Bild von El Lute.
Er war wie Robin Hood und es ging lange gut.
Dann schloss sich die Falle, das Ende schien nah,
doch ein Wunder geschah in dem sonnigen Land von El Lute.

Er hat nie das Licht der Sonne gesehen, sie nannten Ihn El Lute.
Was er wollte, war nur ein Zuhaus' und mehr Brot
und ein Ende von Hunger und Not.
Und es kam ein neuer Morgen ins Land, er kam auch für El Lute,
denn die Freiheit, dir dort für die Menschen heut' gilt,
sie gilt für auch für El Lute.

M + T: Frank Farian, Fred Jay, Hans Blum
© Far Musikverlag GmbH.
Mit freundlicher Genehmigung von Far Musikverlag GmbH & Co. KG.

# ANGEL OF HARLEM

(U2)

**Intro:** C F C F C F C F

```
          C              F              C              F
1. It was a cold and wet December day, when we touched down at JFK.
   C           F                 C          F           C F C F
Snow was melting on the ground, on BLS I heard the sound of an Angel.
   C          F                 C              F           C F C F
New York like a Christmas tree, tonight this city belongs to me, Angel.
   F   G                         F       G        C F   C F
So long, this love won't let me go, so long, Angel of Harlem.

         C         F        C               F
2. Birdland on 53, the street sounds like a symphony,
             C                 F
   we got John Coltrane and a love supreme,
   C         F             C F C F
Miles and she's got to be an Angel.
   C         F                  C            F            C F   C F
Lady Day got diamond eyes, she sees the truth behind the lies, Angel.
   F   G                         F       G
So long, this love won't let me go, so long,
         C F   C F        C F   C F
Angel of Harlem,    Angel of Harlem.
Am    G    F              Am    G          F    C F C F C F
Ooh, ooh, ooh, she sings with heart, heart and soul.

          C                F         C             F
3. Blue light on the avenue, God knows they got to you.
          C           F          C             F
An empty glass, the lady sings, eyes swollen like a bee sting.
   C         F                 C            F
Blinded you lost your way, on the side streets and the alleyways,
             C          F              C                  F
Like a star exploding in the night, filling to the city with broad
daylight.
     F                       G
An Angel in devil's shoes, salvation in the blues.
                         F         G         C F   C F C F C F
You never looked like an angel, yeah! Angel of Harlem,
C  F   C    F        C F   C   F
Angel,    Angel of Harlem...
```

M + T: U2
© Copyright 1988 Blue Mountain Music Limited
All Rights Reserved. International Copyright Secured.

# THE DAY BEFORE YOU CAME

(ABBA)

```
      Em                           C              B
1. I must have left my house at eight because I always do.
                                                    Em
My train I'm certain left the station just when it was due.
                                          D
I must have read the morning paper going into town
                                                      G
and having gotten through the editorial no doubt I must have frowned.
                                   D
I must have made my desk around a quarter after nine
                                                 G
with letters to be read and heaps of papers waiting to be signed.
     C                    G/B
I must have gone to lunch at half past twelve or so.
          Am
The usual place, the usual bunch
                            F#°                  B
and still on top of this I'm pretty sure it must have rained
                         Em
the day before you came.

2. I must have lit my seventh cigarette at half past two.
And at the time I never even noticed I was blue.
I must have kept on dragging through the business of the day
without really knowing anything I hid a part of me away.
At five I must have left there's no exception to the rule,
a matter of routine I've done it ever since I finished school.
The train back home again
undoubtedly I must have read the evening paper then.
Oh yes I'm sure my life was well within it's usual frame
the day before you came.

Em C° A° B7 Em E° Em B7 Em

3. I must have opened my front door at eight o'clock or so
and stopped along the way to buy some Chinese food to go.
I'm sure I had my dinner watching something on TV,
there's not I think a single episode of Dallas that I didn't see
I must have gone to bed around a quarter after ten,
I need a lot of sleep and so I like to be in bed by then.
I must have read a while
the latest one by Marilyn French or something in that style.
It's funny but I had no sense of living without aim
the day before you came.

       C
And turning out the light
   G/B                              Am
I must have yawned and cuddled up for yet another night.
                          F#°                         B
And rattling on the roof I must have heard the sound of rain
                         Em
the day before you came.

Em C° A° B7 Em E° Em B7 Em (2x)
```

M + T: Benny Andersson & Bjorn Ulvaeus
© Copyright 1982 Universal/Union Songs Musikforlag AB.
Bocu Music Limited for Great Britain and the Republic of Ireland.
Universal Music Publishing Limited for World excluding Great Britain and the Republic of Ireland.
All Rights Reserved. International Copyright Secured.

# CHAMPS ELYSEES

(JOE DASSIN)

**Intro:** C G/B Am C7/G F C/E D7 G

```
         C              G/B        Am              C7/G
1. Je m'baladais sur l'avenue le coeur ouvert à l'inconnu,
   F              C/E              D7         G
   j'avais envie de dire bonjour à n'importe qui.
   C              G/B        Am             C7/E
   N'importe qui et ce fut toi, je t'ai dit n'importe quoi
   F              C             F     G7 C
   il suffisait de te parler, pour t'apprivoiser.
```

**Refrain:**
```
C    E7/B    Am  C7/G F    C/E      D7  G7
Aux Champs-Elysées,   aux Champs-Elysées.
C         E7/B         Am         C7/G
Au soleil, sous la pluie, à midi ou à minuit
F                 C/E              F     G7 C
il y a tout ce que vous voulez aux Champs-Elysées.
```

2. Tu m'as dit "J'ai rendez-vous dans un sous-sol avec des fous
qui vivent la guitare à la main, du soir au matin."
Alors je t'ai accompagnée, on a chanté, on a dansé
et l'on n'a même pas pensé à s'embrasser.

Refrain

3. Hier soir deux inconnus et ce matin sur l'avenue
deux amoureux tout étourdis par la longue nuit.
Et de l'Étoile à la concorde, un orchestre à mille cordes,
tous les oiseaux du point du jour chantent l'amour.

Refrain

(HANS BRADTKE)
```
          C              G/B            Am             C7/E
1. Ich ging allein durch diese Stadt, die allerhand zu bieten hat,
   F              C/E             D7        G
   da sah ich dich vorübergehn und sagte "Bonjour!"
   C              G/B         Am            C7/E
   Ich ging mit dir in ein Café, wo ich erfuhr, du heißt Reneé.
   F              C/E           F     G7  C
   Wenn ich an diese Stunden denke, singe ich nur:
```

**Refrain:**
```
C    E7/B       Am  C7/G F    C/E      D7  G7
Oh Champs-Elysées,   oh Champs-Elysées.
C         E7/B          Am             C7/G
Sonne scheint, Regen rinnt, ganz egal, wir beide sind
F                 C/E               F      G7 C
so froh, wenn wir uns wiedersehn. Oh Champs-Elysées.
```

2. Wie wunderschön der Abend war da drüben in der kleinen Bar,
wo Joe auf der Gitarre spielte nur für uns zwei.
Da habe ich die ganze Nacht mit dir getanzt, mit dir gelacht.
Und als wir wieder gingen, war es zehn nach drei.
Refrain

Original Titel: WATERLOO ROAD
M + Orig.T: Mike Wilsh / Mike Deighan
frz. T: Pierre Delanoe
© 1969 Intersong Music Ltd, London.
Reproduced by permission of Faber Music Limited.
All Rights Reserved.

# THE GAMBLER

(KENNY ROGERS)

```
      G                       C              G
1. On a warm summer's evening, on a train bound for nowhere
                                               D
   I met up with a gambler, we were both too tired to speak.
      G                          C             G
   So we took turns a-starin' out the window at the darkness
       C         G          D         G
   'til boredom overtook us and he began to speak.
```

2. He said "Son, I've made a life out of reading people's faces,
   knowing what their cards were by the way they held their eyes,
   and if you don't mind me saying, I can see you're out of aces,
   and for a taste of your whiskey I'll give you some advice."

3. So I handed him my bottle and he drank down my last swallow.
   Then he bummed a cigarette and asked me for a light.
   And the night got deathly quiet, and his face lost all expression, said
   "If you're gonna play the game, boy, you gotta learn to play it right."

**Refrain:**
```
           G                     C              G
You got to know when to hold 'em, know when to fold 'em,
  C             G                D
know when to walk away and know when to run.
           G                   C              G
You never count your money when you're sitting at the table,
               C         G         D                 G
there'll be time enough for counting. When the dealing's done.
```

```
   A                  D              A
4. Every gambler knows that the secret to surviving
                                            E
   is knowing what to throw away and knowing what to keep.
     A                         D              A
   Cause every hand's a winner, and every hand's a loser,
       D              A            E           A
   and the best that you can hope for is to die in your sleep.
```

5. And when he finished speaking, he turned back toward the window,
   crushed out his cigarette and faded off to sleep,
   and somewhere in the darkness, the gambler, he broke even,
   but in his final words I found an ace that I could keep.

You got to know when to hold 'em, know when to fold 'em,
know when to walk away and know when to run.
You never count your money when you're sitting at the table,
there'll be time enough for counting when the dealing's done.

M + T: Don Schlitz
© Copyright 1978 Cross Keys Publishing Company Incorporated, USA.
Sony/ATV Music Publishing (UK) Limited.
All Rights Reserved. International Copyright Secured.

# ICH WILL SPASS

(MARKUS)
[TRANSP. +1]

```
   C
1. Mein Maserati fährt 210, schwupp, die Polizei hat's nicht geseh'n,
        F        G                C
   das macht Spaß! Ich geb Gas, ich geb Gas!

   Will nicht spar'n, nicht vernünftig sein, tank nur das gute Super rein.
       F       G                C
   Ich mach Spaß! Ich geb Gas, ich geb Gas!
```

**Refrain:**
```
                C        Am                  F       G
   Ich will Spaß, ich will Spaß! Ich will Spaß, ich will Spaß!
                C        Am                  F       G
   Ich geb Gas, ich geb Gas! Ich will Spaß, ich will Spaß!

   C
2. Ich schubs die Enten aus dem Verkehr, ich jag' die Opels vor mir her,
       F      G                     C
   ich mach Spaß! Ich mach Spaß, ich mach Spaß!

   Und kost' Benzin auch drei Mark zehn, scheißegal, es wird schon geh'n.
       F       G                     C
   Ich will fahr'n! Ich will fahr'n, ich will fahr'n!
```

Refrain

```
   C
3. Deutschland, Deutschland, spürst du mich? Heut nacht komm ich über
   dich.
        F       G                          C
   Das macht Spaß! Das macht Spaß, das macht Spaß!
   C
   Der Tankwart ist mein bester Freund, hui, wenn ich komm, wie der sich
   freut.
        F       G                    C
   Er braucht Spaß! Er hat Spaß, er hat Spaß!

                 C        Am                   F       G
   Wir wolln Spaß, wollen Spaß! Wollen Spaß, wollen Spaß!
         F         Am              F       G
   Geben Gas, geben Gas! Wollen Spaß, wollen Spaß.
                 C        Am                    F       G
   Ich mach Spaß, ich mach Spaß! Ich brauch Spaß, ich brauch Spaß!
                 C        Am                   F       G
   Ich will fahrn, ich will fahrn! Ich will fahrn, ich will fahrn!
```

M + T: Klopprogge, Axel
© Chartbreaker Musikverlag GmbH. With courtesy of Budde Music, Berlin.

# GROSSVATER

(STS)

**Intro:** Bb Eb F Eb Bb Eb F

```
        Bb                  Eb
1. Bei jedem Wickel mit der Mutter
           F              Bb  Eb  F
war mei erster Weg von daham zu dir!
      Bb                Eb                  F
Und du hast gsagt, sie is allein, des muasst verstehn,
                            Bb   Eb  F
alles vergeht, komm drink a Bier!
   Eb       Bb          Eb           F
Dann hast du gmeint, das ganze Leben
  Eb         Bb           Eb         F
besteht aus Nehmen und viel mehr Geben!
```

2. Worauf i aus dein Kasten in der Nacht
die paar tausend Schilling gfladert hab!
Zum Verputzen in der Diskothek,
a paar Tag drauf hast mi danach gfragt.
I habs bestritten, hysterisch plärrt,
dei Blick war traurig, dann hab I geredt!

```
  F           Eb                    F
Du hast nur gsagt, komm lass ma's bleiben.
        Bb      D/A       Gm      F
Geld kann gar nie so wichtig sein!
```

3. Wann du vom Krieg erzählt hast,
wie du eim Russen Aug in Aug gegenüber gstanden bist.
Ihr habts euch gegenseitig angschickt am Boden,
die Hand am Abzug hat zittert vor lauter Schiss.
Oder dei Frau, die den ganzen Tag
dir die Ohren voll gsungen hat!

Du host nur gsogt, I hab sie gern,
i muass net alles, was sie sagt, immer hörn!

**Refrain:**
```
F     Bb               Eb            C                  F
Großvater, kannst du net oba kommen, auf an schnelln Kaffee?
     Bb              Eb            C                   F
Großvater, i möcht dir so viel sagen, was i erst jetzt versteh!
     Bb              Eb              C            F               Bb
Großvater, du warst mei erster Freund und des vergiss i nie! Großvater!
```

4. Du warst ka Übermensch, hast a nie so tan,
grad deswegen war da irgendwie a Kraft.
Und durch die Art, wie du dei Leben glebt hast,
hab i a Ahnung gkriegt, wie mans vielleicht schafft!
Dei Grundsatz war, zuerst überlegen,
a Meinung haben, dahinter stehen,

niemals Gewalt, alles bereden,
aber a ka Angst vor irgendwem!

Refrain

M + T: Gert Steinbäcker
© Copyright by Edition SCHEIBMAIER
All Rights Reserved. International Copyright Secured.

# S.O.S.

(ABBA)

```
      Dm                      C#°                       Dm
1. Where are those happy days, they seem so hard to find.
Dm                      C#°                    Dm
I try to reach for you but you have closed your mind.
F                      C              Gm           Dm
What ever happened to our love? I wish I understood.
Dm                      C#°                    Dm       C#° Dm C7 F Gm F C7
It used to feel so nice, it used to be so good.
```

**Refrain:**
```
F              C              Gm              Bb        F
So when you're near me, darling can't you hear me S.O.S.
F              C              Gm              Bb        F
The love you gave me, nothing else can save me S.O.S.
            Bb             Db           Eb        F
When you're gone, how can I even try to go on?
            Bb             Db           Eb        F
When you're gone, well I try, how can I carry on?


      Dm                      C#°                       Dm
2. You seem so far away but you are standing near.
Dm                      C#°                    Dm
You make me feel alive but something died I fear.
F                      C              Gm           Dm
I really tried to make it out, I wish I understood.
Dm                      C#°                    Dm       C#° Dm C7 F Gm F C7
What happened to our love, it used to be so good.
```

Refrain 2x

```
F           Bb           Db         Eb        F
When you're gone, how can I even try to go on?
            Bb           Db         Eb        F
When you're gone, ooh I try, how can I carry on?
```

M + T: Benny Andersson, Björn Ulvaeus & Stig Anderson
© Copyright 1975 Universal/Union Songs Musikforlag AB
Universal Music Publishing Limited.
All Rights Reserved. International Copyright Secured.

# BROTHERS IN ARMS

(DIRE STRAITS)

**Intro:** Em C/G Am7 C/G Em C/G Am7 Em

```
        Em                  C      D
1. These mist covered mountains
                    G    Gsus4    G
are a home now for me.
       Bm/F#        Em   Bm
But my home is the lowlands
                 C    Dsus4
and always will be.
      D          Em     Bm
Some day you'll return to
                       C     Am7    D4
your valleys and your farms.
               D         Em
And you'll no longer burn
      C          Dsus4   D
to be brothers in arms.
```

**Solo:** Em C/G Am7 C/G Em C/G Am7 Em


2. Through these fields of destruction,
baptisms of fire
l've watched all your suffering
as the battles raged higher.
And though they did hurt me so bad
in the fear and alarm.
You did not desert me,
my brothers in arms.

**Solo:** Em C/G Am7 C/G Em C/G Am7 Em

```
Em          D            Em      D  G                 C
There's so many different worlds, so many different suns.
Dsus4 D                  Em      D      G             C
And we have just one world, but we live in different ones.
```

**Solo:** Em C/G Am7 C/G Em C/G Am7 Em C/G Am7 C/G Em C/G Am7 Em


3. Now the sun's gone to hell
and the moon's riding high.
Let me bid you farewell
every man has to die.
But it's written in the starlight
and every line on your palm.
We're fools to make war
on our brothers in arms.

**Solo:**
Em C/G Am7 C/G Em C/G Am7
Em C/G Am7 C/G Em C/G Am7
Em C/G Am7 C/G Em C/G Am7 Em

M + T: Mark Knopfler
© Copyright 1985 Straitjacket Songs Limited
Universal Music Publishing Limited.
All Rights Reserved. International Copyright Secured.

# WHERE HAVE ALL THE COWBOYS GONE?

(PAULA COLE)

```
   F#m                         C#m
1. Oh you get me ready in your 56 Chevy.
   F#m                        C#m
Why don't we go sit down in the shade?
   F#m                            C#m
Take shelter on my front porch. The dandelion sun scorched,
          F#m                   C#m
would you like a glass of cold lemonade?

D           A         Bm            C#m
I will do the laundry if you pay all the bills.
```

**Refrain:**
```
F#m            C#m       F#m           C#m
Where is my John Wayne? Where is my prairie son?
F#m          C#m        D               E            F#m C#m D E
Where is my happy ending? Where have all the Cowboys gone?
```

2. Why don't you stay the evening, kick back and watch the TV.
And I'll fix a little something to eat?
Oh I know your back hurts from working on the tractor,
how do you take your coffee my sweet?

I will raise the children if you pay all the bills.

Refrain

```
G
I am wearing my new dress tonight
              Bm              C#m D E
but you don't even notice me.
      Bm              C#m                   D          E
Say our goodbyes, say our goodbyes, say our goodbyes.
```

3. We finally sold the Chevy when we had another baby.
And you took that job in Tennessee.
You made friends at the farm, and you joined them at the bar
almost every single day of the week.

I will wash the dishes while you go have a beer.

Refrain

Where is my Marlboro Man? Where is his shiny gun?
Where is my lonely ranger? Where have all the cowboys gone?

Yippee Aw, Yippee Yea Yippee Aw, Yippee Yea Yippee Aw, Yippee Yea.

M + T: Paula Cole
© Copyright 1993 Hing Face Music/Famous Music Publishing Limited.
All Rights Reserved. International Copyright Secured.

# LOSER

(BECK)

Intro und gesamtes Lied in D

**1.** In the time of chimpanzees I was a monkey,
butane in my veins so I'm out to get the junkie
with the plastic eyeballs, spraypaint the vegetables,
dog food stalls with the beefcake pantyhose,
kill the headlights and put it in neutral,
stockcar flaming with a loser in the cruise control,
baby's in Reno with the vitamin D,
got a couple of couches, sleep on the love seat,
someone came sayin' I'm a saint (I'm insane)
to complain about
a shotgun wedding and a stain on my shirt,
don't believe everything that you breathe,
you get a parking violation and a maggot on your sleeve,
so shave your face with some mace in the dark,
saving all your food stamps for burning down the trailer park.

Yo, cut it.
Soy un perdedor, I'm a loser baby, so why don't you kill me?
Double barrel buckshot.
Soy un perdedor, I'm a loser baby, so why don't you kill me?

**2.** Forces of evil on a bozo nightmare,
ban all the music with a phony gas chamber
cause one's got a weasel and others got a flag,
one's on the pole, shove the other in the bag,
with the rerun shows and cocaine nose job,
the daytime crap of the folk singers slop,
he hung himself with a guitar string,
a slab of turkey neck and it's hangin' from a pigeon wing,
I can't write if ya' can't relate,
trade the cash for the beef for the body for the hate,
and my time is a piece of wax, fallen on a termite,
who's chokin' on the splinters.

Soy un perdedor, I'm a loser baby, so why don't you kill me?
Get crazy with the cheez-wiz.
Soy un perdedor, I'm a loser baby, so why don't you kill me?
Drive, by, body pierce.
Yo bring it on down.

I'm a driver, I'm a winner.
Things are gonna' change, I can feel it.

Soy un perdedor, I'm a loser baby, so why don't you kill me?
I can't believe it
Soy un perdedor, I'm a loser baby, so why don't you kill me?

Soy un perdedor, I'm a loser baby, so why don't you kill me?
Sprechen sie deutsch, baby?

Soy un perdedor, I'm a loser baby, so why don't you kill me?
You know what I'm sayin'.

M + T: Beck Hansen/Carl Stephenson
© Copyright 1993 Cyanide Breathmint/Universal Music MGB Songs/Funky Toe Publishing.
Kobalt Music Publishing Limited/Universal Music Publishing MGB Limited.
All Rights Reserved. International Copyright Secured.

# JACK AND DIANE

(JOHN COUGAR MELLENCAMP)

**Intro:** A E/A A E/A D (2x)

```
A          E           D            E
Little ditty about Jack and Diane,
A              E              D       E    A
two American kids growin' up in the heartland.
A          E       D         E
Jacky's gonna be a football star,
A          E            D    E     A
Diane debutante backseat of Jacky's car.
```

Suckin' on chili dogs outside the tastee freeze
Diane's sittin' on Jacky's lap, he's got his hand between her knees.
Jacky say "Hey Diane lets run off behind a shady tree",
dribble off those Bobby Brooks let me do what I please.
And Jacky says:

**Refrain:**
```
A  E       D      E
Oh yeah, life goes on
A                E          D       E
long after the thrill of livin' is gone.
A  E       D      E
Oh yeah, say life goes on
A                E          D       E    A
long after the thrill of livin' is gone, they walk on.
```

Jacky sits back reflects his thoughts for the moment
scratches his head and does his best James Dean.
Well you know Diane, we oughtta run of the city.
Diane says: "Baby, you aint missin' nothing".
Jacky says:

Refrain

```
A           D    A       E
Gonna let it rock, let it roll.
A            D              G        D    A
Let the Bible Belt come down and save my soul.
A       D    G           D
Hold on to 16 as long as you can,
A            D                   E        A
changes come around real soon make us women and men.
```

Little ditty about Jack and Diane,
two American kids doing the best they can.

M + T: John Cougar Mellencamp
© Copyright 1982 Riva Music Limited.
EMI Music Publishing (WP) Limited.
All Rights Reserved. International Copyright Secured.

# ACHY BREAKY HEART

(BILLY RAY CYRUS)

    A
1. You can tell the world, you never was my girl,
                                E7
you can burn my clothes up when I'm gone

You can tell your friends just what a fool I've been
                                 A
and laugh and joke about me on the phone.

   A
2. You can tell my arms go back to the farm,
                       E7
you can tell my feet to hit the floor.

Or you can tell my lips to tell my fingertips,
                              A
they won't be reaching out for you no more.


**Refrain:**
    A
But don't tell my heart, my achy breaky heart,
                    E7
I just don't think he'd understand.

And if you tell my heart, my achy breaky heart,
                      A
he might blow up and kill this man.

   A
3. You can tell your Ma, I moved to Arkansas,
                   E7
you can tell your dog to bite my leg.

Or tell your brother Cliff whose fist can tell my lip
                     A
he never really liked my anyway.

     A
4. Or tell your Aunt Louise, tell anything you please,
                  E7
myself already knows I'm not OK.

Or you can tell my eyes to watch out for my mind,
                         A
it might be walking out on me today.


Refrain 2x

M + T: Donald Von Tress
© Copyright 1992 Universal Millhouse Music.
Universal Music Publishing Limited. All Rights Reserved. International Copyright Secured.

# MY LOVE IS YOUR LOVE

(WHITNEY HOUSTON)

```
G                            Dm
Clap your hands, you're so right.   (4x)
     G       D              Em     Am     G                     D
1.  If tomorrow is judgement day, and I'm standing on the front line.
   G      D         Em                 C
And the Lord asks me what I did with my life,
        G    D              G
I will say I spent it with you.
G                            Dm
Clap your hands, you're so right.   (2x)

     G      D               Em     Am     G                     D
2.  If I wake up in World War III, I see destruction and poverty,
   G      D        Em        C          G     D                     G
and I feel like I wanna go home, it's okay if you're coming with me.
G                            Dm
Clap your hands, you're so right.   (3x)
```

**Refrain:**
```
         G           D           Em         C
'Cause your love is my love, and my love is your love,
G                         D
it would take an eternity to break us,
Em                        C
and the chains of Amistad couldn't hold us.  Refrain

G                            Dm
Clap your hands, you're so right.   (3x)

     G      D              Em     Am     G                 D
3.  If I lose my fame and fortune, and I'm homeless on the street.
   G      D             Em         C
And I'm sleeping in Grand Central Station,
        G     D                       G
it's okay if you're sleeping with me.
G                            Dm
Clap your hands, you're so right.   (2x)

     G      D              Em     Am     G                      D
4.  As the years they pass us by, we stay young through each others eyes.
   G       D         Em      C           G    D                      G
And no matter how old we get, it's okay as long as I got you, babe.
G                            Dm
Clap your hands, you're so right.   (2x)
Refrain

Eb        F                  Gm
If I should die this very day,
         Eb                F                 G
don't cry, cause on earth we wasn't meant to stay.
Eb        F                  Gm
And no matter what the people say,
Eb                F                       D     D7
I'll be waiting for you after the judgement day.        Refrain 2x
G                            Dm
Clap your hands, you're so right.
```

<sub>M: Jerry Duplessis, Nel Wyclef Jean & Vaughan Mason, T: Nel Wyclef Jean & Vaughan Mason
© Copyright 1998 Te-Bass Music, Inc./Huss-Zwingli Publishing Inc/EMI Blackwood Music. Sony/ATV Music Publishing (UK) Limited. Mit freundlicher Genehmigung der EMI Music Publishing Germany GmbH. International Copyright Secured.</sub>

## BAMBOLEO

(GIPSY KINGS)

```
F#m                C#7        F#m                    C#7
Este amor llega asi esta manera, no tiene la culpa,

caballo le dan sabana porque muy depreciado,
                       F#m
por eso no te perdon de llorar.
                      C#7     F#m                    C#7
Este amor llega asi esta manera, no tiene la culpa,

amor de compra y venta, amor del mes pasado,

Bembele, bembele, bembele, bey, bembele, bembele.
```

**Refrain:**
```
    F#m          Bm              C#7                       F#m
Bamboleo, bamboleo, porque mi vida, yo la prefiero vivir asi.
                 Bm              C#7                       F#m
Bamboleo, bamboleo, porque mi vida, yo la prefiero vivir asi.

                  Bm             E                    A
No tiene pardon de dios, tu eres mi vida, la fortuna del destino,
     F#m                 Bm
pero el destino tendressa para dos,
                C#7               F#m
lo mismo yo que ayer lo mismo soy yo.
                          Bm
No te encuentro a l'abandon,
      E                      A
es imposible no te encuentro de verdad,
          F#m                   Bm
por eso un dia no cuentro si de nada,
                 C#7            F#m
lo mismo you que ayer yo pienso en ti.
```

Refrain 2x

M + T: Tonino Baliardo, Nicolas Reyes, Jalhoul Bouchikhi & Simon Diaz
© Copyright 1988 Hans-Kusters-Music.
Sony/ATV Music Publishing (UK) Limited/Chelsea Music Publishing Company Limited.
All Rights Reserved. International Copyright Secured.

# LUCKY

(BRITNEY SPEARS)
[TRANSP. +1]

```
C  Am    C                                    Am
Intro: This is a story about a girl named Lucky.
   C                    Am             C                   Am
1. Early morning, she wakes up, knock, knock, knock on the door.
C                      Am                   C                  Am
It's time for makeup, perfect smile, it's you they're all waiting for.
              C           Am          F         G            C
They go : "Isn't she lovely, this Hollywood girl?" And they say:
```

**Refrain 1:**
```
C                     Am
She's so lucky, she's a star,
         F                            G
but she cry, cry, cries in her lonely heart, thinking,
C                           Am
"If there's nothing missing in my life,
     F              G
then why do these tears come at night?"
```

```
     C              Am                  C                    Am
2. Lost in an image, in a dream but there's no one there to wake her up.
          C                                G
And the world is spinning, and she keeps on winning,
Am
but tell me what happens when it stops?
              C           Am          F         G            C
They go : "Isn't she lovely, this Hollywood girl?" And they say:
```

**Refrain 2:**
```
C                     Am
She's so lucky, she's a star,
         F                            G       E
but she cry, cry, cries in her lonely heart, thinking,
Am                      C/G
"If there's nothing missing in my life,
     F              G
then why do these tears come at night?"
```

```
C  Am                       G                     C  Am
   "Best actress, and the winner is...Lucky!"
Am
"I'm Roger Johnson for Pop News standing outside the arena,
                                                  C
waiting for Lucky". "Oh, my God, here she comes!"

Fmaj7     G    Am         Dm        G     A
Isn't she lovely, this Hollywood girl?
D         Bm          G                A
She is so lucky, but why does she cry?
D          Bm         G                             A
If there is nothing missing in her life, why do tears come at night?
```

Refrain 1, Refrain 2 (beide einen Ton höher)

M + T: Martin Sandberg / Alexander Kronlund / Rami Yacoub
© Copyright 2000 Grantsville Publishing Limited/Universal/MCA Music Scandinavia AB/GV-MXM.
Kobalt Music Publishing Limited/Imagem London Limited/
Universal/MCA Music Limited. All Rights Reserved.
International Copyright Secured.

# KISS FROM A ROSE

(SEAL)
[TRANSP. +4]

```
         E                   Cmaj7      D          E
1. There used to be a graying tower alone on the sea,
             Cmaj7        D           E
you became the light on the dark side of me.
              Cmaj7        D            E
Love remains a drug that's the high and not the pill.
      E             Em        Cmaj7       D
Did you know that when it snows my eyes become large
    Cmaj7         D          E
and the light that you shine can't be seen.
```

**Refrain:**
```
    E                 Cmaj7       D           E
Baby, I compare you to a kiss from a rose on the gray.
                    Cmaj7        D       E
The more I get of you the stranger it feels, yeah.
             Cmaj7       D         Cmaj7      D            E
Now that your rose is in bloom, a light hits the gloom on the gray.
```

```
   E                      Cmaj7        D          E
2. There is so much a man can tell you, so much he can say.
              Cmaj7       D           E
You remain my power, my pleasure, my pain, baby.
  Cmaj7             D                             E
To me you're like a growing addiction that I can't deny,
                  Cmaj7         D
won't you tell me is that healthy, babe?
          E             Em        Cmaj7       D
But did you know that when it snows my eyes become large
    Cmaj7         D          E
and the light that you shine can't be seen
```

Refrain

**Bridge:**
```
D         A          G        D            A          G
I've been kissed by a rose on the gray, I've been kissed by a rose.
D         A          G        D
I've been kissed by a rose on the gray.
          A          G        E
I've been kissed by a rose on the gray.
```

Strophe 2

Refrain (2x)

```
             Cmaj7            D                       E
Now that your rose is in bloom, a light hits the gloom on the gray.
```

M + T: Seal
© Copyright 1994 Beethoven Street Music.
Perfect Songs Limited.
All Rights Reserved. International Copyright Secured.

# AB IN DEN SÜDEN

(BUDDY VS. DJ THE WAVE)

**Intro:** F Bb/F (8x)

```
           F            Bb/F           F        Bb/F
1. Oh willkommen, willkommen, willkommen, Sonnenschein,
            F                Bb/F        F      Bb/F
wir packen unsere sieben Sachen in den Flieger rein.
      F          Bb/F                   F         Bb/F
Ja wir kommen, wir kommen, wir kommen, macht euch bereit,
        F          Bb/F              F          Bb/F
reif für die Insel, Sommer, Sonne, Strand und Zärtlichkeit.
```

**Bridge:**
```
            F              Bb/F        F       Bb/F       F
Raus ausm Regen ins Leben, ab in den Süden, der Sonne entgegen,
   Bb/F             F             Bb/F           F
was erleben, einen Heben und dann Bikinis erleben.
Bb/F                  F            Bb/F              F
Jetzt kommt es dick, Mann! Ich rette den Tag, ich sag:

ab geht die Party und die Party geht ab.
```

**Refrain:**
```
             F Bb/F F    Bb/F      F Bb/F F
Und ich sag heeeeeeeeee ab in den Süden,
Bb/F          F      Bb/F         F
der Sonne hinterher (ey jo was geht),
Bb/F          F      Bb/F         F
der Sonne hinterher (ey jo was geht).
Refrain

F            Bb/F                F            Bb/F
Sommer, Sonne, Sonnenschein, Sommer, Sonne, Sonnenschein.
F            Bb/F                F            Bb/F
Sommer, Sonne, Sonnenschein, Sommer, Sonne, Sonnenschein.

F
2. Oh willkommen, willkommen, willkommen, Sonnenschein,
den ganzen Tag am Strand ziehn wir uns die Melonen rein.
Ja Tequila, Tequila, Tequila, Wonderbra
und heute Nacht machen wir noch die ganze Insel klar.
```

Bridge

Refrain 2x

M + T: Olaf Jeglitza, Boris Koehler, Sebastian Erl
© 2003 Edition Phat Monday administered by Hanseatic Musikverlag GmbH & Co KG,
Warner/Chappell Overseas Holdings Ltd, London. Reproduced by permission of Faber
Music Ltd. All Rights Reserved.

# **SANTA MARIA**

(ROLAND KAISER)
[TRANSP. -2]

**Intro:**
```
C                                F
Um dada, um dada, um dada uha. Um dada, um dada, um dada uha.
```

Intro

**Refrain:**
```
C                                    F
Santa Maria, Insel, die aus Träumen geboren,
                  G                         C                 G
ich hab meine Sinne verloren, in dem Fieber, das wie Feuer brennt.

      C                                 F
1. Santa Maria, nachts an deinen schneeweißen Stränden hielt ich ihre
G                                    C
Jugend in den Händen, Glück, für das man keinen Namen kennt.

Am                  E7              F                 D
Sie war ein Kind der Sonne, schön wie ein erwachender Morgen.
Am                  E7              F
Heiß war ihr stolzer Blick, und tief in ihrem Inneren verborgen
D                         C
brannte die Sehnsucht. Santa Maria, den Schritt zu wagen,
G                                F
Santa Maria, vom Mädchen bis zur Frau.
```

Intro
Refrain

```
      C                                   F
2. Santa Maria, ihre Wildheit ließ mich erleben, mit ihr auf bunten
G                                           C
Flügeln entschweben, in ein fernes, unbekanntes Land.

Am                  E7              F                     D
Wehrlos trieb ich dahin, im Zauber ihres Lächelns gefangen.
Am                  E7                  F
Doch als der Tag erwacht, sah ich die Tränen auf ihren Wangen,
D                         C
Morgen hieß Abschied. Santa Maria, und meine Heimat,
G                                   F
Santa Maria, war so unendlich weit.
```

1 Ton höher

Intro
Refrain

```
      D                                 G
3. Santa Maria, niemals mehr hab ich so empfunden, wir im Rausch der
A                                     D                    A
nächtlichen Stunden, die Erinnerung, sie wird nie vergehn.
```

Intro

M + T: De Angelis, Guido / De Angelis, Maurizio / De Natale, Cesare C. /
Gane, Leonie / Duncan-Smith, Susan
© Edition Roma/MCA Music GmbH.

# DISCO 2000

(PULP)

**Intro:** F Fsus4 F  Bb  Bbsus4 Bb
```
              F
```
1. Well we were born within an hour of each other,
our mothers said we could be sister and brother.
```
             Bb
```
Your name is Deborah. Deborah - it never suited you.
```
            F
```
2. Oh and they said that when we grew up
we'd get married and never split up.
```
             Bb
```
We never did it, although I often I thought of it.

**Refrain:**
```
                     Cm
```
Oh Deborah, do you recall?
```
                     Cm                           Cm
```
Your house was very small with wood-chips on the wall.
```
                Cm                        F
```
When I came around to call you didn't notice me at all.

And I said:
```
 Bb
```
"Let's all meet up in the year 2000.
```
Dm                                Gm
```
Won't it be strange when we're all fully grown?
```
                        Cm             Fsus4 F
```
Be there two o'clock by the fountain down the road."
```
Bb
```
I never knew that you'd get married,
```
Dm                          Gm
```
I would be living down here on my own,
```
                   Cm                 F
```
on that damp and lonely Thursday, years ago.

```
             F
```
3. You were the first girl in school to get breasts,
Martyn said that you were the best.
```
             Bb
```
The boys all loved you but I was a mess,
I had to watch them try to get you undressed.

```
        F
```
4. We were friends that was as far as it went,
I used to walk you home sometimes but it meant.
```
                       Bb
```
Oh, it meant nothing to you cause you were oh so popular.

Refrain 2x

```
       Bb
```
|: Oh, what are you doing Sunday, baby?
```
Dm
```
Would you like to come and meet me maybe?
```
Gm                          Cm  F
```
You can even bring your baby, oh.  :|

M + T: Jarvis Cocker, Russell Senior, Candida Doyle, Stephen Patrick Mackey, Nick Banks & Mark Andrew Webber
© Island Music Limited. Universal/Universal Music Publishing GmbH

# WHEN I'M SIXTY-FOUR

(THE BEATLES)

```
   C                                                    G
1. When I get older, losing my hair, many years from now,

will you still be sending me a Valentine,
G7                                    C
birthday greetings, bottle of wine?

If I'd been out 'till quarter to three,
C7                      F
would you lock the door?
            F#°        C/G              A7
Will you still need me, will you still feed me,
D7       G7      C
when I'm sixty-four?


Am    G    Am
Hmm mmm mmmh.
Am                  E7
You'll be older, too.
Am          Dm          F        G7         C
Aaah, and if you say the word, I could stay with you.


2. I could be handy, mending a fuse, when your lights have gone.
You can knit a sweater by the fireside,
sunday mornings, go for a ride.
Doing the garden, digging the weeds, who could ask for more?
Will you still need me, will you still feed me,
when I'm sixty four?


Every summer we can rent a cottage in the Isle of Wight
if it's not to dear.
We shall scrimp and save.
Ah, grandchildren on your knee, Vera, Chuck, and Dave.


3. Send me a postcard, drop me a line stating point of view.
Indicate precisely what you mean to say,
yours sincerely wasting away.
Give me your answer, fill in a form, mine forever more.
Will you still need me, will you still feed me,
when I'm sixty four?
```

M + T: John Lennon & Paul McCartney
© Copyright 1967 Sony/ATV Music Publishing (UK) Limited.
All Rights Reserved. International Copyright Secured.

# I AM A ROCK

(SIMON & GARFUNKEL)

```
            C           F              C
1. A winter's day, in a deep and dark December.
Dm G7 F    C
I am alone,
Dm7             Em7       Dm7              Em7
gazing from my window to the streets below
      Dm              F              G
on a freshly fallen silent shroud of snow.

         C          G C    Am
I am a rock, I am an island.


           C           F              C
2. I've built walls, a fortress deep and mighty
    Dm    G   F    C
that none may penetrate.
   Dm7            Em7       Dm7             Em7
I have no need of friendship, friendship causes pain.
       Dm              F          G
It's laughter and loving I disdain.

         C          G C    Am
I am a rock, I am an island.


             C             F              C
3. Don't talk of love but I've heard the word before.
       Dm   G7        F    C
It's sleeping in my memory.
   Dm7            Em7           Dm7            Em7
I won't disturb the slumber of the feelings that have died
       Dm            F              G
if I never loved I never would have cried.

         C          G C    Am
I am a rock, I am an island.


              C           F              C
4. I have my books and my poetry to protect me.
       Dm    G7       F    C
I am shielded in my armour.
Dm7        Em7   Dm7            Em7
Hiding in my room, safe within my womb,
   Dm              F          G
I touch no one and no one touches me.

         C          G C
I am a rock, I am an island.

       Dm7 G         C        Dm7    G       C
And a rock feels no pain, and an island never cries.
```

M + T: Paul Simon
© Copyright 1965 Paul Simon Music, USA.
All Rights Reserved. International Copyright Secured.

# SOMETHING STUPID

(ROBBIE WILLIAMS & NICOLE KIDMAN)
(FRANK SINATRA & NANCY SINATRA)

```
        G
1. I know I stand in line, until you think you have the time
            Am          D    Am  D
to spend an evening with me.
  Am              D                Am                  D
And if we go some place to dance, I know that there's a chance
              G
you won't be leaving with me.
   G                     G7
And afterwards we drop into a quiet little place
         Cmaj7          Eb7
and have a drink or two.

    Am            D              Am                 D
And then I go and spoil it all, by saying something stupid
       G
like: I love you.

           G7
I can see it in your eyes, you still despise the same old lies
            Cmaj7
you heard the night before.
       A7
And though it's just a line to you, for me it's true,
                    D           D+
I never seemed so right before.


     G
2. I practice every day to find some clever lines to say,
             Am          D    Am  D
to make the meaning come true.
     Am            D             Am                D
But then I think I'll wait until the evening gets late,
          Gmaj7
and I'm alone with you.
     G7
The time is right, your perfume fills my head, the stars get red,
            Cmaj7           Eb7
and oh, the night's so blue.

    Am            D              Am                 D
And then I go and spoil it all, by saying something stupid
       G
like: I love you.

       G7
The time is right, your perfume fills my head, the stars get red,
            Cmaj7           Eb7
and oh, the night's so blue.

    Am            D              Am                 D
And then I go and spoil it all, by saying something stupid
       G     Eb7 G       Eb7 G       Eb7 G
like: I love you. I love you. I love you. I love you.
```

M + Orig.T: Carson Parks
© 1967 Greenwood Music Company.
Chappell Morris Ltd, London.
Reproduced by permission of Faber Music Limited.
All Rights Reserved.

# BELFAST CHILD

(SIMPLE MINDS)

```
        G                  D         C    G          D
1. When my love said to me meet me down by the gallowtree
           C    G    D      C           G
for it's sad news I bring about this old town
                          D         C       G     D
and all that it's suffering. Some say troubles are abound,
         C                G                    D
some day soon they're gonna pull the old town down,
D       G/D    D          C      G          D
one day we'll return here when the Belfast child sings again.

     G                           D
2. Brothers, sisters where are you now
      C     G                     D
as I look for you right through the crowd?
        C         G    D
For all my life here I have spent
        C          G                    D
with my faith in god and church and the government.
      C         G    D
Some say troubles are abound,
         C                G                    D
some day soon they're gonna pull the old town down,
D       G/D    D          Am     G          D
one day we'll return here when the Belfast child sings again.

   D    C   G                        D
3. Come back Billy, won't you come on home?
   D    C   G                     D
Come back Mary, you've been away so long.
   D               C   G                    D
The streets are empty and your mother's gone,
   D            C   G                  D
the girls are crying and it's been oh so long.
   D                 C   G           D
And your father's calling: come on home,
   D                  C   G            D
won't you come on home, come on home.

   D    C   G                            D
4. Come back people, you've been gone a while
   D          C   G                       D
and the war is raging through the emerald isle.
   D                C          G               D
But that's flesh and blood, man, that's flesh and blood,
   D            C   G                D
the girls are crying but all's not lost.
   D              C   G              D
The streets are empty cause the streets are cold,
   D                    C   G               D
won't you come on home, won't you come on home?
   D              C   G          D
The streets are empty life goes on,
D       G/D    D          C      G          D
one day we'll return here when the Belfast child sings again.
           C    G         D
When the Belfast child sings again.
```

Traditional
Arranged by James Kerr, Charles Burchill and Michael McNeil
© 1989 Simple Minds Limited, Jim Kerr Management Consultancy Limited and Charles Burchill Limited. EMI Virgin Music Limited, London, W8 5SW. Reproduced by permission of International Music Publications Limited (a trading name of Faber Music Limited).
All Rights Reserved.

# SUMMER IN BERLIN
(ALPHAVILLE)

```
   Em              Bm           D               A
1. This day's an invitation and it's just for you.
   Em              Bm           D               A
You've got a reservation for the 17th of June.
B          F#                B                F#
Open your eyes and let the sun break in for a while,
B          F#                        B           F#
there may be something that you've never seen inside.

   Em              Bm              D          A
2. Feel how your heart beats, like a heavy machine.
   Em              Bm              D          A
The sound of the traffic is like a silent dream.
B          F#                       B       F#
The dust in the park, the exhaust from the cars
B           F#              B                  F#
ascends in that heated afternoon. You touch a sweaty body.
```

**Refrain:**
```
Em         Bm           D          A
Summer in Berlin, it's alright, it's alright.
Em              Bm                       D
The day feels so tired from the lead in the air
                A
and the fire in the skies.
Em              Bm         D              A
Life seemed to be a fault of grace. But it's ok.
                Em         Bm         D    A
It gave you a kiss in the middle of the crossroads.
```

2. Strophe

Refrain

Summer in Berlin

**Refrain 2:**

Summer in Berlin, it's alright, it's alright, it's alright.

The heat of the sun which is stored in the pavement feels so fine.

Here stands the innocent and there it comes, oh so wild.

That's when you're longing for a summer by the wall.

Summer in Berlin

```
            Em              Bm     D A
Summer in Berlin, it's alright.
                Em              Bm    D A
Summer in Berlin, it's ok.
```

M: Gold, Marian / Lloyd, Bernhard / Mertens, Frank
T: Gold, Marian
© 1984 Rolf Budde Musikverlag GmbH, Berlin.

# DIRTY OLD TOWN

(THE POGUES)

```
            G
1. Met my love by the gas yard wall,
         C                  G
dreamed a dream by the old canal.

Kissed my girl by the factory wall.
            D            Em
Dirty old town, dirty old town.


            G
2. Heard a siren from the dock,
       C                  G
saw a train cut the night on fire.

Smelled the breeze on the smokey wind.
            D            Em
Dirty old town, dirty old town.


                  G
3. I'm going to make a big sharp ax,
         C                G
shining steel tempered in the fire.

I'll cut you down like an old dead tree.
            D            Em
Dirty old town, dirty old town.


                        G
4. Clouds are drifting on the street,
         C             G
cats are prowling on their beats.

Springs a girl on the streets at night.
            D            Em
Dirty old town, dirty old town.


            G
5. Met my love by the gas yard wall,
         C                  G
dreamed a dream by the old canal.
            G
Kissed my girl by the factory wall.
            Am           Em
Dirty old town, dirty old town.
            D            Em
Dirty old town, dirty old town.
```

M + T: Ewan MacColl
© Copyright 1956 Robbins Music Corporation Limited.
All Rights Reserved. International Copyright Secured.

89

# IN THE SHADOWS

(THE RASMUS)

```
             D              F#m    Bm  F#m
Intro: Oh oh. Oh oh. Oh oh. Oh oh.         (2x)

       Bm      F#m           Bm                    F#m
1. No sleep. No sleep until I'm done with finding the answer.
       Bm      F#m           Bm                    F#m
Won't stop. Won't stop before I find the cure for this cancer.
   D        F#m              Bm                 F#m
Sometimes I feel like going down, I'm so disconnected.
   D        F#m           Bm              F#m Fm E
Somehow I know that I am haunted to be wanted.
```

**Refrain:**
```
                   D              F#m         Bm             F#m
I've been watching, I've been waiting in the shadows for my time.
                   D              F#m         Bm             F#m
I've been searching, I've been living for tomorrows all my life.

       D              F#m         Bm    F#m
Oh oh. Oh oh. Oh oh. Oh oh. In the shadows.
       D              F#m         Bm    F#m
Oh oh. Oh oh. Oh oh. Oh oh. In the shadows.

       Bm   F#m              Bm                      F#m
2. They say that I must learn to kill before I can feel safe.
    Bm F#m                  Bm                F#m
But I, I'd rather kill myself than turn into their slave.
   D        F#m            Bm                      F#m
Sometimes I feel that I should go and play with the thunder.
   D        F#m              Bm                 F#m Fm E
Somehow I just don't wanna stay and wait for a wonder.
```

Refrain

```
D                        E         F#m
Lately, I've been walking, walking in circles.

Watching, waiting for something.
Bm                                       F#m Fm E
Feel me, touch me, heal me, come take me higher.
```

Refrain

```
           D     F#m           Bm   F#m
I've been watching, I've been waiting
              D    F#m         Bm             F#m
I've been searching, I've been living for tomorrow
       D              F#m         Bm    F#m
Oh oh. Oh oh. Oh oh. Oh oh. In the shadows.
       D              F#m         Bm    F#m
Oh oh. Oh oh. Oh oh. Oh oh. In the shadows.
             Bm
I've been waiting.
```

M: Lauri Ylönen, Pauli Rantasalmi, Aki Hakala, Eero Heinonen
T: Lauri Ylönen
© Copyright 2004 Sony/ATV Music Publishing (UK) Limited.
All Rights Reserved. International Copyright Secured.

# THE MAN WHO SOLD THE WORLD

(DAVID BOWIE)

**Intro:** A D F

```
      Dm                  A                       Dm
1. We passed upon the stair, we spoke of whats and when.
              A                      F
Although I wasn't there, he said I was his friend
                       C                    A
which came as a surprise. I spoke into his eyes.
                    Dm                   C
I thought you died a long a long, long time ago.
       F      Bbm             F
Oh no, not me, I never lost control.
    C          F            Bbm              A
You're face to face with the man who sold the world.


      Dm                   A                      Dm
2. I laughed and shook his hand and made my way back home.
               A                         F
I searched for former land, for years and years I roamed
                  C                       A
I gazed a gazely stare. And all the millions here.
                     Dm                  C
We must have died a long a long, long time ago.
            F      Bbm            F
Who knows not me. We never lost control.
    C          F            Bbm              A
You're face to face with the man who sold the world.

C          F      Bbm            F
Who knows not me. We never lost control.
    C          F            Bbm              A
You're face to face with the man who sold the world.
```

M + T: David Bowie
© 1970 Tintoretto Music/Mainman-Saag Ltd New York. Chrysalis Music Limited, a BMG Chrysalis Company/RZO Music Limited/EMI Music Publishing Limited.
Mit freundlicher Genehmigung von Tintoretto Music/RZO Music Limited.
All Rights Reserved. International Copyright Secured.

# ICH HAB DAS FRÄUL'N HELEN BADEN SEH'N

(CHRIS HOWLAND)

```
      C           G7                C
1. Immer, wenn man sieht den guten Friedrich,
                   G7             C
   jammert er: "Das Leben ist so widrig!"
   F         C        F           C
   Aber gestern Nacht hat er so gelacht,
   D7                                    G7
   als hätt' einen Treffer er gemacht! Gemacht! Gemacht! Gemacht!
   C              G7                  C
   Wie er ins Hotel nach Haus gekommen,
             G7              C   C7
   hat er eine falsche Tür genommen,
   F         Fm              C         Csus4
   wo das schöne Fräul'n Helene g'rad im Bade saß.
   C         C#sus4    G7
   Da rief er in heller Ekstas':
```

**Refrain:**
```
                    G7
Ich hab' das Fräul'n Helen' baden seh'n, das war schön!
                C
Da kann man Waden seh'n, rund und schön im Wasser steh'n!
       Csus4    G7          Dm7         G7
Und wenn sie ungeschickt tief sich bückt so,
     G+        C           G+          C
da sieht man ganz genau bei der Frau, oh!
                    G7
Ich hab' das Fräul'n Helen' baden seh'n, das war schön!
                C
Da kann man Waden seh'n rund und schön im Wasser steh'n!
                  Ab7             C
Man fühlt erst dann sich recht als Mann,
                    G7                  C
wenn man beim Baden geh'n Waden seh'n kann!
```

2. Wie verwandelt ist der Friedrich heute,
freundlich grüßt er unbekannte Leute.
Auch beim Business ist er voll Noblesse,
will man ihn betrügen, sagt er: "Yes! Oh yes! Oh yes! Oh yes!"
Er, der punkto Reinlichkeit ein Hasser,
schwärmt begeistert plötzlich nur für Wasser.
Die Gemeinde seiner Freunde weiß nicht aus noch ein.
Doch er lacht in sich nur hinein:

Refrain

3. Unser Freund, der nahm zur Frau Helene;
doch die Waden, welche einst so schöne,
schlank und zart und süß, wurden später mies
und so dick wie vom Klavier die Füß'! Die Füß', die Füß', die Füß'!
Geht die Gattin heut' ins Badezimmer,
schaut der Mann sich nicht mehr an die Trümmer,
sondern weise schließt er leise hinter ihr die Tür
und spielt am verstimmten Klavier:

Refrain

M: Fred Raymond
T: Fritz Grünbaum
© Universal/ MCA Music Publishing GmbH
(Universal Music Publishing Group).

## ZEHN NACKTE FRISEUSEN

(MICKIE KRAUSE)

**Intro:** B G#m E F# B G#m E F#  G A

```
      D              G              D              G
1. Es gibt hunderttausend Frauen, denen ist alles zuzutrauen,
                A
   doch ich sag no, no no no no.
      D                G              D              G
   Es gibt fünfzigtausend Weiber, die haben einwandfreie Leiber,
                A          F#
   doch ich sag no, no no no no.
```

**Refrain:**
```
           B            G#m     E                F#
   Ich will zehn nackte Friseusen, zehn nackte Friseusen, oh oh.
      B            G#m       E              F#
   Zehn nackte Friseusen mit richtig feuchten Haaren.
```

2. Es gibt hunderttausend Mädel, die sind alle schön und edel.
   Da wird ich weich, wa wa wa weich.
   Es gibt fünfzigtausend Damen, die wollen alle meinen Namen,
   doch ich bleib hart, ha ha ha hart.

Refrain

3. Es gibt hunderttausend Schnitten, die haben wunderschöne Augen,
   da bin ich weg, weg weg weg weg.
   Es gibt fünfzigtausend Hasen, die woll'n mir alle ein'n erzählen.
   Ich hör nicht hin, hi hi hi hin.

Refrain

```
OK, ich will hier nicht unnötig 'n Riesenfass aufmachen, ja, aber
folgendes:
   F#          B                            G#m
   Ich hab sie alle gehabt, ich hab sie alle gesehn,
             E                       F#
   doch es gibt nur ein paar, die mich wirklich verstehn.
            B                              G#m
   Ich hab sie niemals gezählt, doch ich weiß, was mir fehlt.
           E                        F#
   Ja ich weiß, was mir fehlt, ja ich weiß, was mir fehlt.
```

Refrain

M + T: Clemens Winterhalter, Lou Richter
© 1999 Neue Welt Musikverlag GmbH & Co KG.
Warner/Chappell North America Ltd, London.
Reproduced by permission of Faber Music Limited.
All Rights Reserved.

# FROM A DISTANCE

(BETTE MIDLER)

```
          G            C             D           G
1. From a distance, the world looks blue and green
        C          D          G        D C
and the snow capped mountains white.
         G            C        D          G
From a distance, the ocean meets the stream
        C     D       G     D G
and the eagle takes to flight.
        Cmaj7         D       Em
From a distance, there is harmony
        C    G/B         D
and it echoes through the land.
         C      G/B            C       G/B
It's the voice of hope, it's the voice of peace.
         C      D     G     D C G C G D
It's the voice of every man.
```

2. From a distance, we all have enough
and no one is in need.
There are no guns, no bombs, no disease,
no hungry mouths to feed.
From a distance, we are instruments
marching in a common band.
Playing songs of hope, playing songs of peace,
they're the songs of every man.

```
G        C         D           G          Em
God is watching us, God is watching us,
     Am7         Dsus4 D       G
God is watching us      from a distance.
```

3. From a distance, you look like my friend
even though we are at war.
From a distance, I just cannot comprehend
what all this fighting is for.
From a distance, there is harmony
and it echoes through the land.
It's the hope of hopes, it's the love of loves,
it's the heart of every man.
It's the hope of hopes, it's the love of loves,
this is the song of every man.

```
    G        C         D           G          Em
And God is watching us, God is watching us,
     Am7         Dsus4 D       G
God is watching us      from a distance.
            C        D          G          Em
Oh God is watching us, God is watching,
     Am7         Dsus4 D       G         C G C G Am7 D G
God is watching us      from a distance.
```

M + T: Julie Gold
© Julie Gold Music, Irving Music / BMG Rights
Management GmbH / Wing and Wheel Music,
Julie Gold Music, Cherry Lane Music Publishing, Rondor
Musikverlag GmbH, Wintrup Musikverlag, Detmold.

# YUMMY, YUMMY, YUMMY

(OHIO EXPRESS)

```
   G
1. Yummy, Yummy, Yummy, I got love in my tummy
      F                G
   and I feel like a-lovin you.

   Love, you're such a sweet thing, good enough to eat thing
              F                     G
   and that's just a what I'm gonna do.
   C
   Ooh love, to hold ya, ooh love, to kiss ya,
                         G   F/G
   Ooh love, I love it so. Oh.
   C
   Ooh love, you're sweeter, sweeter than sugar,
                            G    F
   ooh love, I wont let you go. Oh.

   G
2. Yummy, Yummy, Yummy, I got love in my tummy
      F                G
   and as silly as it may seem.

   The loving that you're giving is what keeps me living
            F                      G
   and your love is like peaches and cream.
   C
   Kind-a like sugar, kind-a like spices,
                          G   F/G
   Kind-a like, like what you do. Oh.
   C
   Kind-a sounds funny, but love, honey,
                        G   F
   honey, I love you. Oh.
   C            G             C            G
   Ba da, ba da da da da, ba da da da da, ba da da da.

      G#
3. Yummy, Yummy, Yummy, I got love in my tummy
      F#               G#
   that your love can satisfy.

   Love, you're such a sweet thing, good enough to eat thing
              F#                    G#
   and sweet thing, that ain't no lie.
   C#
   I love to hold ya, I love, to kiss ya,
                          G#  F#/G#
   Ooh love, I love it so. Oh.
   C#
   Ooh love, you're sweeter, sweeter than sugar,
                            G#   F#
   ooh love, I wont let you go. Oh.
   C#           G#            C#           G#
   Ba da, ba da da da da, ba da da da da, ba da da da.
```

M + T: Bob Levine, Arthur Resnick
© 1986 by Carlin Music Corporation and Bug Music-Trio Music Company.
This arrangement © 2011 by Alley Music Corp. and Bug Music-Trio Music Company. Copyright Renewed.
Reprinted by permission of Hal Leonard Corporation / Greenhorn Musikverlag GmbH & Co. KG.

# PRIVATE DANCER

(TINA TURNER)

```
     Em7                      Bm  Cmaj7 Em7       Bm         Am7       Am7/D
1. Well, the men come in these places   and the men are all the same.
   Em7                    Bm  Cmaj7 Em7 D6        Am7       Am7/D
   You don't look at their faces    and you don't ask their names.
   Em7                    Bm  Cmaj7 Em7 Bm           Am7       Am7/D
   You don't think of them as human,   you don't think of them at all.
   Em7                    Bm  Cmaj7 Em7    D6        Am7       Am7/D
   You keep your mind on the money    keeping your eyes on the wall.
```

**Refrain:**
```
       C/G      G
I'm your private dancer, a dancer for money,
       G         Em7         Dsus4  D
I'll do what you want me to do.
                           Fmaj7
I'm your private dancer, a dancer for money
     F#°     B7         Em   C/D
and any old music will do.
```


2. I wanna make a million dollars, I wanna live out by the sea.

Have a husband and some children yeah, I guess I want a family.

All the men come in these places and the men are all the same.

You don't look at their faces and you don't ask their names.

Refrain

**Refrain 2:**
```
       C/G      G
I'm your private dancer, a dancer for money,
       G         Em7         Dsus4  D
I'll do what you want me to do.
                           Fmaj7
I'm your private dancer, a dancer for money
     F#°              C#°  C7
and any old music will do.
```

**Bridge:**
```
A7
Deutschmarks or dollars,

a few pounds sterling will do nicely, thank you.

Let me loosen up your collar,
         C#°            C7      B7
tell me, do you wanna see me do the shimmy again?
```

Refrain
Refrain 2

M + T: Mark Knopfler
© Copyright 1984 Straitjacket Songs Limited.
All Rights Reserved. International Copyright Secured.

## I'LL MEET YOU AT MIDNIGHT

(SMOKIE)

**Intro:** F#m

```
       F#m                      Bm
1. A summer evening on Les Champs Elysees,
                         F#m
  a secret rendezvous they planned for days.
                    Bm
  I see faces in the crowded cafe,
                           F#m
  a sound of laughter as the music plays.

      F#m                          Bm
2. Jean-Claude was a student at the University,
                    F#m
  Louise-Marie is just a world away.
                              Bm
  He recalls the night they met was warm with laughter,
                           F#m
  the words and music as she turned away.
```

**Refrain:**
```
E             F#m       E           F#m
I'll meet you at midnight, under the moonlight.
E             F#m                              Bm         F#m
I'll meet you at midnight but Jean-Claude, Louise-Marie will never be.


       F#m                    Bm
3. Each cigarette will light a thousand faces,
                      F#m
  each hour passing like a thousand years.
                      Bm
  Midnight was turning to empty spaces,
                           F#m
  The sound of laughter had disappeared.
```

Refrain

```
       F#m                      Bm
4. A summer morning on Les Champs Elysees,
                       F#m
  the empty table in the street cafe.
                                Bm
  The sunlight melting through an open doorway,
                           F#m
  Jean-Claude has left to face another day.

E             F#m       E           F#m
I'll meet you at midnight, under the moonlight.
E             F#m
I'll meet you at midnight.
```

Refrain

M + T: Nicky Chinn / Mike Chapman
© Chinnichap Publ. Limited. Universal Music Publishing Limited. All Rights Reserved. International Copyright Secured.

## CAN'T HELP FALLING IN LOVE

(ELVIS PRESLEY)

```
     F     Am  Dm    Dm/C Bb    F     C7
1. Wise men say,  only fools rush in.
    Bb C7    Dm    Gm        F     C7    F
But I can't help falling in love with you.


     F     Am  Dm    Dm/C    Bb F C7
2. Shall I stay? Would it be a sin?
    Bb C7    Dm   Gm       F    C7    F
If I can't help falling in love with you.


Am           Bm E7 Am           Bm E7
Like a river flows surely to the sea.
Am           Bm E7 Am        D7         Gm7 C7
Darling so it goes. Some things are meant to be.


     F     Am  Dm    Dm/C Bb F     C7
3. Take my hand, take my whole life, too.
    Bb C7    Dm   Gm       F    C7    F
For I can't help falling in love with you.


Am           Bm E7 Am           Bm E7
Like a river flows surely to the sea.
Am           Bm E7 Am        D7         Gm7 C7
Darling so it goes. Some things are meant to be.


     F     Am  Dm    Dm/C Bb F     C7
3. Take my hand, take my whole life, too.
    Bb C7    Dm   Gm       F    C7    F
For I can't help falling in love with you.

    Bb C7    Dm   Gm       F    C7    F
For I can't help falling in love with you.
```

M + T: George David Weiss, Hugo Peretti & Luigi Creatore
© Copyright 1961 Gladys Music. All Rights Reserved.
International Copyright Secured.

# I TURN TO YOU

(MELANIE C)
[TRANSP. -1]

**Intro:**  Em Am Em Am Am D Em Am D Em
                                You.      You.

```
Em              C            D       Em           D C
When the world is darker than I can understand,
Em           D          C       Em      D C
when nothing turns out the way I planned,
Em              C              D          Em    D C
when the sky turns gray and there's no end in sight,
Em           D              C       Em      D
when I can't sleep through the lonely night.
```

**Refrain:**
```
            C          Am              Em
I turn to you like a flower leaning toward the sun.
            Am        D            Em
I turn to you cause you're the only one
              C          Am               Em
who can turn me around when I'm upside down.
          D C Em
I turn to you.

Em                  C           D       Em D C
When my insides are wrecked with anxiety
Em          D               C       Em D C
you have the touch that will quiet me.
Em          C             D        Em   D
You lift my spirit, you melt the ice
Em              D              C       Em     D
when I need inspiration, when I need advice.
```

Refrain

```
C                       G
Where would I be? What would I do
C                      D
if you'd never helped me through?
C                   G
I hope someday if you've lost your way
              C                  D
you could turn to me like I turn to you.
```

Em Am Em Am

Refrain

```
            C          Am              Em
I turn to you when fear tells me to turn around.
            Am        D            Em
I turn to you cause you're the only one
              C          Am               Em
who can turn me around when I'm upside down.
          D C Em
I turn to you.
          D C Em
I turn to you.
```

M + T: Richard Nowels, Billy Steinberg and Melanie Chisholm
© Jerk Awake / Future Furniture / Red Girl Productions Limited. Kobalt Music Publishing Ltd / Peermusic (UK) Limited / BMG Rights Management (UK) Limited.
All Rights Reserved. International Copyright Secured.

## JOE, NOCH EINEN

(HANS HARTZ)

**Intro:** G D/F# G C G/B Dsus4

```
     G              Bm                    Am
1. Kalte Asche, müde Mädchen, ein letzter Schluck im Neonlicht,
      Dsus4
   das sich im leeren Glas hier bricht.
   G                Bm                            Am
   Jetzt einen Kaffee, stark wie immer, nur nicht gehen müssen, jetzt noch
                  Dsus4
   nicht. Noch einen Joe, sonst sterbe ich.
   C       G    C       G                                Am
   Joe, noch einen für den Magen, und ein Streichholz für den letzten Zug.
        Dsus4
   Die Zeit verging heut wie im Flug.
   C       G   C      G         Am
   Drück B-7, meine Nummer, die Musicbox spielt "Baby Blue"
       Dsus4                    C
   und Baby Blue ist so wie du Marleen.
```

**Refrain:**
```
C       D             G    C          D             G
Joe, wie könnt ich jetzt gehn? Ich trink noch einen hier im Stehn.
C    D         G       C           Dsus4
Und alles ist so schön. Ich hab noch Geld für Zehn.
C       D          G    C     D              G
Joe, wo könnt es besser sein? Hier bin ich nicht allein.
C     D            G     C        Dsus4
Komm schenk noch einen ein, für einen wahren Freund.
```

```
      G                Bm                      Am
2. Sechs Uhr vierzig. Licht von draußen. Nur mein Stuhl ist nicht
               Dsus4
   hochgestellt, der einzige, der mit mir durchhält.
   G            Bm                         Am
   Ann und Mandy gehen nach Hause, nur noch Joe und ich auf dieser Welt,
       Dsus4
   hey hab ich Dir schon den erzählt?
   C       G    C       G                    Am
   Joe, noch einen für die Träume. Drei Zehner für das Baby Blue,
                 Dsus4
   denn Baby Blue ist so wie Du Marleen.
   C         G      C     G                 Am
   Drei Minuten sind doch gar nichts. Joe, mach den Laden noch nicht zu.
       Dsus4
   Nur einen noch, dann geb ich Ruh.
```

Refrain

M + T: Johann-Christoph Busse
© 1982 Albert Bennefeld, Berlin.

## ALLES WIRD SICH ÄNDERN

(ECHT)

**Intro:**
```
        D              G           Em           G
Du du du du du, du du duah, du du du du, du du duah
        D              G           Em           G
Du du du du du, du du duah, du du du du, du du duah
```

```
              Bm                              A
1. Die besten Plätze sind besetzt und selbst wenn ich wollte
             Em                          G
könnt' ich's nicht ändern, ich könnt' es nicht ändern
            Bm                        A
leb' im Hier und Jetzt und Dinge die ich sollte
          Em                  G
machen daß ich schlender, ich schlender

Bm                   A                            Em
Müßiggang ist aller Laster Anfang hör' ich meine Mutter sagen
                              G
doch ich kann nicht drauf hören, nein
           Bm
ich kann nicht drauf hören
                              A
nein ich kann nicht drauf hören, nein
           Em
ich kann nicht drauf hören, nein, nein
```

**Refrain:**
```
D                              G
Alles wird sich ändern, wenn wir groß sind
         Em                       G
Alles wird sich ändern, wird sich ändern
D                              G
Alles wird sich ändern, wenn wir groß sind
         Em          G
Alles wird sich ändern.
```

2. Ich hänge Dinge die ich tu nicht an die große Glocke
muß die Welt nicht regieren, oder zensieren
komm laß mich heute in Ruh' mit deinem Pseudo-Geschocke
kannst Du mir nicht imponieren, nicht imponieren

Hochmut kommt vor dem Fall, immer und überall
wann wirst du's kapieren, endlich kapieren

Refrain

```
A            F#                Bm                        G
Unser Leben ist ein weißes Blatt Papier da können wir nichts dafür
A            F#                Bm          G     A                  F#
komm laß' uns etwas schreiben was uns wichtig ist, was uns wichtig ist
```

Intro

Refrain 2x

M + T: Stefan Oliver Knoess
© EMI Music Publishing Germany GmbH.

# SHE LOVES YOU

(THE BEATLES)

**Intro:**
```
    Em
She loves you, yeah, yeah, yeah.
    A
She loves you, yeah, yeah, yeah.
    C                       G6
She loves you, yeah, yeah, yeah.
```

```
       G              Em           Bm           D
1. You think you've lost your love, well I saw her yesterday.
       G              Em           Bm           D
   It's you she's thinking of and she told me what to say.
```

**Refrain:**
```
              G                            Em
She says she loves you and you know that can't be bad.
              Cm                            D
Yes, she loves you and you know you should be glad.
```

```
       G              Em           Bm           D
2. She said you hurt her so, she almost lost her mind.
       G              Em           Bm           D
   But now she says she knows you're not the hurting kind.
```

Refrain

**Bridge:**
```
    Em
She loves you, yeah, yeah, yeah.
    A
She loves you, yeah, yeah, yeah.
         Cm            D                G
With a love like that you know you should be glad.
```

```
       G              Em      Bm              D
3. And so its up to you, I think it's only fair.
G                     Em      Bm         D
Pride can hurt you too. Apologize to her.
```

Refrain

Bridge

```
         Cm            D                G     Em
With a love like that you know you should be glad.
         Cm            D                G
With a love like that you know you should be glad.
```

M + T: John Lennon & Paul McCartney
© Copyright 1963 Sony/ATV Music Publishing.
All Rights Reserved. International Copyright Secured.

# CARRIE

(EUROPE)

**Intro:** Em  G/D  C  G/B  Am  G/B  C  D  Am  G/B  C  D  G

```
       G       D/F#      Em              G/D  C      G/B      Am
1. When  lights  go  down  I  see  no  reason  for  you  to  cry.
   G/B                C          D              Em              G/D  C
We've been through this before in every time, in every season.
         G           Am       G/B              C           D
God knows I've tried, so please don't ask for more.
              C              D           C                Am         D      C D
Can't you see it in my eyes?  Well this might be our last goodbye.
```

**Refrain:**
```
G  D/F#  Em      D  C  D  Em
Carrie,  Carrie
             Dsus4        D
things, they change my friend.
G  D/F#  Em      D  C  D  Em
Carrie,  Carrie
             Dsus4  D  Am    G/B  C         G
maybe we'll meet     again somewhere again.

       D/F#       Em              G/B  C
2. I read your mind with no intensions
   G/B     Am      G/B       C         D
of being unkind, I wish I could explain.
              Em                  G/D  C
It all takes time, a whole lot of patience.
   G/B      Am      G/B         C       D
If it's a crime, how come I feel no pain?
              C              D
Can't you see it in my eyes?
C                    Am          D     C D
This might be our last goodbye.
```

Refrain

M + T: Joey Tempest and Mic Michaeli
© Copyright 1986 EMI Music Publishing Limited, London, 8W 5SW.
Reproduced by permission of International Music Publications Limited
(a trading name of Faber Music Ltd).
All Rights Reserved.

# I WANT IT THAT WAY

(BACKSTREET BOYS)

**Intro:** F#m D A  F#m D A

```
        F#m    D A        F#m      D A
1. You are my fire, the one desire.
   F#m      D A    F#m       E      A
Believe, when I say, I want it that way.

         F#m    D  A      F#m      D   A
2. But we are two worlds apart, can't reach to
      F#m        D A         F#m      E    A
your heart, when you say, that I want it that way.
```

**Refrain:**
```
           D              E    F#m
Tell me why ain't nothin' but a heartache.
           D              E    F#m
Tell me why ain't nothin' but a mistake.
           D            E        A
Tell me why I never wanna hear you say,
F#m     E    A
I want it that way.
```

```
        F#m    D A       F#m    D A
3. Am I your fire, your one desire.
        F#m       D  A         F#m     E   A
Yes I know it's too late, but I want it that way.

           D              E    F#m
Tell me why ain't nothin' but a heartache.
           D              E    F#m
Tell me why ain't nothin' but a mistake.
           D            E        A
Tell me why I never wanna hear you say,
F#m       C#
I want it that way.
```

**Bridge:**
```
F#m                     A/E
Now I can see that we're fallin' apart,
         D             Bm   E
from the way that it used to be, yeah.
        F#m             A/E
No matter the distance, I want you to know,
       D               E
that deep down inside of me.
```

```
         D   E  F#m       D   E F#m
4. You are my fire, the one desire.
D                      E        F#m  E
You are, you are, you are, you are. Don't want to hear you.
```

Refrain 3x (ein Ton höher)
```
G#m       F#   B
I want it that way.
```

M + T: Martin Sandberg / Andreas Carlsson
© Copyright 1999 GV-MXM/GV-Maratone
Kobalt Music Publishing Limited
All Rights Reserved. International Copyright Secured.

# SWEET CAROLINE

(NEIL DIAMOND)
[TRANSP. +2]

```
       A            D
1. Where it began I can't begin to know it
   A                      E
but then I know it's growing strong.
   A            D
Was in the spring and spring became the summer,
   A                       E
who'd have believed you'd come along?

   A     A6         E           D                  E
Hands touching hands, reaching out, touching me, touching you.
```

**Refrain:**
```
   A             D                    E
Sweet Caroline, good times never seemed so good.
   A         D                  E      D   C#m Bm
I've been inclined to believe they never would but now I
```

```
      A              D
2. look at the night and it don't seem so lonely.
   A           E
We fill it up with only two.
   A              D
And when I hurt, hurting runs off my shoulders,
   A               E
how can I hurt when holding you?

   A     A6        E           D                  E
Warm touching warm, reaching out, touching me, touching you.
```

**Refrain:**
```
   A             D                    E
Sweet Caroline, good times never seemed so good.
   A         D                  E      D   C#m Bm   E
I've been inclined to believe they never would, oh no, no.
   A             D                    E
Sweet Caroline, good times never seemed so good.
   A             D                E
Sweet Caroline, I believe they never could.
   A             D                    E    A
Sweet Caroline, good times never seemed so good.
```

M + T: Neil Diamond
© Copyright 1969 Stonebridge Music Incorporated, USA.
Universal/MCA Music Limited.
All Rights Reserved. International Copyright Secured.

# GAUDEAMUS IGITUR

```
      G         C       D7         G
1. Gaudeamus igitur, juvenes dum sumus.
G         C       D7         G
Gaudeamus igitur, juvenes dum sumus.
D        G        D                   G   D
Post jucundam juventutem, post molestam senectutem
G      C     G D7  G      C      D D7 G
nos habebit humus! Nos habebit humus!
```

2. Vita nostra brevis est, brevi finietur.
Vita nostra brevis est, brevi finietur.
Venit mors velociter, rapit nos atrociter,
nemini parcetur. Nemini parcetur.

3. Ubi sunt qui ante nos in mundo fuere?
Ubi sunt qui ante nos in mundo fuere?
Vadite ad superos, transite ad inferos,
hos si vis videre. Hos si vis videre.

4. Vivat academia, vivant professores.
Vivat academia, vivant professores.
Vivat membrum quodlibet, vivant membra quaelibet,
semper sint in flore! Semper sint in flore!

5. Vivant omnes virgines faciles, formosae.
Vivant omnes virgines faciles, formosae.
Vivant et mulieres, tenerae, amabiles,
bonae, laboriosae! Bonae, laboriosae!

6. Vivat et respublica et qui illam regit.
Vivat et respublica et qui illam regit.
Vivat nostra civitas, maecenatum caritas,
quae nos hic protegit! Quae nos hic protegit!

7. Pereat tristitia, Pereant osores.
Pereat tristitia, Pereant osores.
Pereat diabolus, quivis antiburschius,
atque irrisores! Atque irrisores!

8. Quis confluxus hodie academicorum?
Quis confluxus hodie academicorum?
E longinquo convenerunt, protinusque successerunt
in commune forum; In commune forum.

9. Vivat nostra societas, vivant studiosi.
Vivat nostra societas, vivant studiosi.
Crescat una veritas, floreat fraternitas,
patriae prosperitas. Patriae prosperitas.

10. Alma mater floreat, quae nos educavit.
Alma mater floreat, quae nos educavit.
Caros et commilitones, dissitas in regiones
sparsos, congregavit. Sparsos, congregavit.

Traditionell
© 2005 by Edition DUX, Manching

# OH PRETTY WOMAN

(ROY ORBISON)

```
         A                F#m
1. Pretty woman, walking down the street.
         A                F#m
Pretty woman, the kind I like to meet.
         D              E
Pretty woman, I dont believe you,
```

you're not the truth. No one could look as good as you. Mercy!

```
2. Pretty woman, won't you pardon me?
Pretty woman, I couldnt help but see.
Pretty woman, that you look lovely as can be,
are you lonely just like me?

Dm            G7           C            Am
Pretty woman, stop a while. Pretty woman, talk a while.
Dm            G7                 C
Pretty woman, give your smile to me.
Dm            G7           C            Am
Pretty woman, yeah yeah yeah. Pretty woman, look my way.

Dm            G7                 C  A
Pretty woman, say you'll stay with me

       F#m       Dm           E
'cause I need you, I'll treat you right.
A          F#m      Dm        E
Come with me baby, be mine tonight.
```

3. Pretty woman, don't walk on by.
Pretty woman, don't make me cry.
Pretty woman, don't walk away, hey.

E
Okay, if that's the way it must be, okay.

I guess I'll go on home, it's late.

There'll be tomorrow night, but wait!

What do I see?

Is she walking back to me?

Yeah, she's walking back to me!
             A
Oh, pretty woman!

M + T: Bill Dees, Roy Orbinson
© Copyright 1964 (renewed 1992) Roy Orbison Music Company/Barbara Orbison Music Company,
USA/Sony/ATV Acuff Rose Music. Kobalt Music Publishing Limited/Sony/ATV Music Publishing
All Rights Reserved. International Copyright Secured.

# DESERT ROSE

(STING)

**Intro:** Am G F Dm E Am

```
         Am                            G
1. I dream of rain, elay elay, I dream of gardens in the desert sand,
F                           Dm              E                    Am
I wake in pain, elay elay, I dream of love as time runs through my hand.
```

I dream of fire, elay elay,

those dreams are tied to a horse that will never tire, and in the

                                                                        C
flames, elay elay, her shadows play in the shape of a man's desire.

```
                           Em7
2. This desert rose, elay elay, each of her veils, a secret promise,
G                          F
this desert flower, elay elay, no sweet perfume ever
E                    Am
tortured me more than this. And as she turns, elay elay,
```

this way she moves in the logic of all my dreams,

this fire burns, elay elay, I realize that nothing's as it seems.

```
         Am                            G
3. I dream of rain, elay elay, I dream of gardens in the desert sand,
F                           Dm              E                    C
I wake in pain, elay elay, I dream of love as time runs through my hand.
                           Em7
I dream of rain, elay elay, I lift my gaze to empty skies above,
G
I close my eyes,
                           F           E              Am
this rare perfume is the sweet intoxication of her love.
```

```
         Am                            G
4. I dream of rain, elay elay, I dream of gardens in the desert sand,
F                           Dm              E                    C
I wake in pain, elay elay, I dream of love as time runs through my hand.
                           Em7
Sweet desert rose, elay elay, each of her veils, a secret promise,
G
this desert flower, elay elay,
F                  E                C
no sweet perfume ever tortured me more than this.
```

```
                           Em7
5. Sweet desert rose, elay elay, this memory of Eden haunts us all,
G
this desert flower,
                           F           E              Am
this rare perfume, is the sweet intoxication of the fall.
```

M + T: Sting
© Copyright 1999 Magnetic Publishing Limited/EMI Music Publishing Limited.
All Rights Reserved. International Copyright Secured.

# PINBALL WIZARD

(THE WHO)

**Intro:** Bsus4 B Bsus4 B Bsus4 B Bsus4 B

```
      B    Bsus4                              B
1. Ever since I was a young boy, I've played the silver ball.
         Asus4                  A
From Soho down to Brighton I must have played them all.
         Gsus4                              G
But I ain't seen nothing like him in any amusement hall.
         F#sus4                F#                B   A D E  B A D E
That deaf dumb and blind kid sure plays a mean pinball.


      B    Bsus4                              B
2. He stands like a statue, becomes part of the machine.
Asus4                   A
Feeling all the bumpers always playing clean.
         Gsus4                     G
He plays by intuition, the digit counters fall.
         F#sus4                F#                B   A D E  B A D E
That deaf dumb and blind kid sure plays a mean pinball.


       E  F#  B          E        B
He's a pinball wizard there has to be a twist.
    E   F#  B         G          D
A pinball wizard, got such a supple wrist.
D
How do you think he does it? I don't know! What makes him so good?


      B    Bsus4                              B
3. He ain't got no distractions can't hear no buzzes and bells,
         Asus4                A
Don't see lights a flashing plays by sense of smell.
Gsus4                                G
Always gets a replay, and never tilts at all.
         F#sus4                F#                B   A D E  B A D E
That deaf dumb and blind kid sure plays a mean pinball.


    E       F# B     E   F#     B
I thought I was the bodytable king.
     E  F#  B         G          D
But I just handed my pinball crown to him.


      B    Bsus4                    B
4. Even on my usual table he can beat my best.
         Asus4                   A
His disciples lead him in and he just does the rest.
         Gsus4                           G
He's got crazy flipper fingers never seen him fall.
         F#sus4                F#                B   A D E
That deaf dumb and blind kind sure plays a mean pinball.
```

M + T: Pete Townshend
© Copyright Fabulous Music Limited.

# FLUGZEUGE IM BAUCH

(HERBERT GRÖNEMEYER)

**Intro:** Cm Gm Ab Gsus4 G
```
              Em                      Bm
1. Du hast'n Schatten im Blick, Lachen ist gemalt.
       Fmaj7                     Em
Deine Gedanken sind nicht mehr bei mir.
Am           G/B         C
Streichelst mich mechanisch, völlig steril.
Fmaj7                       G
Eiskalte Hand, mir graut vor dir!
            Em                      Bm
2. Fühl mich leer und verbraucht, alles tut weh,
       Fmaj7            Em
hab Flugzeuge in meinem Bauch.
Am           G/B    C
Kann nichts mehr essen, kann dich nicht vergessen,
Fmaj7                       G
aber auch das gelingt mir noch.
```

**Refrain:**
```
C           Fmaj7  G                  C
Gib mir mein Herz zurück, du brauchst meine Liebe nicht.
C           Fmaj7  G                      Am
Gib mir mein Herz zurück, bevor es auseinander bricht.
    Em         F      G
Je eher, je eher du gehst,
        Em         F        G         C    Fm C Fm B7
um so leichter, um so leichter wird's für mich.

          Em                             Bm
3. Ich brauch niemand, der mich quält, niemand, der mich zerdrückt,
Fmaj7                          Em
niemand, der mich benutzt, wann er will.
Am          G/B    C
Niemand, der mit mir redet nur aus Pflichtgefühl,
Fmaj7                       G
der nur seine Eitelkeit an mir stillt.
        Em                              Bm
4. Niemand, der nie da ist, wenn man ihn am nötigsten hat,
Fmaj7                         Em
wenn man nach Luft schnappt, auf dem Trocknen schwimmt.
Am       G/B   C
Lass mich los, lass mich in Ruhe,
Fmaj7         G
damit das ein Ende nimmt.
```

Refrain

```
2. Fühl mich leer und verbraucht, alles tut weh,
hab Flugzeuge in meinem Bauch.
Kann nichts mehr essen, kann dich nicht vergessen,
aber auch das gelingt mir noch.
```

Refrain

**Outro:** Fm C Fm C

M + T: Herbert Grönemeyer
© Copyright Grönland Musikverlag
All Rights Reserved. International Copyright Secured

## ONLY YOU

(THE FLYING PICKETS)
[TRANSP. +1]

```
   G            D/F#    Em           Em7/D    C
1. Looking from a window above is like a story of love,
        G     D
can you hear me?
G             D/F#    Em            Em7/D    C
Come back only yesterday, we're moving further away,
          G    D
want you near me.
```

**Refrain:**
```
C                     D
All I needed was the love you gave,
G    D/F#        Em     Em7/D
all I needed for another day,
     C          D          G
and all I ever knew, only you.
```

```
   G            D/F#         Em             Em7/D  C
2. Sometimes when I think of her name, when it's only a game,
        G    D
and I need you.
G             D/F#         Em            Em7/D     C
Listen to the words that you say, it's getting harder to stay,
        G    D
when I see you.
```

Refrain

```
   G            D/F#      Em         Em7/D         C
3. This is gonna take a long time, and I wonder what's mine,
        G   D
can't take no more.
G             D/F# Em              Em7/D         C
Wonder if you'll understand, it's just the touch of your hand,
        G    D
behind closed door.
```

Refrain

M + T: Vincent Clarke
© Copyright 1982 Musical Moments Limited.
Sony/ATV Music Publishing (UK) Limited.
All Rights Reserved. International Copyright Secured

# DIE GLOCKEN VON ROM

(HEIKE SCHÄFER)

```
      F                        C
1. Zweitausend Jahre geh'n zur Neige
Bb            C   F         C
und niemand brachte sie zum Schweigen.
  F                    C
Sie geben uns von allem Kunde
Bb           C    F
und läuten auch zur letzten Stunde.
     F                 C              F
Die Glocken von Rom, die Glocken von Rom.
     F                 C              F
Die Glocken von Rom, die Glocken von Rom.


      F                       C
2. Sie klingen für ein neues Leben,
Bb              F      C
sind Warnung und sind auch Gebete.
  F                      C
Und niemand konnte sie zerstören,
Bb            C    F
sie waren nicht zu überhören.
     F                 C              D
Die Glocken von Rom, die Glocken von Rom.

G              C                 D               G
Wem die Stunde schlägt, was die Welt bewegt, sie erzählen davon.
G             C               D               G
Doch ist unser Glück nur einen Augenblick für die Glocken von Rom.
G#             C#                D#                    G#
Viele schlugen laut, and're nur ganz still, viele blieben oft stumm.
G#                  C#           D#                    F
Doch der Glockenklang hat von Anfang an unser Leben begleitet.

     F                      C
3. An einem Tag noch fern von heute,
Bb              F         C
da werden alle Glocken läuten.
  F                      C
Und jeder Ton ist ganz verschieden,
Bb              C    F
doch alle schlagen für den Frieden.
     F                 C              F
Die Glocken von Rom, die Glocken von Rom.
```

M + T: Ralph Siegel, Bernd Meinunger
© 1979 Edition Meridian Ralph Siegel KG, Germany.
Warner/Chappell Overseas Holdings Limited, London.
Reproduced by permission of Faber Music Limited.
All Rights Reserved

# GANZ ODER GAR NICHT

(WOLFGANG PETRY)

**Refrain:**
```
D                        Bm
Ganz oder gar nicht, gehn oder bleiben,
G                       A
ganz oder gar nicht, du musst dich entscheiden.
      D                        Bm
Denn weil ich dich liebe, will ich's auch wissen,
G                       A                    G
ganz oder gar nicht, und nicht nur ein bisschen,
A
nicht nur ein bisschen!
```

```
   D
1. Kann sein, dass ich altmodisch bin,
                                     Bm
doch glaub' mir, ich weiß genau, wovon ich sprech'.

Willst du jetzt mich oder ihn?
                                         G                A
Auf zwei Parties tanzen, das geht nun mal schlecht, da hast du Pech!
   D
Entscheiden, das willst du dich nicht,
                                  Bm
du pickst dir aus allem das Beste heraus. Doch zufällig liebe ich dich,
                                    G   Em  A
und dich zu teilen macht mir noch 'was aus.
```

Refrain

```
   D                                                    Bm
2. Wir haben lange genug einfach von Stunde zu Stunde gelebt,

und es gefiel uns auch gut,
                                                G
doch wenn ich mich frag', was hat wirklich gezählt,
           A
dann bleibt nicht viel.
D                                                              Bm
Fang' nicht noch mal damit an, von Freiheit zu reden ist heut ja so in.

Dass man auch zwei lieben kann, sagt immer nur der,
                          G   Em  A
der nicht weiß, was er will.
```

Refrain 2x

Orig. Titel: TEN O' CLOCK POSTMAN
M + T: Tim Norell / Bjorn Hakanson
© Sonet Music AB. Universal Music Publishing GmbH. All Rights Reserved. International Copyright Secured.

## DIE WEISSEN TAUBEN SIND MÜDE

(HANS HARTZ)
[TRANSP. +2]

```
      C              G            F              C
1. Komm her, Marie, ein letztes Glas, genießen wir den Augenblick,
   F              C           G
ab morgen gibt's statt Wein nur Wasser.
        C            G                F              C
Komm her und schenk uns noch mal ein, so viel wird morgen anders sein,
   F       G             C       F G
Marie, die Welt wird langsam blasser.
```

**Refrain:**
```
C         F/C          C    C G Am       F              G    F G C
Die weißen Tauben sind müde,    sie fliegen lange schon nicht mehr.
          F/C              C    C G F                         G    F G C
Sie haben viel zu schwere Flügel   und ihre Schnäbel sind längst leer.
         F/C              C    C G Am      F                 G    F G C
Jedoch, die Falken fliegen weiter,   sie sind so stark wie nie vorher.
         F/C                C    C G F          G               F
Und ihre Flügel werden breiter    und täglich kommen immer mehr,
      C          G          C
nur weiße Tauben fliegen nicht mehr.
```

```
        C              G              F             C
2. Bleib noch, Marie, der letzte Rest reicht für uns beide alle Mal,
   F              C          G
ab morgen gibt's statt Brot nur Steine.
        C            G                F                       C
Komm her und schenk uns noch mal ein, denn so wie heut' wird's nie mehr
sein,
   F        G               C    F G
Marie, die Welt kreist von alleine.
```

Refrain

```
        C              G              F                 C
3. Sieh dort, Marie, das leere Bett, der Spiegel uns'rer großen Zeit,
   F              C           G
ab morgen gibt's statt Glas nur Scherben.
        C            G                F                         C
Komm her und schenk uns noch mal ein, den letzten Schluck vom letzten
Wein,
   F       G          C
Marie, die Welt beginnt zu sterben.
```

Refrain
```
C         F/C          C    C G Am       F              G    F G C
Die weißen Tauben sind müde,    sie fliegen lange schon nicht mehr.
          F/C              C    C G F                         F
Sie haben viel zu schwere Flügel   und ihre Schnäbel sind längst leer.
      C          G          C
Die weißen Tauben fliegen nicht mehr.
      F    C     G          C
Die weißen Tauben fliegen nicht mehr.
```

M + T: Johann-Christoph Busse
© 1982 Albert Bennefeld, Berlin.

# LEAN ON ME

(CLUB NOUVEAU)
(BILL WITHERS)

```
Intro: C  C  Dm  Em  F  F  Em  Dm  C  C  Dm  Em  Em  Dm
       C  C  Dm  Em  F  F  Em  Dm  C  C  Dm  Em  G   C
```

```
      C         Dm Em  F          Em  Dm   C         Dm  Em        Dm
1. Sometimes in our lives we all have pain, we all have sorrow.
   C      Dm Em  F Bb F  Em    Dm     C          Dm     Em G C
   But if we are wise we know that there's always tomorrow.
```

**Refrain:**
```
            C        Dm      Em   F            Em  Dm       C
   Lean on me when you're not strong and I'll be your friend,
        Dm      Em         Dm
   I'll help you carry on.
   C       Dm      E   F          Em Dm  C
   For it won't be long till I'm gonna need
                    G      C
   somebody to lean on.
```

```
      C         Dm  Em   F          Em  Dm    C         Dm   Em       Dm
2. Please swallow your pride if I have things you need to borrow.
   C      Dm  Em  F          Em  Dm   C         Dm  Em      G    C
   For noone can fill those of your needs that you won't let show.
```

Refrain

```
            C                           C
   You just call on me, brother, when you need a hand.
            C             G      C
   We all need somebody to lean on.
            C                         C
   I just might have a problem that you'll understand.
            C             G      C
   We all need somebody to lean on.
```

Refrain

M + T: Bill Withers
© Copyright 1972 Interior Music Corporation, USA.
Universal/MCA Music Limited.
All Rights Reserved. International Copyright Secured.

# MONEY FOR NOTHING

(DIRE STRAITS)

**Intro:** Gm Gm7 C   Gm Bb C
Gm Gm7 C   Gm F Gm

```
Gm7                                      C
Now look at them yoyo's that's the way you do it.
Gm7                      Bb   C
You play the guitar on the M.T.V.
Gm7                                  C
That ain't working that's the way you do it.
Gm7                        F         Gm7
Money for nothing and chicks for free.
```

Now that ain't working that's the way you do it.
Lemme tell ya them guys ain't dumb.
Maybe get a blister on your little finger.
Maybe get a blister on your thumb.

**Refrain:**
```
Eb            Bb                Eb                    F
We gotta install microwave ovens, custom kitchen deliveries.
Gm7                        C              D           E
We gotta move these refrigerators. We gotta move these colour TV's

Gm7                                                C
See the little faggot with the earring and the makeup.
Gm7               Bb      C
Yeah buddy that's his own hair.
Gm7                                   C
That little faggot got his own jet airplane.
Gm7                        F         Gm7
That little faggot he's a millionaire.       Refrain Intro Refrain

Gm7                                  C
I shouldda learned to play the guitar.
Gm7                       Bb      C
I shouldda learned to play them drums.
Gm7                                                C
Look at that mama, she's got it sticking in the camera.
Gm7          F         Gm7
Man we could have some fun.
```

And he's up there, what's that? Hawaiian noises?
Banging on the bongoes like a chimpanzee.
That ain't working that's the way you do it.
Get your money for nothing and chicks for free.     Refrain

```
Gm7                                      C
Now that ain't working that's the way you do it.
Gm7                      Bb   C
You play the guitar on the M.T.V.
Gm7                                  C
That ain't working that's the way you do it.
Gm                         F         Gm7
Money for nothing and your chicks for free.
Gm7            Bb         C     Gm7                F          Gm7
Money for nothing chicks for free. Money for nothing chicks for free.
```

M + T: Mark Knopfler & Gordon Matthew Sumner
© Copyright 1985 Straitjacket Songs Limited.
Universal Music Publishing Limited/GM Sumner.
All Rights Reserved. International Copyright Secured.

## BLAUE AUGEN

(IDEAL)
[TRANSP. +1]

```
   D       G   D                G
1. Ideal im TV lässt mich völlig kalt
   D           G      D        G
   und die ganze Szene hängt mir aus'm Hals.
         D   G      D    G
   Da bleib ich kühl, kein Gefühl.

   D                G              D             G
2. Grelle Fummel aus den Fifty/Sixties, alles hohl und hundsgemein,
   D        G       D                    G
   auf Skoda oder Fiorucci flieg ich nicht mehr ein.
         D   G      D    G
   Da bleib ich kühl, kein Gefühl.
```

**Refrain:**
```
      Bm              C                         A
   Nur deine blauen Augen machen mich so sentimental: so blaue Augen.
   Bm                   C                       G
   Wenn du mich so anschaust wird mir alles andre egal: total egal.
   Bm              C               A
   Deine blauen Augen sind phänomenal: kaum zu glauben.
   Bm                  C                G
   Was ich dann so fühle ist nicht mehr normal.
   G                 A
   Das ist gefährlich, lebensgefährlich, zuviel Gefühl!

      D            G                  D                  G
3. Insider-Feten, da' schlaf ich ein. Ich will auch nicht in London
   sein.
   D              G            D             G
   Bei Sex and Drugs and Rock'n'Roll ist das Maß an Stumpfheit voll.
         D   G      D    G
   Da bleib ich kühl, kein Gefühl.

      D          G             D                  G
4. Der ganze Hassle um die Knete macht mich taub und stumm,
   D              G    D                  G
   für den halben Luxus leg ich mich nicht krumm.
         D     G       D     G
   Nur der Scheich ist wirklich reich.
```

Refrain

M + T: ANNETTE HUMPE
© 1980, P.O.E.M. Musikverlag Klaus D. Mueller, Berlin.

# ONLY TIME

(ENYA)
[TRANSP. +1]

```
    D                  Bm                 G              D
1. Who can say where the road goes? Where the day flows? Only time.
    D                  Bm                 G              D
And who can say if your love grows? As your heart chose. Only time.

Bm           G           A         D
Di da da deh, di da da deh, dih dah deh.
Bm           G           A
Di da da deh, da di da de, di da, da dei di da.


    D                  Bm                 G              D
2. Who can say why your heart sighs? As your love flies. Only time.
    D                  Bm                 G              D
And who can say why your heart cries? When your love lies. Only time.

Bm           G           A         D
Di da da deh, di da da deh, dih dah deh.
Bm           G           A
Di da da deh, da di da de, di da, da dei di da.


    D                  Bm                     G              D
3. Who can say when the roads meet that love might be in your heart?
    D                  Bm                 G              D
And who can say when the day sleeps if the night keeps all your heart,
G                          D
night keeps all your heart?

F  C  Bb  F    F  C  Bb  F    F  C  Bb  F    F  C  Bb A  D
Di da da dei, Di da da dei, Di da da dei, Di da da dei.


    D                  Bm                 G              D
4. Who can say if your love grows? As your heart chose. Only time.
    D                  Bm                 G              D
And who can say where the road goes? Where the day flows? Only time.
G           D      G           D
Who knows? Only time. Who knows? Only time.
```

M + T: Enya, Nicky Ryan and Roma Ryan
© 2000 EMI Music Publishing Limited, London, W8 5SW.
Reproduced by permission of International Music Publications
Limited (a trading name of Faber Music Limited)
All Rights Reserved.

## I JUST CALLED TO SAY I LOVE YOU

(STEVIE WONDER)

```
       G
1. No New Year's day to celebrate,
                                        Am
no chocolate covered candy hearts to give away.
AmMaj7         Am         AmMaj7       Am7
No first of spring, no song to sing,
AmMaj7             Am            D7        G
in fact here's just another ordinary day.
```

2. No April rain, no flowers bloom,
no wedding Saturday with in the month of June.
But wath it is. Is something true
made up of these three words that I must say to you.

**Refrain:**
```
  G       Am7        D       G
I just called to say I love you.
          Am7        D              Em
I just called to say how much I care.
          Am7        D       Em
I just called to say I love you
         Am7             D7          G
and I mean it from the bottom of my heart.
```

3. No summer's high, no warm July,
no harvest moon to light one tender August night.
No autumn breeze, no falling leaves,
not even time for birds to fly to southern skies.

4. No Libra sun, no Halloween,
no giving thanks to all the Christmas joy you bring.
But what it is, though old so new,
to fill your heart like no three words could ever do.

Refrain 2x

M + T: Stevie Wonder
© Copyright 1984 by Jobete Music Incorporated/ Black Bull Music. Mit freundlicher Genehmigung der EMI Music Publishing Germany GmbH / EMI Songs Musikverlag GmbH.

# ANOTHER DAY IN PARADISE

(PHIL COLLINS)

**Intro:** Am G Dm7 Am G Dm7  (2x)

```
   Am                  G              Dm
1. She calls out to the man on the street,
   Am           G
"Sir, can you help me?"
   Am                G            Dm
It's cold and I've nowhere to sleep,
   Am                       G
is there somewhere you can tell me?"

      Am            G         Dm
2. He walks on, doesn't look back,
   Am                    G
he pretends he can't hear her.
   Am                    G               Dm
Starts to whistle as he crosses the street,
   Am                      G
seems embarrased to be there.
```

**Refrain:**
```
Am         Em/A            Fmaj7/A                           Em/A
Oh, think twice, cos' it's another day for you and me in paradise.
Am         Em/A            Fmaj7/A              G      (Am   G F) Am
Oh, think twice, cos' it's another day for you, you and me in paradise.

Am G Dm7 Am G Dm7 Am G Dm7 Am G Dm7
```

```
    Am                  G              Dm
3. She calls out to the man on the street,
   Am                   G
he can see she's been crying.
   Am                    G             Dm
She's got blisters on the soles of her feet,
   Am                      G
she can't walk, but she's trying.   Refrain + Zwischenspiel wie oben

G/B Am             G                         C
Oh  Lord, is there nothing more anybody can do.
G/B Am               G                  C
Oh  Lord, there must be something you can say.

    Am                    G               Dm
4. You can tell from the lines on her face,
   Am                      G
you can see that she's been there.
   Am                          G        Dm
Probably been moved on from every place,
   Am                      G
cos she didn't fit in there.    Refrain + Zwischenspiel wie oben

            Am           G         Dm7    Am      G Dm7
It's just another day for you and me in paradise.
              Am           G         Dm7    Am
It's just another day for you and me in paradise.
```

M + T: Phil Collins
© Copyright 1989 Philip Collins Limited.
Imagem Music.
All Rights Reserved. International Copyright Secured.

# LUCKY MAN

(EMERSON, LAKE & PALMER)

```
   G              D           G              D
1. He had white horses and ladies by the score,
   G              D           G              D
   all dressed in satin and waiting by the door.

   Am         Em          D     Am         Em          D
   Oooh, what a lucky man he was. Oooh, what a lucky man he was.

   G              D           G              D
2. Of white lace and feathers they made up his bed,
   G              D           G              D
   a gold covered mattress on which he was laid.

   Am         Em          D     Am         Em          D
   Oooh, what a lucky man he was. Oooh, what a lucky man he was.

   G              D           G              D
3. He went to fight wars for his country and his king,
   G              D           G              D
   of his honor and his glory the people would sing.

   Am         Em          D     Am         Em          D
   Oooh, what a lucky man he was. Oooh, what a lucky man he was.

   G              D           G              D
4. A bullet had found him his blood ran as he cried,
   G              D           G              D
   no money could save him so he laid down and he died.

   Am         Em          D     Am         Em          D
   Oooh, what a lucky man he was. Oooh, what a lucky man he was.
```

M + T: Greg Lake
© Copyright 1970 Leadchoice Limited.
Bosworth Music Publishing GmbH, Berlin.
All Rights Reserved. International Copyright Secured.

# HARD HEADED WOMAN

(CAT STEVENS)

**Intro:** Dm G Dm G

```
Dm  G                             C         Cm         F             Dm    Am F
I'm looking for a hard headed woman, one who'll take me for myself
Bb        G           C              F
and if I find my hard headed woman
Bb            C        F        Am        Dm
I won't need nobody else, no, no, no.

Dm  G                             C         Cm         F             Dm    Am F
I'm looking for a hard headed woman, one who'll make me do my best
Bb        G           C              F
and if I find my hard headed woman
Bb            C                        F                Am
I know the rest of my life will be blessed, yes, yes, yes.

Dm  G                    C         Cm         F             Dm    Am F
I know a lot of fancy dancers, people who can glide you on a floor.
Bb        F           Bb           F   C
They move so smooth but have no answers
Gm              C                         F    Am
when you ask "why'd you come here for?"

Solo  (wie Strophe)

Am           D             Am
I know, many fine feathered friends
         D           F         E
but their friendliness depends on how you do,
Am                   D           Am
they know many sure fine ways
         D              F        E       A7
to find out the one who pays and how you do.

Dm  G                             C         Cm         F             Dm    Am F
I'm looking for a hard headed woman, one who'll make me feel so good.
Bb  F  Bb                  F      C
And if I find my hard headed woman,
Gm         C                   F            Am
I know my life will be as it should, yes, yes, yes.

Dm  G                             C         Cm         F             Dm    Am F
I'm looking for a hard headed woman, one who'll make me do my best.
Bb  F  Bb                  F      C
And if I find my hard headed woman,
Gm         C                   F            Am
I know my life will be as it should, yes, yes, yes.
```

M + T: Cat Stevens
© Copyright 1970 Salafa Limited.
All Rights Reserved. International Copyright Secured.

# UNCLE JOHN FROM JAMAICA

(VENGABOYS)

```
F          C           G      C  F         C           G      C
Na na na na na na na he he he, na na na na na na na he he he.

C                                     G
Eight o'clock: Get up, get out of bed,
                                        Am            F       G
I feel like a truck went over my head, another day of stress and sorrow.
C                                G
Skip breakfast 'cause I have to go,
                                  Am                  F        G
ain't got no time to take it slow and I will do my hair tomorrow.
Am               F            Am                         G
I can take it no more, o no no no. Is this what I'm living for?
```

**Refrain:**
```
              F             C             G             C
But my uncle John from Jamaica keeps on calling every day:
             F            C            G           C
"Just buy a ticket and take a summer holi- holiday!"
           F            C             G            C
My uncle John from Jamaica keeps on calling every day:
             F            C            G           C
"Just buy a ticket and take a summer holi- holiday!"


F          C           G      C  F         C           G      C
Na na na na na na na he he he, na na na na na na na he he he.

C                                G
Six o'clock: My job is still not done.
                           Am                   F        G
The life I'm living ain't no fun, too many days of stress and sorrow.
C                                G
My boss just won't give me a break
                                 Am                    F       G
and this is more than I can take. Think i will quit this job tomorrow
Am               F            Am                         G
I can take it no more, o no no no. Is this what I'm living for?
```

Refrain

```
F          C           G      C  F         C           G      C
Na na na na na na na he he he, na na na na na na na he he he.
F          C           G      C  F         C           G      C
Na na na na na na na he he he, na na na na na na na he he he.

C         G           C                  G           C
I need a holi- holiday. You need a holi- holiday.
            G            C                   G           C
We need a holi- holiday. Everybody needs a holi- holiday.
```

Refrain

M + T: Danski & Delmundo
© Deldan Publishing. Universal Music Publishing GmbH.
All Rights Reserved. International Copyright Secured.

# JUST LIKE A WOMAN

(BOB DYLAN)

```
      C    F    G    C
1. Nobody feels any pain
   C           F        G              C
tonight as I stand inside the rain.
   F          G             F               G
Everybody knows that baby's got new clothes
     F   Em Dm C        F                 G
but lately I see her ribbons and her bows
       Am      C         G
have fallen from her curls.
```

**Refrain:**
```
      C       Em    Dm      F
She takes just like a woman, yes she does.
      C         Em     Dm       F
She makes love just like a woman, yes she does.
          C      Em    Dm     F
And she aches just like a woman
          G                           C
but she breaks just like a little girl.
```

```
            C    F    G   C
2. Queen Mary, she's my friend,
                   F      G        C
yes, I believe I'll go see her again.
    F         G              F                G
Nobody has to guess that baby can't be blessed
       F    Em    Dm     C    F                G
till she finally sees that she's like all the rest.
           Am              C/G   F         G
With her fog, her amphetamine and her pearls.
```

Refrain

```
        E7
It was rainin' from the first and I was dying there of thirst.
         C
So I came in here
            E7
and your longtime curse hurts but what's worse
           F              Gsus4
is this pain in here, I can't stay in here, ain't it clear.
```

```
       C F   G     C
3. That I just can't fit,
            C         F          G        C
yes, I believe it's time for us to quit.
   F          G         F              G
When we meet again introduced as friends
   F    Em    Dm  C  F                    G
please don't let on that you knew me when
          Am              C/G    F    G
I was hungry and it was your world.
```

Refrain

M + T: Bob Dylan
© Copyright 1966; Renewed 1994 Dwarf Music, USA.
All Rights Reserved. International Copyright Secured.

## CATCH ME

(BANDITS)

```
   A         D              A
1. I heard she drove the silvery sports-car
        Bm             A
   along the empty streets last night,
         G                D
   hanging around with hairdos like mine.
        G                       A
   No, I haven't seen the kids for some time.

               D                   A
2. Picked up her shoes from the red-brick-stairway,
        Bm              A
   just like harpsichord as she moved
         G                 D
   and back upstairs at half past two
        G                  A
   with a paper folded outside the loo.
```

**Refrain:**
```
Em       G           D      A
Rain falls like Elvis-tears. Oh no, no sugar tonight.
Em       G         A                Em        G      A
Out on the highstreets dim all the lights now bright color tears again.
D                   A                   Bm
Baby, don't forget to catch me, don't forget to catch me,
                     A
don't forget to catch me.
G                            D
Hold on princes, don't you think that it's time
G                   D              A
on this platform with the drizzle in my eye.

            D               A
3. I had a friend from over the harbour,
        Bm                        A
   he said he stayed with a neighbourhood girl
            G              D
   and sometimes when it won't go right
        G                        A
   I can hear his voice inside me at night.
```

Refrain

Baby, don't forget to catch me, don't forget to catch me,
don't forget to catch me.
Hold on princes, don't you think that it's time.
The ticket's in my hand, the train pulls down the line.

Baby, don't forget to catch me, don't forget to catch me,
don't forget to catch me.
Hold on princes, don't you think that it's time
on this platform with the drizzle in my eye.

M + T: Bob Stanley, Peter Stewart Wiggs
© 1992 Warner/Chappell Music Ltd, London.
Reproduced by permission of Faber Music Limited.
All Rights Reserved.

# CLAIRE

(GILBERT O'SULLIVAN)

**Intro:** F#m7 Bm7 E E7

```
     F#m7           Bm7                   E7
1. Claire. The moment I met you, I swear.
   C#m7                        F#m
I felt as if something, somewhere,
     Bm7                 Bm/G#        E7
had happened to me, which I couldn't see.

       F#m7          Bm7              E7
And then, the moment I met you, again.
   C#m7                       F#m
I knew in my heart that we were friends.
     Bm7              Bm/G#        E7
It had to be so, it couldn't be no.
      A        G°                  Bm7
But try as hard as I might do, I don't know why.
E7                        Amaj7
You get to me in a way I can't describe.
Dmaj7/A                     B9/A
Words mean so little when you look up and smile.
          A6                       B9
I don't care what people say, to me you're more than a child.
     Bm7       E7
Oh Claire. Claire.

       F#m7           Bm7                  E7          C#m7                      F#m
2. Claire. If ever a moment so rare was captured for all to compare.
       Bm7              Bm/G#         E7
That moment is you in all that you do.
       A        G°                          Bm7
But why in spite of our age difference do I cry?
E7                      Amaj7
Each time I leave you I feel I could die.
Dmaj7/A                     B9/A
Nothing means more to me than hearing you say,
            A6                       B9
"I'm going to marry you. Will you marry me? Oh, hurray!"
     Bm7       E7
Oh Claire. Claire.

       F#m7           Bm7                        E7
3. Claire, I've told you before, don't you dare?
     Amaj7     F#m7            Bm7            E7
Get back into bed. Can't you see that it's late?
          Amaj7        F#m7          Bm7              E7         A
No, you can't have a drink. Oh alright then, but wait just a minute.
            G°                Bm7         E7
While I, in an effort to babysit, catch up on my breath,
              Amaj7
what there is left of it.
Dmaj7/A                     B9/A
You can be murder at this hour of the day.
            A6                         B9
But in the morning the sun will see my lifetime away.
     Bm7      E7      F#m/D# Dmaj7 A/C# Bm7    Amaj7
Oh Claire. Claire.                          Oh Claire.
```

M + T: Gilbert O'Sullivan
© Copyright 1972 Sony/ATV Music Publishing (UK) Limited.
All Rights Reserved. International Copyright Secured.

## LET'S TWIST AGAIN

(CHUBBY CHECKER)

Come on everybody, clap your hands, are you looking good?

I'm gonna sing my song and it won't take long.

We're gonna do the twist and it goes like this:

```
              G                            Em
Come on, let's twist again, like we did last summer.
             C                      D7
Yeah, let's twist again, like we did last year.
         G                       Em
Do you remember when things were really humming?
              C          D              G    C G7
Yeah, let's twist again, twistin' time is here.
C                                       G
And round and round and up and down we go again.
C                           D7
Oh, baby make me know you love me so and then
     G                          Em
let's twist again, like we did last summer.
                  C          D7             G
Come on, let's twist again, like we did last year.
```

Who's that flyin' up there?
Is it a bird? No!
Is it a plane? No!
Is it the twister? Yeah!

```
        G                          Em
Yeah, twist again, like we did last summer.
                  C                      D7
Come on, let's twist again, like we did last year.
         G                       Em
Do you remember when things were really humming?
                  C          D              G    C G7
Come on, let's twist again, twistin' time is here.
C                                       G
And round and round and up and down we go again.
C                           D7
Oh, baby make me know you love me so and then
       G                          Em
come on, twist again, like we did last summer.
              C          D7             G
Girl, let's twist again, like we did last year.
              C      D7            G
Come on, twist again, twistin' time is here, Bop Bop.
```

M + T: Kal Mann / Dave Appell
© 1961 Kalmann Music Inc. administered by Chappell & Co Inc,
warner/Chappell North America Ltd, London.
Reproduced by permission of Faber Music Limited.
All Rights Reserved.

# FIELDS OF GOLD

(STING)

```
         Bsus2            G
You'll remember me when the west wind moves
                       D
upon the fields of barley,
         Bsus2            G        D
you'll forget the sun in his jealous sky
     G/B     A          Bm7       G      D
as we walk in fields of gold.
         Bsus2            G
So she took her love for to gaze awhile
                       D
upon the fields of barley,
         Bsus2            G        D
in his arms she fell as her hair came down
     G/B     A        D
among the fields of gold.
         Bsus2            G
Will you stay with, will you be my love
                       D
among the fields of barley
         Bsus2            G        D
we'll forget the sun in his jealous sky
     G/B     A          Bm7       G      D
as we walk in fields of gold.
         Bsus2            G
See the west wind move like a lover so
                       D
upon the fields of barley,
         Bsus2            G        D
feel her body rise when you kiss her mouth
     G/B A            D
among the fields of gold
G           D             G                   D
I never make promises lightly, and there have been some that I've
         G              D              G/B     A             D
broken, but I swear in the days still left we'll walk in fields of gold.
     G/B     A        D    Bsus2 G D Bsus2 G D G/B A D
We'll walk in fields of gold.
         Bsus2                      G
Many years have passed since those summer days
                       D
among the fields of barley,
         Bsus2            G        D        G/B A             D
see the children run as the sun goes down among the fields of gold.
         Bsus2            G                                   D
You'll remember me when the west wind moves upon the fields of barley,
         Bsus2            G        D        G/B        A
you can tell the sun in his jealous sky when we walked in fields of
     D       G/B      A         D        G/B      A
gold. When we walked in fields of gold. When we walked in fields of
gold.
Outro:  D G/D D G/D D G/D D
```

M + T: Sting
© Copyright 1992 Steerpike Limited/Steerpike (Overseas) Limited/EMI Music Publishing Limited.
All Rights Reserved. International Copyright Secured.

# THANK YOU FOR THE MUSIC

(ABBA)

**Intro:** E G° F#m7 B7

```
    E              G°         F#m7         B7       E      Bm7  E7
1. I'm nothing special, in fact I'm a bit of a bore.
   A                        C#7              F#m    F#m7 B7
If I tell a joke, you've probably heard it before.
   E                    B
But I have a talent, a wonderful thing
         E      E7         A          Am
'cause everyone listens when I start to sing.
       C#m7            A/C#
I'm so grateful and proud.
        F#m7                     B7
All I want is to sing it out loud, so I say:
```

**Refrain:**
```
E                F#m        B7           E
Thank you for the music, the songs I'm singing.
C#m       C#m7        F#7          B7
Thanks for all the joy they're bringing.
E             F#m        G#      C#m7         A
Who can live without it, I ask in all honesty,
            Am
what would life be?
              E          E7             C#7
Without a song or a dance what are we?
        F#m              A
So I say thank you for the music,
    B7           E G° F#m7 B7
for giving it to me.
```

```
2. Mother says I was a dancer before I could walk.
She says I began to sing long before I could talk.
And I've often wondered, how did it all start?
Who found out that nothing can capture a heart
like a melody can?
Well, whoever it was, I'm a fan.
```

Refrain

```
Am6          E             Am6                  E
I've been so lucky, I am the girl with golden hair,
       Am6      G#7      C#m   C#m7
I wanna sing it out to everybody.
F#m7                    B7
What a joy, what a life, what a chance!
```

Refrain
```
         F#m               A
So I say thank you for the music,
    B7           E  F#m E Am E
for giving it to me.
```

M + T: Benny Andersson & Bjorn Ulvaeus
© Copyright 1977 Universal/Union Songs Musikforlag AB.
Universal Music Publishing Limited.
All Rights Reserved. International Copyright Secured.

# WHERE THE STREETS HAVE NO NAME

(U2)

```
        D
1. I want to run, I want to hide,
                                    G
I want to tear down the walls that hold me inside.
           Bm                 A
I want to reach out and touch the flame
          Csus2
where the streets have no name.


        D
2. I want to feel sunlight on my face,
                                      G
see that dust cloud disappear without a trace.
           Bm                      A
I want to take shelter from the poison rain
          Csus2
where the streets have no name.
```

**Refrain:**

```
                         D
Where the streets have no name. Where the streets have no name.
                          G
We're still building then burning down love, burning down love.
          Bm              A                        D
And when I go there I go there with you, it's all I can do.


         D
3. The city's a flood and our love turns to rust.
                                              G
We're beaten and blown by the wind, trampled in dust.
           Bm                  A
I'll show you a place, high on the desert plain
          Csus2
where the streets have no name.
```

Refrain

```
D
Our love turns to rust
                    G
and we're beaten and blown by the wind, blown by the wind,
       D
oh and I see love, see our love turn to rust.
                         G
And we're beaten and blown by the wind, blown by the wind,
            Bm                    A                  D
oh when I go there I go there with you, it's all I can do.
```

M + T: Larry Mullen, Adam Clayton, Dave Evans & Paul David Hewson
© Copyright 1987 Mother Music (for the Republic of Ireland)/Blue Mountain Music Limited (for the UK)/Universal International Music Publishing B.V. (for the rest of the world).
All Rights Reserved. International Copyright Secured.

# UND IRGENDWANN BLEIB I DANN DORT
(STS)

```
            G                            Am
1. Der letzte Sommer war sehr schön, i bin in irgendeiner Bucht glegn.
             G                         Am
Die Sonn' wie Feuer auf der Haut, riechst des Wasser und nix is laut.
          C                   D
Irgendwo in Griechenland, jede Menge weißer Sand,
                     G
auf mei'm Rücken nur dei' Hand.

                                  G
2. Nach zwei, drei Wochen hab ich's gspürt.
                   Am
I hab das Lebensgfühl dort inhaliert.
                 G                    Am
Die Gedanken drehn sich um, was zuhaus wichtig war ist jetzt ganz dumm.
                   C                             D
Du sitzt bei einem Olivenbaum, und du spielst mit einem Stein,
              G
es ist so anders als daheim.
```

**Refrain:**
```
G                        C                       D
Und irgendwann bleib' i dann dort. Lass alles liegen und stehn,
                          G
Geh von daheim für immer fort.
              C                   D
Darauf geb i dir mein Wort, wieviel Jahr auch noch vergehn,
                         G
Irgendwann bleib i dann dort.

                         G                         Am
3. In unsrer Hektomatikwelt dreht sich alles nur um Macht und Geld.
                       G
Finanzamt, Banken steign mer drauf,
                          Am
die Rechnung, die geht sowieso nie auf.
                   C                             D
Und irgendwann fragst du, wieso quäl i mi da so schrecklich ab
                         G
und bin net längst schon weiß Gott wo.
```

Solo. Wie Strophe.

```
                    G                            Am
4. Aber noch ist net so weit, noch was zu tun befiehlt die Eitelkeit.
                                    Am
Doch bevor der Herzinfarkt mi mit vierzig in die Windel brackt,
                  C                             D
lieg I schon irgendwo am Strand, a Bottle Rotwein in der Hand,
                            G
und steck die Füß in weißen Sand.
```

Refrain 2x

M + T: Gert Steinbäcker
© Copyright by Edition SCHEIBMAIER
All Rights Reserved. International Copyright Secured.

# YOU SANG TO ME

(MARC ANTHONY)
[TRANSP. +5]

**Intro:** G Em C D G Em C D G D

```
         G
1. I just wanted you to comfort me,
when I called you late last night you see,
         Em
I was falling into love, yes, I was crashing into love.
         C
Oh, of all the words you sang to me,
         D
about life, the truth, and being free,
         G                      D
yeah, you sang to me, oh, how you sang to me.

              G
2. Girl, I live for how you make me feel,
so I question all this being real,
              Em
cause I'm not afraid to love, for the first time I'm not afraid to love.
         C
Oh, this day seems made for you and me
         D
and you showed me where I want to be,
         G                  D
yeah, you sang to me, oh, you sang to me.
```

**Refrain:**
```
         G
All the while you were in front of me I never realized,
         Em
I just can't believe I didn't see it in your eyes.
         C              D
I didn't see it, I can't believe it,
         G              D
oh, but I feel it when you sing to me.
         G
How I long to hear you sing beneath the clear blue skies,
         Em
and I promise you this time I'll see it in your eyes.
         C              D
I didn't see it, I can't believe it,
         G              D
oh, but I feel it when you sing to me.

              G
3. Just to think you live inside of me,
I had no idea how this could be,
         Em
now I'm crazy for your love, can't believe, I'm crazy for your love.
         C
The words you sang, just sang to me,
         D
and you showed me what life needs to be
         G              D
you sang to me, oh, you sang to me.
Refrain Intro Refrain
```

M + T: Marc Anthony & Mark Rooney
© Copyright 1999 Sony/ATV Tunes LLC/Cori Tiffani Publishing, USA.
Sony/ATV Music Publishing (UK) Limited.
All Rights Reserved. International Copyright Secured.

# DESPERADO

(EAGLES)

**Intro:** G G7 C Cm G Em A7 D

```
         G              G7                C              Cm
Desperado, why don't you come to your senses?
         G             Em           A7        D7
You been out riding fences for so long now.
                  G               G7          C              Cm
Oh, you're a hard one, I know that you got your reasons,
      G/D           B7/D# Em        A7       D7  G   D/F#
these things that are pleasing you can hurt you somehow.

         Em                 Bm
Don't you draw the queen of diamonds boy,
    C                   G    D/F#
she'll beat you if she's able,
         Em7              C              G    D/F#
you know the queen of hearts is always your best bet.
      Em              Bm                    C        G    D/F#
Now it seems to me some fine things have been laid upon your table
         Em          A7            Am7   D
but you only want the ones you can't get.

D7  G       G7            C              Cm
Desperado, oh you ain't getting no younger,
    G        B7/F# Em       A7           D7
your pain and your hunger, they're driving you home.
    G              G7           C
And freedom, well, that's just some people talking
    G       B7/F# Em            A7    D7  G   D/F#
your prison is    walking through this world all alone.

          Em                      Bm
Don't your feet get cold in the winter time?
    C                   G          D/F#
The sky won't snow and the sun won't shine.
    Em7             C             G    D/F#
It's hard to tell the night time from the day.
         Em              Bm
You're losing all your highs and lows,
         C            G           Am7   D
ain't it funny how the feeling goes away.

  D7 G       G7                C              Cm
Desperado, why don't you come to your senses?
      G        B/F# Em       A7       D7
Come down from your fences, open the gate.
         G            G7         C              Cm
It may be raining, but there's a rainbow above you.
           G      B7/F# Em   G/D   C      G/B  Am7
You better let somebody   love you, let somebody love you.
            G/D    B7/F# Em        Am7      D7  G   G7 C Cm G
You better let somebody  love you before it's too late.
```

M + T: Don Henley, Glenn Lewis Frey
© 1973 Cass County Music / Red Cloud Music. Warner/Chappell
North America Ltd, London / Universal/MCA Music Limited.
Reproduced by permission of Faber Music Ltd.
All Rights Reserved. International Copyright Secured.

## WE DON'T NEED ANOTHER HERO

(TINA TURNER)

```
       G            D         G            D
1. Out of the ruins, out from the wreckage,
   C            D               A
can't make the same mistake this time.
Em           D            Em           D
We are the children, the last generation,
C            D           A
we are the ones they left behind.
            C            D          Am7
And I wonder when we are ever gonna change,
          C               D          Am7
living under the fear, till nothing else remains.
```

**Refrain:**
```
D       C    D       C D           C      D      C   D
We don't need another hero, we don't need to know the way home.
          C        D      C D       Am
All we want is life beyond thunderdome.
```

```
       G           D         G         D
2. Looking for something we can rely on,
   C              D                A
there's gotta be something better out there.
Em        D             Em          D
Love and compassion, their day is coming,
C            D              A
all else are castles built in the air.
            C            D          Am7
And I wonder when we are ever gonna change,
          C               D          Am7
living under the fear, till nothing else remains.
D       C        D
All the children say
```

Refrain

```
                D                     F              Am
So what do we do with our lives, we leave only a mark,
Bb               C              Bb              C
will our story shine like a light, or end in the dark ?
D
Give it all or nothing
```

Refrain

```
D       C        D
All the children say
```

Refrain

M + T: Graham Lyle, Terry Britten
© 1984 Goodsingle Limited. Rechte für Deutschland, Österreich, Schweiz und Osteuropa: TJ MUSICSERVICE GMBH, W B Music Corp, Warner/ Chappell North America Ltd, London. Reproduced by permission of Faber Music Limited.
All Rights Reserved.

# RUNAWAY

(BON JOVI)

**Intro:** Am Asus2/4 Dm/A Am Asus2/4 Am Gsus4 G Gsus2 G Gsus4 G Gsus2 G (3x)

```
   Am                                                    G
1. On the streets where you live the girls talk about their social
lives.
            Em                         F           G           Am
They're made of lipstick, plastic and paint. A touch of sable in their
eyes.

        Am                                               G
2. All your life, all you asked when is your daddy gonna talk to you.
           Em                     G                Am
But you where living in another world trying to get your message
through.

Em         G          Am
No one heard a single word you said,
                  Dm                         C                G
they should have seen it in your eyes what was going around your head.
```

**Refrain:**
```
Am            G        C                    Em
Oooh, she's a little runaway. Daddy's girl learned fast
G             Am          G    E                Am
all those things he couldn't say. Ooh, she's a little runaway.

   Am                                           G
3. A different line every night guaranteed to blow your mind.
Em               G           Am
See you out on the streets call me for a wild time.
   Am                                                  G
4. So you sit home alone cause there's nothing left that you can do.
              Em                     G                Am
There's only pictures hung in the shadows left there to look at you.

Em          G                    Am
You know she likes the lights at night on the neon Broadway signs
   Dm                         C                        G
and she don't really mind, it's only love she hoped to find.
```

Refrain

```
Em         G          Am
No one heard a single word you said,
                  Dm                         C                G
they should have seen it in your eyes what was going around your head.

Am            G        C                    Em
Oooh, she's a little runaway. Daddy's girl learned fast
G             Am          Am                    G
all those things he couldn't say. Ooh, she's a little runaway.
C              Em    G              Am
Daddy's girl learned fast, now she was a night away.
G                    Am
Oooh, she's a little runaway.
```

M + T: Jon Bon Jovi, George Karakoglou
© Copyright 1984 Simile Music Incorporated, Minder Music Limited, Famous Music Corp.
Warner/Chappell Music Limited, London.
All Rights Reserved. International Copyright Secured.

# SPANISH TRAIN

(CHRIS DE BURGH)

```
          Dm                          Bb
There's a Spanish train that runs between Guadalquevir

and old Seville
              C
and at dead of night the whistle blows and
       A7                   Dm
people hear she's running still.
                Dm
And then they hush their children back to sleep,
Bb
lock the doors upstairs they creep,
   C                                              A7
for it is said that the souls of the dead fill up the train,
                Dm
ten thousand deep.

          Dm                      Bb      C      Dm
Well a railway-man lay dying with his people by his side.
                               Bb            A7
His family were crying knelt in prayer before he died,
       Bb                 C
But above his head just waiting for the dead
       A7                  Dm
was the devil with a twinkle in his eye,
      Bb                     C                       Dm
Well, God's not around look what I've found? This one's mine!
                                 Bb       C      Dm
Just then the Lord himself appeared in a blinding flash of light.
                             Bb            A7
And shouted at the devil, get thee hence to endless night.
       Bb                       C
But the devil just grinned and said I may have sinned
          A7                  Dm
but there's no need to push me around,
   Bb                  C
I got here first so you can do your worst,
                Dm
he's going under ground.

          Dm                              Bb     C     Dm
Well I think I give you one more chance said the devil with a smile,
                                    Bb              A7
so throw away that stupid lance. It's really not your style.
Bb            C
Joker is the name, poker is the game,
       A7              Dm
we'll play right here on this bed.
      Bb                     C                          Dm
And we'll bet for the biggest stakes yet the souls of the dead.
```

```
          Bb         C                      Dm
And I said, look out Lord he's gonna win!
     Bb               C                  Dm
The sun is down and the night's riding in.
     Bb            A7       Dm                 Gm
The train is dead on time, many souls are on the line,
     Bb       A7      Dm
oh Lord, he's gonna win.
```

Now the railway-man he cut the cards
and he dealt such a hand of five.
And for the Lord he was praying hard for that train
he'd have to drive,
Well, the devil he had three aces and a king
and the Lord he was running for a straight he had
the queen the knave the nine and ten of spades
all he needed was the eight,
and then the Lord, he called for one more card
but he drew the diamond eight.
And the devil said to the Son of God, 'I believe you got it straight,
so deal me one for the time has come
to see who'll be the king of this place',
But as he spoke from beneath his cloak he slipped another ace.
Ten thousand souls was the opening bid,
but soon went up to fifty-nine,
but the Lord didn't see what the devil did and he said,
'that suits me fine.'
I'll raise you high to hundred-five and
forever put an end to your sin.
But the devil let out a mighty shout: 'my hand wins'.

And I said, Lord oh, Lord you let him win.
The sun is down and the night's riding in.
The train is dead on time, many souls are on the line,
oh Lord, he's gonna win.

There's a Spanish train that runs between Guadelquevir
and old Seville
and at dead of night the whistle blows
and people hear she's running still.
And far away in some recess the Lord and the devil
are now playing chess.
The devil still cheats and wins more souls and as for the Lord, well,
he's just doing his best,

```
And I said, Lord oh, Lord you've gotta win.
The sun is down and the night's riding in.
The train is still on time, oh my soul is on the line,
     Bb    C             Dm
oh Lord, you've got to win.
```

M + T: Chris de Burgh
© Copyright 1975 Big Secret Music Limited/ Chrysalis Music Limited.
Alle Rechte für Deutschland, Österreich und Schweiz bei Global
Musikverlag, München.

# DANCING QUEEN

(ABBA)

```
Intro: Bb Eb/Bb Bb F/A Eb/G Bb/F
F            D7           Gm7                    C7/E
You can dance, you can jive, having the time of your life.
Eb          Cm7                     Bb         Eb/Bb Bb Eb/Bb
See that girl, watch that scene, dig in the dancing queen.

      Bb                      Eb/Bb
1. Friday night and the lights are low,
Bb                       Gm
looking out for the place to go.
F             Bb/F    F          Bb/F
Where they play the right music, getting in the swing,
          F           Gm
you come to look for a king.

      Bb                      Eb/Bb
2. Anybody could be that guy,
Bb                          Gm
night is young and the music's high.
F             Bb/F    F          Bb/F
With a bit of rock music, everything is fine,
          F     Gm    F
you're in the mood for a dance
Gm          Cm7           F7
and when you get the chance,
```

**Refrain**:
```
              Bb           Eb/Bb         Bb       Eb/Bb
You are the dancing queen, young and sweet, only seventeen.
Bb        Eb/Bb              Bb       F/A Eb/G
Dancing queen, feel the beat from the tambourine.
F            D7           Gm7                    C7/E
You can dance, you can jive, having the time of your life.
Eb          Cm7                     Bb         Eb/Bb Bb Eb/Bb
See that girl, watch that scene, dig in the dancing queen.

      Bb                      Eb/Bb
3. You're a teaser, you turn 'em on,
Bb                           Gm
leave them burning and then you're gone.
F             Bb/F    F          Bb/F
Looking out for another, anyone will do,
          F     Gm    F
you're in the mood for a dance
Gm          Cm7           F7
and when you get the chance,
```

Refrain

M + T: Benny Andersson, Björn Ulvaeus & Stig Anderson
© Copyright 1976 Universal/Union Songs Musikforlag AB.
All Rights Reserved. International Copyright Secured.

# WIEDER ALLES IM GRIFF

(JÜRGEN DREWS)
[TRANSP. -1]

**Refrain:**
```
G                C                      G
Wieder alles im Griff auf dem sinkenden Schiff,
      Dm            F        C                   G
keine Panik auf der Titanic, Land in Sicht, ich sterbe nicht.
                 C                      G
Wieder alles im Griff auf dem sinkenden Schiff,
      Dm            F        C                   G
keine Panik auf der Titanic, Land in Sicht, ich sterbe nicht.
```

```
              C                   G
1. Kurz vor dem Hafen der Liebe war alles aus.
         F
Hast nur noch gegengelenkt, das Schiff versenkt,
C              G
du wolltest einfach raus.
                C                             G
Nahmst mir den Wind aus den Segeln. Nichts hat mehr geklappt.
    F                                    C             G
S.O.S., Herz in Not, doch im Rettungsboot da ging es wieder ab.
```

Refrain

```
              C                        G
2. Im wilden Meer der Gefühle kein Land in Sicht,
      F
du lässt mich einfach stehn, einfach untergehn,
C            G
hast mich weggewischt.
                C                             G
Nahmst mir den Wind aus den Segeln. Nichts hat mehr geklappt.
    F                                    C             G
S.O.S., Herz in Not, doch im Rettungsboot da ging es wieder ab.
```

Refrain

M + T: Drews, Jürgen
© Cornfield Musikverlag,
administriert von Fortunator Musik GmbH.

# (TAKE A LITTLE) PIECE OF MY HEART

(JANIS JOPLIN)

**Intro:** F#m    A    B     C#m   B    D    B

```
B          B           B           B
Come on!   Come on!    Come on!    Come on!
```

```
       E                    A   B    A              E      A B A
1. Didn't I make you feel like you were the only man?
                E                   A                          B
Yeah, and didn't I give you nearly ev'rthing that a woman possibly can?
                      B
Honey you know I did!

C#m                                    B
But each time I tell myself that I, that I think I've had enough.
              D                           B
Oh, but I'm gonna show ya baby, that a woman can be tough.
              B        B         B         B
I want you to come on, come on, come on, come on and
```

**Refrain:**
```
E             A                    B                A
Take it! Take another little piece of my heart now, baby.
E              A                       B
Break a, break another little bit of my heart, now, darlin' yeah, yeah,
yeah, yeah.
E             A                      B                B  Bb  A
Have a, have another little piece of my heart now, baby.
                           A      G#m F#m  E
Well you know you got it if it makes you feel good, oh yes indeed.
```

2. You're out on the streets, lookin' good, and baby deep down in your heart.
I guess you know that it ain't right.
Now, now, now, now, now, now hear me when I cry at night.
Yeah, but I cry all the time!

And each time I tell myself that I, that I can't stand the pain.
When you hold me in your arms, I'm singin' once again.
I said come on, come on, come on, come on yeah.

Refrain

B
I need you to come on, come on, come on, come on, and

Refrain

Well you know you go it.

Refrain

M + T: Jerry Ragovoy & Bert Berns
© Copyright 1967 Web IV Music Incorporated, USA and (Renewed) Chappell & Co Inc.
Sony/ATV Music Publishing (UK) Limited, Warner/Chappell Music Limited, London. Reproduced by permission of Faber Music Ltd.
All Rights Reserved. International Copyright Secured.

# HELLO

(LIONEL RICHIE)

**Intro:** Am G Fmaj7 G Fmaj7 Am G Fmaj7 G Fmaj7

```
            Am              G             Fmaj7 G Fmaj7
1. I've been alone with you inside my mind
      Am           G                Fmaj7       G Fmaj7
and in my dreams I've kissed your lips a thousand times.
     Am           G              Fmaj7 G Fmaj7
I sometimes see you pass outside my door.
    Am  G    Fmaj7         A
Hello, is it me you're looking for?
```

**Refrain:**
```
         Dm             G
I can see it in your eyes,
         C              F
I can see it in your smile,
         Bb             E
you're all I've ever wanted
      Am       G/B  Am/C G/B
and my arms are open wide.
         Dm             G
Cause you know just what to say
         C              F
and you know just what to do
         Bb             E         Am  G Fmaj7 G Fmaj7
and I want to tell you so much, I love you.
```

2. I long to see the sunlight in your hair
and tell you time and time again how much I care.
Sometimes I feel my heart will overflow.
Hello, I've just got to let you know.

'Cause I wonder where you are
and I wonder what you do.
Are you somewhere feeling lonely
or is someone loving you?
Tell me how to win your heart
for I haven't got a clue
but let me start by saying, I love you.

Hello, is it me you're looking for?
'Cause I wonder where you are
and I wonder what you do
or is someone loving you?
Tell me how to win your heart
for I haven't got a clue
but let me start by saying, I love you.

M + T: Lionel Richie
© Copyright 1983, 1984 Brenda Richie Publishing, USA/Brockman Music.
Kobalt Music Publishing Limited/Imagem Music.
All Rights Reserved. International Copyright Secured.

# MUSIK, MUSIK, MUSIK (ICH BRAUCHE KEINE MILLIONEN)
(MARIKA RÖKK)

```
         F7        Bb7      Eb              F7       Bb7        Eb
1. Ich hab' am Anzug viele Taschen, doch in den Taschen ist nichts drin
    Bb7       Eb          Gm         Cm7            F7         Bb7
als nur ein kleines Bild der Frau, mit der ich glücklich bin.
    D7   Gm              Gm            D7   Gm           Gm
Und außerdem noch ein paar Noten, doch keine Noten von der Bank,
     Cm    G#° Cm Gm  D7   Gm   Cm           D     Bb7
nur Noten einer Melodie, die sing' ich stundenlang:
```

**Refrain:**
```
Eb    F#°     Fm6          Bb7   Eb   F#°      Fm6                 Bb7
Ich brauche keine Millionen, mir fehlt kein Pfennig zum Glück,
C7             Fm7                   B7           Bb7 Eb
ich brauche weiter nichts als nur: Musik! Musik! Musik!
    F#°        Fm6            Bb7   Eb   F#°      Fm6                 Bb7
Ich brauch' kein Schloß um zu wohnen, kein Auto, funkelnd und schick,
C7            Fm7                  B7        Bb7 Eb
ich brauche weiter nichts als nur Musik! Musik! Musik!
Eb7       Ab6           Eb7            Ab6
Doch eine ganze Kleinigkeit die brauch' ich noch dazu,
 F7       Bb6                F7              Bb Bb9 Ab/Bb Bb7
und diese große Kleinigkeit bist du, nur du, nur du du du du!
Eb    F#°     Fm6         Bb7  Eb   F#°     Fm6                Bb7
Ich brauche keine Millionen mir fehlt kein Pfennig zum Glück,
C7              Fm7               B7        Bb7 Eb
ich brauch' nur deine Liebe und Musik! Musik! Musik!
```

```
         F7        Bb7      Eb               F7      Bb7        Eb
2. Ein junger Mann, den ich sehr liebe, weil er bezaubernd ist und nett,
   Bb7     Eb          Gm         Cm7            F7        Bb7
der sagte neulich, dass er mich zur Ehefrau gern hätt':
     D7    Gm      D7       Gm            D7    Gm    D7     Gm
Doch weil er leider schrecklich arm wär, hätt er zu fragen nicht gewagt,
     Cm    G#°  Cm  Gm      D7  Gm   Cm           D     Bb7
da habe ich als Antwort ihm nur Folgendes gesagt:
```

Refrain

M: Peter Kreuder
T: Hans-Fritz Beckmann
© Dreiklang-Dreimasken Bühnen- und Musikverlag GmbH
(Universal Music Publishing Group).

# CALIFORNIA GIRLS

(THE BEACH BOYS)

```
        B                           A/B
1. Well, East Coast girls are hip, I really dig those styles they wear,
        E
and the Southern girls with the way they talk,
             F#
they knock me out when I'm down there.
      B                                      A/B
The midwest farmers' daughters really make you feel alright,
        E
and the Northern girls with the way they kiss,
             F#
they keep their boyfriends warm at night.
```

**Refrain:**
```
      B                 C#m
I wish they all could be California,
      A                 Bm
I wish they all could be California,
      G                 Am          B
I wish they all could be California girls.

        B                                    A/B
2. The West coast has the sunshine, and the girls all get so tanned.
        E
I dig a French bikini on Hawaiian Island dolls
     F#
by a palm tree in the sand.
    B
I've been all around this great big world
         A/B
and I've seen all kinds of girls.
           E
Yeah, but I couldn't wait to get back in the states,
            F#
back to the cutest girls in the world.
```

Refrain

```
B
I wish they all could be California,
C#m
wish they all could be California,
B
I wish they all could be California,
C#m                                    B
wish they all could be California girls.
```

M + T: Edward Michael Love, Brian Wilson
© Copyright 1965 Irving Music Incorporated, USA.
Rondor Music International.
All Rights Reserved. International Copyright Secured.

# SHE'S ALWAYS A WOMAN TO ME

(BILLY JOEL)
[TRANSP. +1]

**Intro:** D Dsus4 D A D Dsus4 D

```
       A         D         A         D
1. She can kill with a smile, she can wound with her eyes.
             G          Gmaj7  G
She can ruin your faith with her casual lies.
      A7     D           A           F#
And she only reveals what she wants you to see.
    Bm        Bm/A          G         A7       D
She hides like a child, but she's always a woman to me.
```

```
2. She can lead you to love, she can take you or leave you.
She can ask for the truth, but she'll never believe.
And she'll take what you give her as long it's free.
Yes, she steals like a thief, but she's always a woman to me.
```

**Refrain:**
```
Bm     E7              A
Ohhh, she takes care of herself.
F#m     D          G        Em      A7         D
She can wait if she wants, she's ahead of her time.
Dm          G           C
Ohhh, and she never gives out,
Am                Bb   E       E7         A
and she never gives in, she just changes her mind.
```

```
3. And she'll promise you more than the garden of Eden.
Then she'll carelessly cut you and laugh while you're bleeding.
But she brings out the best and the worst you can be.
Blame it all on yourself cause she's always a women to me.
```

Refrain

```
4. She's frequently kind and she's suddenly cruel.
She can do as she pleases, she's nobody's fool.
But she can't be convicted, she's earned her degree.
And the most she will do is throw shadows at you,
but she's always a woman to me.
```

M + T: Billy Joel
© Copyright 1977, 1978 Impulsive Music.
Rondor Music International.
All Rights Reserved. International Copyright Secured.

# I SAVED THE WORLD TODAY

(EURYTHMICS)

```
      Am         G#+               C/G
1. Monday finds you like a bomb,
             F#m7b5         Fmaj7
that's been left ticking there too long.
E       Am
You're bleeding.

      Am              G#+         C/G
2. Some days there's nothing left to learn
       F#m7b5       Fmaj7
from the point of no return.
E       Am
You're leaving.
```

**Refrain:**
```
Dm    G     C              F
Hey hey, I saved the world today
Dm              G
and everybody's happy now.
     C               F
The bad thing's gone away
Dm              G
and everybody's happy now.
     C                 F
The good thing's here to stay,
Ab      Bb      Am
please let it stay.

      Am        G#+            C/G
3. There's a million mouths to feed
          F#m7b5       Fmaj7
and I've got everything I need.
E    Am
I'm breathing.

      Am       G#+            C/G
4. There's a hurting thing inside
          F#m7b5       Fmaj7
and I've got everything to hide.
E    Am
I'm grieving.


Refrain 2x
```

M + T: Annie Lennox / David A. Stewart
© Copyright 1999 La Lennoxa Music Company Limited/Eligible Music Limited.
BMG Music Publishing Limited.
All Rights Reserved. International Copyright Secured.

# ANGELS

(ROBBIE WILLIAMS)

**Intro:** E

```
        E                         A           B
1. I sit and wait, does an angel contemplate my fate
         E                                     A    B
and do they know the places where we go when we're grey and old,
          F#m7          A              C#m         A
cause I've been told that salvation lets their wings unfold.

           D
So when I'm lying in my bed
         A/C#
thoughts running through my head
       E
and I feel that love is dead,
  D       A/C#      E
I'm loving angels instead.
```

**Refrain:**
```
              B                   C#m
And through it all she offers me protection,
                      A
a lot of love and affection
                 E
whether I'm right or wrong
                B                    C#m
and down the waterfall wherever it may take me,
                       A
I know that life won't break me
              E/G#              F#m7
when I come to call, she won't forsake me.
  D       A      E
I'm loving angels instead

       E                                  A              B
2. When I'm feeling weak and my pain walks down a one way street,
          E                          A              B
I look above and I know I'll always be blessed with love
      D                              A/C#
and as the feeling grows she breathes flesh to my bones
      E             D       A       E
and when love is dead I'm loving angels instead.
```

Refrain

**Solo:** (Bm F#m E E) 4x

Refrain

M + T: Robbie Williams & Guy Chambers
© Copyright 1997 Kobalt Music Publishing Limited/BMG VM Music Limited.
All Rights Reserved. International Copyright Secured.

# NIKITA

(ELTON JOHN)

```
   G      Bm         C Csus4 C              G
1. Hey Nikita is it cold?    In your little corner of the world
                       D
you could roll around the globe
       D7            G
and never find a warmer soul to know.
                      C                      G
Oh I saw you by the wall. Ten of your tin soldiers in a row
                                D
With eyes that looked like ice on fire,
D7                        G
the human heart a captive in the sow.
```

**Refrain:**
```
G7              C                     G
Oh Nikita you will never know anything about my home.
                                  D          D7      G
I'll never know how good it feels to hold you, Nikita I need you so.
G7              C                  G
Oh Nikita is the other side of any given line in time,
                                D
counting ten tin soldiers in a row.
    D7               G
Oh no, Nikita you'll never know.

Bm Bm7 C Am7 D G

   G      Bm         C                           G
2. Do you ever dream of me? Do you ever see the letters that I write?
                        D
When you look up through the wire,
D7                              G
Nikita, do you count the stars at night?
                      C                      G
And if there comes a time, guns and gates no longer hold you in
G                   D
and if you're free to make a choice
D7                             G
just look towards the west and find a friend.
```

Refrain

M + T: Elton John & Bernie Taupin
© Copyright 1985 Rouge Booze Incorporated.
Universal Music Publishing Limited. All Rights Reserved.
International Copyright Secured.

# ROCK ME AMADEUS

(FALCO)

**Intro**: Am F D G Am F D G

```
         Am
1. Er war ein Punker und er lebte in der großen Stadt.
     F
Es war in Wien, war im Jänner, wo er alles tat.
    D                                            G
Er hatte Schulden, denn er trank, doch ihn liebten alle Fraun
          Am
und jede rief: Hey, come and rock me, Amadeus.


             Am
2. Er war ein Superstar, er war populär.
        F
Er war so exaltiert, because er hatte Flair.
    D                          G
Er war ein Virtuose, war ein Rock-Idol
         Am
und alles rief: Hey, come and rock me, Amadeus.
```

**Refrain:**
```
Am                                F
Amadeus, Amadeus, Amadeus, - Amadeus, Amadeus, Amadeus,
  D               G              Am
Amadeus, Amadeus, oh, oh, oh, Amadeus. (Hey come and rock me Amadeus)
Am                                F
Amadeus, Amadeus, Amadeus, - Amadeus, Amadeus, Amadeus,
  D               G              Am
Amadeus, Amadeus, oh, oh, oh, Amadeus.


             Am
3. Es war um 1780 und es war in Wien.
         F
No plastic money, alle money Banken gegen ihn.
       D                                       G
Woher die Schulden kamen, war wohl jedermann bekannt.
               Am
Er war ein Mann der Fraun, Frauen liebten seinen Punk.


             Am
4. Er war ein Superstar, er war populär.
        F
Er war so exaltiert, genau das war sein Flair.
    D                          G
Er war ein Virtuose, war ein Rock-Idol
         Am
und alles ruft noch heute: Come and rock me, Amadeus.
```

Refrain 2x

M + T: R. Bolland, F. Bolland, Falco & J. Hoelzel
© Copyright 1985 Edition Falco Privatstiftung / Nada International / Falkenhorst / Rolf Budde Musikverlag GmbH / Warner/Chappell Music Holland B.V. Warner/Chappell Overseas Holdings Limited, London / Nanada Music B.V. Reproduced by permission of Faber Music Limited. Mit freundlicher Genehmigung von Sony/ATV Music Publishing (Germany) GmbH.
All Rights Reserved. International Copyright Secured.

# DAS KUFSTEINER LIED (DIE PERLE TIROLS)

(FRANZL LANG)

```
   G    D7   G                  D
1. Kennst du die Perle, die Perle Tirols,
            D7                    G
   das Städtchen Kufstein, das kennst du wohl;
                         G7               C
   umrahmt von Bergen, so friedlich und still:
         G      D7            G       G7
   Ja das ist Kufstein an dem grünen Inn,
      C         G   D7  G   D7 G
   ja das ist Kufstein am grünen Inn.
         D7   G
   Hollrädiri...


   G    D7   G                D
2. Es gibt so vieles bei uns in Tirol.
          D7                  G
   A guates Weinderl aus Südtirol.
                   G7                    C
   Da denkt a jeder, 's möcht immer so sein:
         G        D7          G      G7
   Bei einem Maderl und am Flascherl Wein.
       C       G       D7       G   D7 G
   Bei einem Maderl und am Flascherl Wein.
         D7   G
   Hollrädiri...


   G    D7    G                D
3. Und ist der Urlaub dann wieder aus,
              D7                      G
   dann nimmt man Abschied und fährt nach Haus.
                  G7                    C
   Man denkt an Kufstein, man denkt an Tirol.
          G         D7           G    G7
   Mein liebes Maderl, leb wohl, leb wohl.
         C         G      D7   G   D7 G
   Mein liebes Maderl, leb wohl, leb wohl.
         D7   G
   Hollrädiri...
```

M+T: Karl Ganzer
© 1957 by Eberle Verlag, Wien.
Der Abdruck erfolgt mit freundlicher Genehmigung.

## I BELIEVE I CAN FLY

(R. KELLY)

```
      C                        Fm/C
1. I used to think that I could not go on.
      C                   Fm/C
And life was nothing but an awful song.
      C                        Fm/C
But now I know the meaning of true love.
      C                        Fm/C
I'm leaning on the everlasting arms.

   E+       Am7              Fm/Ab
If I can see it, then I can do it,
            C/G                     G7sus4
If I just believe it, there's nothing to it.
```

**Refrain:**
```
              C                  Am7
I believe I can fly, I believe I can touch the sky.
                 Dm7                          G7sus4
I think about it every night and day, spread my wings and fly away.
   E/G#       Am7                           Fm/Ab
I believe I can soar, I see me running through that open door,
              C/G              Fm/Ab          Am G7sus4
I believe I can fly, I believe I can fly, I believe I can fly.
```

```
         C                        Fm/C
2. See I was on the verge of breaking down.
         C                Fm/C
Sometimes silence can seem so loud.
            C                       Fm/C
There are miracles in life I must achieve.
         C                        Fm/C
But first I know it starts inside of me.

   E+       Am7              Fm/Ab
If I can see it, then I can be it,
            C/G                     G7sus4
If I just believe it, there's nothing to it.
```

Refrain

**Outro:** C

# VIENNA

(ULTRAVOX)

```
    C                      F/C
1. We walked in the cold air. Freezing breath on a window pane.
   C                    F/C
Lying and waiting. A man in the dark in a picture frame.
    C                      F/C
So mystic and soulful. A voice reaching out in a piercing cry.
    C
It stays with you until.

Bb                                                    F Bb F
The feeling has gone only you and I. It means nothing to me.
         Bb         F Bb    F
This means nothing to me. Oh, Vienna.


       C                    F/C
2. The music is weaving. Haunting notes, pizzicato strings.
       C                    F/C
The rhythm is calling. Alone in the night as the daylight brings
   C                    F/C
a cool empty silence. The warmth of your hand and a cold grey sky
         C
it fades to the distance.

Bb                                                  F Bb F
The image has gone only you and I. It means nothing to me.
         Bb         F Bb    F
This means nothing to me. Oh, Vienna.
```

M + T: Midge Ure, Billy Currie, Warren Cann & Christopher Allen
© Copyright 1980 PolyGram Music Publishing Limited.
Universal Music Publishing Limited.
All Rights Reserved. International Copyright Secured.

# COME TO SIN

(BANANAFISHBONES)

**Intro:** Em C G A Em C A

```
      Em         C                  G                   A
1. Sun, all our dreams are dreams of fun handing out the watergun,
                                Em             C
shoot me and I'll drink you into the shade, I'll shrink you.
A
Finally we're done and stare up into the

2. Sky, flat on our backs we lie in quicksand slowly my hand
flies up and away with the yellow bird, driven by

3. Wind, I think I'll come to sin with all this heaty windy skin
around my neck and what glory the sand in my pants
reminds me of Doreen.

4. Sand, we cannot fight getting tanned
all the limits banned into the nightflight's time's right no fight
there goes the sun into the the nightlife. Yeah
```

**Refrain:**
```
Em                       C
Whang I sing while the others swing
         G               A          Em             C          G
like a beam of light through a bottle. Souzie swings her phoney rings.
Em                       C
Whang I sing while the others swing
         G               A          Em             C          A
like a beam of light through a bottle. Souzie swings her phoney rings.
```

```
5. Time, bugs crawling up our spine and the memory is mine
I'm a grain of sand in your hand so hand me mine. Yeah
that would be fine.

6. Heat, I kiss the blisters on your feet a lizard's eye I greet
I'm afraid there's no aid 'til we get laid
into the nightlife time's right no flight.
```

Refrain

```
Em                  C                G              A              Em
I think I'll come to sin with all that heaty windy skin around my neck
                    C                     G
and now what glory the sand in my pants reminds me of Doreen,
Em          C         G           A
mocking photography shocking in the sand with me.
Em                  C              A
Sand in my pants. Sand in my pants. Sand in my pants.
```

Refrain

M + T: Peter Horn, Florian Rein & Sebastian Horn
© Edition Base Two Music Germany der State One Musikverlag GmbH

# RASPUTIN

(BONEY M.)

```
         Bm
1. There lived a certain man in Russia long ago,
      Em                F#                 Bm
he was big and strong, in his eyes a flaming glow,

most people looked at him with terror and with fear,
      Em                F#            Bm
but to Moscow chicks he was such a lovely dear.
                                   Em                      F#
He could preach the Bible like a preacher, full of ecstasy and fire.
Bm                                  Em    F#      Bm
But he also was the kind of teacher, women would desire.
```

**Refrain:**
```
Bm     D         E            B
Ra-Ra-Rasputin, lover of the Russian queen,
    A          E       B
there was a cat that really was gone.
       D           E                 B
Ra-Ra-Rasputin, Russia's greatest love machine,
    A       E         B
it was a shame how he carried on.
```

```
2. He ruled the Russian land and never mind the Czar,
but the kasachok he really danced wunderbar.
In all affairs of state, he was the man to please,
but he was real great when he had a girl to squeeze.
For the queen he was no wheeler dealer, though she'd heard the things
he'd done. She believed he was a holy healer, who would heal her son.
```

```
Refrain
              Bm  A                       G           A           Bm
Gesprochen: But when his drinking and lusting and his hunger for power
                                           A
became known to more and more people, the demands to do something
             G        A       Bm
about this outrageous man became louder and louder.
```

```
3. "This man's just got to go!" declared his enemies,
but the ladies begged "Don't you try to do it, please."
No doubt this Rasputin had lots of hidden charms,
though he was a brute, they just fell into his arms.
Then one night some men of higher standing,
set a trap, they're not to blame,
"Come to visit us" they kept demanding, and he really came.

Ra-Ra-Rasputin, lover of the Russian queen,
they put some poison into his wine.
Ra-Ra-Rasputin, Russia's greatest love machine,
He drank it all and he said "I feel fine."

Ra-Ra-Rasputin, lover of the Russian queen,
They didn't quit they wanted his head.
Ra-Ra-Rasputin, Russia's greatest love machine,
and so they shot him till he was dead.
Gesprochen: Oh, those Russians!
```

M + T: Frank Farian / George Reyam / Fred Jay
© Far Musikverlag GmbH. Mit freundlicher Genehmigung
von Far Musikverlag GmbH & Co. KG.

# HELP ME RHONDA

(THE BEACH BOYS)
[TRANSP. +1]

```
      C                      G              C
1. Since she put me down I've been out doing in my head.
                             G                       C
Come in late at night and in the morning I just lay in bed.
   Am                        F                        D7
Well, Rhonda you look so fine and I know it wouldn't take much time
         C             Dm                  C
for you to help me Rhonda, help me get her out of my heart.
```

**Refrain:**
```
G7
Help me Rhonda, help, help me Rhonda!
C
Help me Rhonda, help, help me Rhonda!
G7
Help me Rhonda, help, help me Rhonda!
C
Help me Rhonda, help, help me Rhonda!
F
Help me Rhonda, help, help me Rhonda!
Am            G
Help me Rhonda, help, help me Rhonda!
Dm            G                  C
Help me Rhonda, yeah get her out of my heart!
```

```
            C              G              C
2. She was gonna be my wife and I was gonna be her man.
                             G                        C
But she let another guy come between us and it ruined our plans.
      Am                     F                         D7
Well, Rhonda you caught my eye and I'll give you lots of reasons why
           C             Dm                C
you got to help me Rhonda, help me get her out of my heart.
```

Refrain

M + T: Brian Wilson & Mike Love
© Sea of Tunes Publishing Co. Inc.
Subverlag: EMI Music Publishing Germany GmbH.

## ALONE

(HEART)

**Intro:** Bm G A A/G Bm G A F#7

```
   Bm           G              A
1. I hear the ticking of the clock,
     A/G             Bm             G A F#7
I'm lying here the room's pitch dark.
Bm          G            A          A/G           Bm          G A F#7
I wonder where you are tonight, no answer on your telephone.
            G            D/F#      Em  D
And the night goes by so very slow,
          G            D/F#     Em A
oh I hope that it won't end so.
    D
All alone.
```

**Refrain:**
```
Em      C         G          D
  Till now, I always got by on my own.
Em C            G          D
  I never really cared until I met you.
Em C           G         D
  And now it chills me to the bone.
G/B       C         D
How do I get you alone?
G/B       C         D
How do I get you alone?
```

```
   Bm           G               A
2. You don't know how long I have wanted
     A/G            Bm      G    A F#7
to touch your lips and hold you tight.
Bm           G             A
You don't know how long I have waited,
   A/G          Bm             G A F#7
and I was gonna tell you tonight.
          G          D/F#        Em D
But the secret is still my own
          G            D/F#         Em A
and my love for you is still unknown.
    D
All alone.
```

Refrain

1. Strophe

Refrain

M + T: Billy Steinberg & Tom Kelly
© Copyright 1983 Sony/ATV Tunes LLC, USA.
Sony/ATV Music Publishing.
All Rights Reserved. International Copyright Secured.

# WEM

(HOWARD CARPENDALE)

**Intro:** Bbm

**Refrain:**
```
Bbm
Wem erzählst du nach mir deine Träume?
Gb
Wem erzählst du nach mir deine Träume?
F                    Bbm
Wem erzählst du deine Träume?

Bbm
Wem erzählst du nach mir deine Träume?
Gb
Wem erzählst du nach mir deine Träume?
F                    Bbm
Wem erzählst du deine Träume?

    Bbm                         F
1. Es ist Nacht, wir liegen da, und trotzdem sind wir uns nicht nah.
Ebm             Ab              Db                   F
Wenn ich auch deine Wärme spür, du wendest dein Gesicht von mir.
Bbm                      Ebm
Ich leg die Decke über dich und die Kälte fühle ich.
F                                Ebm
Zwei Menschen hier und doch sind wir allein.
```

Refrain

```
2. Ich kenne dich, weiß wie du bist. Wie schwer für dich so manches ist.
Und ich hab Angst, dass du dich trennst von allem was du liebst und
kennst.
Ich weiß, du brauchst Geborgenheit. Nicht eine Nacht der Zärtlichkeit.
Weil ich das weiß, will ich dich nicht verlieren.
```

Refrain 2x (Einen Halbton höher)

```
D
Immer wenn ein Lichtstrahl auf dich fällt,
Em         A
denk ich mir, dass du schön bist.
D                                       Em        A
Und dass nichts für mich in meiner Welt ohne dich zu verstehen ist.
D          Bm           Em          Gm
Irgendwann fingst du an von mir wegzugehen.
```

Refrain 2x

M + T: Howard Carpendale / Joachim Horn-Bernges / Fred Jay
© 1981 Musikverlag Intersong GmbH and Co KG,
Warner/Chappell Overseas Holdings Limited, London.
Reproduced by permission of Faber Music Limited.
All Rights Reserved.

## KALKUTTA LIEGT AM GANGES

(VICO TORRIANI)

**Refrain:**
```
A                                E
Kalkutta liegt am Ganges, Paris liegt an der Seine,
                                      A
doch das ich so verliebt bin, das liegt an Madeleine.
```

```
   A                                       E
1. Am schönen Rhein liegt Basel, und Kairo liegt am Nil,
              E7                         A
   doch ich träum von Madeleine, an der liegt mir viel.

      A7                    D
2. Die schwarzen Kulleraugen, das ganze Drum und Dran,
      B7                E
   das schau ich an und sag mir dann.
```

Refrain

```
      A                                  E
3. Der Tower steht in London, der Louvre an der Seine,
                                       A
   doch ich in meinem Falle, ich steh auf Madeleine.

      A                                 E
4. New York liegt am Atlantik, Athen am Mittelmeer,
              E7                         A
   doch ich träum von Madeleine, die liegt mir so sehr.

      A7                      D
5. Sie hat die schönsten Beine, so schlank und wunderbar,
      B7                E
   die schau ich an und mir wird klar.
```

Refrain

```
       A                                    E
6. Die Nacht ist heiß am Kongo, die Nacht ist kalt am Pol,
                                         A
   bei ihr, da wird mir beides und das tut so wohl.

      A                                        E
7. So dreht sich diese Erde im Kreis und bleibt nicht stehen,
                E7                 A
   bei mir, da dreht sich alles, allein um Madeleine.

       A7                         D
8. Wir sind ein schönes Pärchen, seit gestern liebt auch sie,
       B7                    E
   nur mich und meine Geographie.
```

Refrain 2x

M: Gaze, Heino
T: Bradtke, Hans
© Edition Takt und Ton
Mit freundlicher Genehmigung von Budde Music.

## DA NAHM ER SEINE GITARRE

(HOWARD CARPENDALE)

**Intro:** A Amaj7 A7 D A E7

```
          A                             D
1. Wo er herkam, wusste sie nicht, doch sie las in seinem Gesicht,
            A                   E
   stell keine Fragen, ich will nichts sagen.
              A                     D
   Und sie fragte nicht, wer er war, sie erkannte wohl die Gefahr,
            A                 E
   doch er gefiel ihr, oh, er gefiel ihr.

   A              E      F#m               Em7    A7
   Da nahm er seine Gitarre und sang nur für sie allein.
   D    E       A     F#m B              E
   Er sang seine Liebeslieder  bis tief in die Nacht hinein.
   A               E       F#m            Em7      A7
   Und dem Klang seiner Gitarre konnte sie nicht widerstehen.
   D     E            A    F#m D    E            A
   Draußen dämmerte der Morgen,  aber sie ließ ihn nicht gehen.

            A                         D
2. Wie im Flug verging ihr die Zeit und sie fühlte sich wie befreit,
           A           E
   er war die Liebe, die große Liebe.
           A                       D
   Eines Tages sagte sie dann, bleib für immer da von nun an,
             A             E  ´
   du bist mein Alles, mein Ein und Alles.

   A              E      F#m                  Em7    A7
   Da nahm er seine Gitarre, doch das Spielen ließ er sein,
   D    E       A     F#m B              E
   er sang keine Liebeslieder  bis tief in die Nacht hinein.
   A              E       F#m              Em7   A7
   Er nahm nur seine Gitarre und er sagte, ich muss gehen.
   D     E            A    F#m D    E              A
   Draußen dämmerte der Morgen,  es gibt noch soviel zu sehn.
```

M: Howard Carpendale
T: Fred Jay
© ROBA MUSIC VERLAG GMBH / RADIO MUSIC INTERNATIONAL.

# SO SCHMECKT DER SOMMER

(EDWARD REEKERS)

```
   A              E              Bm7            D
1. Weißt du noch im letzten Jahr, weißt du noch, weißt du noch?
   A              E              Bm7
   Ein Sonnenstrahl und er war da. Weißt du noch?
   D              D/E
   So schmeckt der Sommer, so schmeckt der Sommer.
```

**Refrain:**
```
A              E      Bm              D         E
So schmeckt der Sommer. So schmeckt der Sommer.
A              E      Bm              D         E
So schmeckt der Sommer. So schmeckt der Sommer.
```

```
   A              E              Bm7            D
2. Weißt du, was mit uns geschah, weißt du noch, weißt du noch?
   A              E              F#m
   Die wahre Liebe wurde wahr. Weißt du noch?
   D                          E
   So schmeckt der Sommer, so schmeckt der Sommer.
```

Refrain

```
F#m          E         A         D/F#       E         A
Wir waren ein Paar in jenem Sommer, gingen Hand in Hand.
F/A      G/B       C                  E    D/F#      E/G#
Und wenn du willst, seh'n wir uns wieder an uns'rem Strand.
```

```
D                        E
So schmeckt der Sommer. So schmeckt der Sommer.
```

Refrain

M + T: Eggermont, Jacobus / Schoen, Peter /
Schwingeler, Marie Theres / Wunderlich, Frank / Maas, Rainer
© Edition Antenna Musik / Universal Music Publishing GmbH.

# EIN GUTER TAG ZUM STERBEN

(J.B.O.)

```
      F#              C#             B     G#m D#m      B
1. Ich stehe morgens auf, es ist halb drei. Die Birne tut mir weh, ich
   C#              F#               C#              B               G#m
könnte spei'n. Als erstes hau' ich mir den Fuß an meinem Nachttisch an,
   D#m            B                   C#                F#
dann stolpere ich über das Telefonkabel und reiß es aus der Wand.
   F#                    C#                           B
Ich kriege gerade noch den Vorhang zu fassen, doch der hält auch nichts
G#m       D#m               B
aus. Drum haut's mich schwungvoll auf die Fresse,
           C#
meine Katze klatscht Applaus.
    F#                    C#                 B                G#m
Ich steh' wieder auf und schmerzerfüllt reibe ich mir mein Gebein.
    D#m                   B                 C#                F#
Und während ich auf einen Reißnagel trete, fällt's mir wieder ein:
```

**Refrain:**
```
            F#            B              C#            F#
Heut' ist ein guter Tag zum Sterben. So hat das Leben keinen Sinn.
         F#       C#/F   D#m
Die Götter wollen mir den Spaß verderben,
    B                  C#
man gönnt mir keinen Lustgewinn.
    F#           B              C#             F#
Ein guter Tag zum Sterben. So macht das Leben keinen Spaß.
      F#       C#/F   D#m              B       C#          F#
Bevor die Zähne ich mir ausbeiße, beiß ich lieber gleich ins Gras!
```

2. Im Kühlschrank ist die Stimmung gut, die Pilzkulturen feiern.
Eine fette Made grinst mich an, ich dreh' mich um zum Reihern.
Die Eier zu weich, die Butter zu hart, der Kaffee fließt daneben,
im Brot tobt sich der Schimmel aus, dann entfällt das Frühstück eben.
Mein Auto hat man demoliert, es hängt ein Zettel dran,
von meiner Freundin, die mir sagt, was ich sie alles kann.
Sie führt die Sache näher aus: Ich wäre zu oft blau,
sie sagt mir damit lebewohl, doch ich weiß ganz genau:

Refrain
```
    G#m         F#/A#     B     C#   G#m       F#/A#     B    C#
Ich schmeiß mich hinter'n Auto, ich schieß mir in den Fuß.
    G#m       F#/A#      B           C#              D#m   C#/F   F#
Irgendwie werd' ich's schon schaffen, bevor ich noch mehr ertragen muss!
```

3. Beim Uli steigt 'ne Party, mit letzter Kraft komm' ich dort an.
An jeder Frau, die ich dort seh', klebt schon 'n Macker dran.
Als letztes bleibt mir nur der Rausch, was soll ich sonst noch hier,
doch auch dieser Wunsch bleibt mir versagt, es gibt nur Pariser Bier.
Ich will mir einen Whisky holen, die Hausbar ist mein Ziel.
Da treff' ich meine Freundin, stöhnend, mit Hannes beim Liebesspiel.
Ich steig ins Auto, fahre los und denke: Hoffentlich denkt die Frau,
die mir gerade vor's Auto läuft, genauso wie auch ich:

Ein guter Tag zum Sterben. So macht das Leben keinen Spaß
Bevor die Zähne ich mir ausbeiße, beiß ich lieber gleich ins Gras!
Ein guter Tag zum Sterben. So hat das Leben keinen Sinn. Ich will den
Spaß euch nicht verderben. Auch nicht, wenn ich gestorben bin.

M + T: Holzmann, Hannes / Kutzer, Veit
© Copyright und freundlicher Genehmigung Blanko Musik GmbH, München
All Rights Reserved. International Copyright Secured.

# WHEN SUSANNAH CRIES

(ESPEN LIND)
[TRANSP. +1]

**Refrain:**
```
            G              D                       Am
When Susannah cries, she cries a rainstorm, she cries a river,
            G          D
she cries a hole in the ground.
            G              D                       Am
She cries for love, she cries a sad song, she cries a shiver,
            G          D
sometimes she cries for me too.
```

```
         Am                           Em              D
1. And I say I'll never hurt her but she knows it isn't true
         Am                           Em                    D
cause although I never told her I think she knows bout me and you.
         Am                     G              D
Now she cries with silent tension, this can't be right
         C            Bm7                Am           D
and the downtown special cries along cause I'm leaving tonight.
```

Refrain

```
         Am                           Em              D
2. Now I slip the night around her and I hope she'll be okay.
         Am                      Em                         D
I just pray someone will find her and guide her along her way
         Am                  G              D
cause I'm leaving on the one a.m. by soon I'm out of sight
         C            Bm7            Am         D
but she'll always be my baby though I'm leaving tonight.
```

**Solo:** G D Am C G D G D Am C D

```
         Am                    Em              D
3. Every night I hear her talking in her sleep.
         Am                        Em                       D
She says "You know I always be there" and I feel like such a creep.
                  Am
Please take back the love she gave to me
         G               D
and in time her grief will pass,
         C            Bm              Am D     G
just tell her that I loved her now, it's all she has.
```

```
Bb C            G
Ohh, when Susanna cries.
```

M + T: Espen Lind & Armund Bjorklund
© Universal Music Publishing. Universal Music Publishing Limited.
All Rights Reserved. International Copyright Secured.

# THE BOYS OF SUMMER

(DON HENLEY)

```
     D#m
1. Nobody on the road, nobody on the beach,
B
I feel it in the air, the summer's out of reach.
C#
Empty lake, empty streets, the sun goes down alone.
B
I'm drivin' by your house though I know you're not at home.
```

**Refrain:**
```
F#                 C#
But I can see you, your brown skin shining in the sun,
                                    B
you got your hair combed back and your sunglasses on, baby.
F#                         C#
And I can tell you my love for you will still be strong
                 B
after the boys of summer have gone.
```

2. I never will forget those nights, I wonder if it was a dream.
Remember how you made me crazy? Remember how I made you scream?
Now I don't understand what happened to our love
but babe, I'm gonna get you back, I'm gonna show you what I'm made of.

**Refrain:**
I can see you, your brown skin shining in the sun,
I see you walking real slow and you're smiling at everyone.
I can tell you my love for you will still be strong
after the boys of summer have gone.

3. Out on the road today, I saw a DEADHEAD sticker on a Cadillac.
A little voice inside my head said: "Don't look back. You can never look back."
I thought I knew what love was. What did I know?
Those days are gone forever I should just let them go but...

**Refrain:**
I can see you, your brown skin shining in the sun,
you got that top pulled down and that radio on, baby.
And I can tell you my love for you will still be strong
after the boys of summer have gone.

**Refrain:**
I can see you, your brown skin shining in the sun,
you got that hair slicked back and those wayfarers on, baby.
I can tell you my love for you will still be strong
after the boys of summer have gone.

M + T: Don Henley, Michael Campbell
© Wild Gator Music, Wixen Music Publishing Inc, Woody Creek Music and Warner Tamerlane Publishing Corp. Warner/Chappell North Africa Ltd, London, W6 8BS.
Abdruck erfolgt mit freundlicher Genehmigung von MELODIE DER WELT, J. Michel GmbH & Co. KG, Musikverlag, Frankfurt/Main.
Reproduced by permission of Faber Music Ltd. All Rights Reserved.

# DON'T WORRY, BE HAPPY

(BOBBY MCFERRIN)
[TRANSP. +4]

**Intro:** G Am C D (Melodie gepfiffen)
```
   G
1. Here's a little song I wrote,
   Am                                        C       D  G
   you might want to sing it note for note, don't worry, be happy.

   In every life we have some trouble
   Am                                       C       D  G
   but when you worry you make it double, don't worry, be happy.
```

**Refrain:**
```
G                                      Am
Uh hu hu, hu hu hu hu hu hu, u hu hu, don't worry,
         C                      D            G
u hu hu hu hu hu hu, be happy, u hu hu hu hu,

don't worry, be happy!
G                                      Am
Uh hu hu, hu hu hu hu hu hu, u hu hu, don't worry,
         C                      D            G
u hu hu hu hu hu hu, be happy, u hu hu hu hu,

don't worry, be happy!

   G
2. Ain't got no place to lay your head,
   Am                                    C       D  G
   somebody came and took your bed, don't worry, be happy.

   The landlord say your rent is late,
   Am                            C       D  G
   he may have to litigate, don't worry, be happy.
```

Refrain

```
   G
3. Ain't got no cash, ain't got no style,
   Am                                         C       D  G
   ain't got no girl to make you smile, don't worry, be happy.

   Cause when you worry your face will frown,
       Am                                        C       D  G
   and that will bring everybody down, so don't worry, be happy.
```

Refrain 2x

M + T: Bobby McFerrin
© Copyright 1988 Probnoblem Music. Universal Music Publishing MGB Limited.
All Rights Reserved. International Copyright Secured.

# IMMORTALITY

(CELINE DION)

```
      D   A/C#    G/B   D         A              Bm
1. So this is who I am, and this is all I know,
                            Em                         G
and I must choose to live, for all that I can give.
                       G
The spark that makes the power grow.

          D            A        G     F#m
And I will stand for my dream if I can,
G          D         Em    Bm              Em
symbol of my faith in who I am, but you are my only.
             D           A       G     F#m
And I must follow on the road that lies ahead,
      G            D       Em    Bm                  Em
and I won't let my heart control my head, but you are my only.

       A         D         A          Bm
And we don't say goodbye, we don't say goodbye,
E                   Em
and I know what I've got to be.

D Em F#m Em  D          Em                 F#m   Em
Immortality, I make my journey through eternity,
D         Em        F#m      Em
I keep the memory of you and me inside.

          A              D        A             Bm
2. Fulfill your destiny, it's there within the child.
                        Em
My storm will never end, my fate is on the wind,
         G
the king of hearts, the joker's wild.
          D         A        Bm
We don't say goodbye, we don't say goodbye.
E                 Em
I'll make them all remember me.

           D          A        G     F#m
Cause I have found a dream that must come true,
G         D          Em    Bm                  Em
Every ounce of me must see it through, but you are my only.
      G     D            A      G      F#m
I'm sorry I don't have a role for love to play,
G             D          Em   Bm                   Em
hand over my heart I'll find my way, I will make them give to me.

D Em F#m Em  D          Em            F#m    Em
Immortality, there is a vision and a fire in me,
D         Em        F#m     Em    G
I keep the memory of you and me, inside.

       A         D         A          Bm
And we don't say goodbye, we don't say goodbye,
E                   Em                        G
with all my love for you, and what else we may do
                D     A    G    D
we don't say, goodbye.
```

M + T: Maurice Gibb, Robin Gibb, Barry Alan Gibb
© Crompton Songs / Universal Music Publishing International MGB Limited. Warner/Chappell Music Limited, London / Universal Music Publishing MGB Limited. Reproduced by permission of Faber Music Limited. All Rights Reserved. International Copyright Secured.

# IN THESE ARMS

(BON JOVI)

**Intro:**  E A E A E A E A

```
          E                       A/E
1. You want commitment, take a look into these eyes.
          E                          A/E
They burn with fire, just for you now until the end of time.
         C#m                          A
I would do anything, I'd beg, I'd steal, I'd die
         B                E    A/E
to have you in these arms tonight.

2. Baby, I want you like the roses want the rain.
You know I need you like a poet needs the pain.
I would give anything, my blood, my love, my life
if you were in these arms tonight.
```

**Refrain:**
```
E             B              C#m            A                E
I'd hold you, I'd need you, I'd get down on my knees for you
       C#m              B                A
and make everything alright if you were in these arms.
E             B                C#m              A
I'd love you, I'd please you, I'd tell you that I'd never leave you
E            E/G#           B             A              E
and love you till the end of time if you were in these arms tonight.

                     E              A/E
3. We started at the sun and we made a promise.
              E                A/E
A promise this world, would never blind us.
            C#m                        A
These are my words, our words were our songs.
                 C#m
Our songs are our prayers, these prayers keep me strong.
         A                  B                E
It's what I believe if you were in these arms tonight.
```

Refrain

```
      B
Your clothes are still scattered all over my room.
   A
This old place still smells like your cheap perfume.
B
Everything here reminds me of you and there's
A
nothing that I wouldn't do.
```

Solo:  E B C#m A E B F#m A
```
                 B
And these were our words they keep me strong. Baby!
```

Refrain

M + T: David Bryan, Jon Bon Jovi & Richie Sambora
© Copyright 1992 Aggressive Music, USA/Bon Jovi Publishing, USA/Moon Junction Music, USA/Sony-ATV Tunes LLC/ EMI April Music Inc. Kobalt Music Publishing Limited/Sony/ATV Music Publishing.
Mit freundlicher Genehmigung der EMI Music Publishing Germany GmbH. All Rights Reserved. International Copyright Secured.

# IMAGINE

(JOHN LENNON)

**Intro:** C Cmaj7 F (2x)

```
        C            Cmaj7 F         C              Cmaj7 F
1. Imagine there's no    heaven.  It's easy if you    try.
   C        Cmaj7 F        C           Cmaj7 F
   No hell be----low us. Above us only      sky.
            Am/E     Dm7 F/C G         C/G G7
   Imagine all the people  living for today. A ha!


        C            Cmaj7 F         C              Cmaj7 F
2. Imagine there's no    countries, it isn't hard to    do.
   C           Cmaj7 F        C           Cmaj7 F
   Nothing to kill or    die for and no religion  too.
            Am/E     Dm7 F/C G         C/G G7
   Imagine all the people  living life in  peace. You!

   F        G         C        C E F         G              C     C E F
   You may say I'm a dreamer      but I'm not the only one.
                G            C       C E F       G              C
   I hope some day you'll join us     and the world will be as one.


        C            Cmaj7 F         C              Cmaj7 F
3. Imagine no pos---sessions, I wonder if you    can.
   C            Cmaj7 F          C           Cmaj7 F
   No need for greed or    hunger, a brotherhood of     man.
            Am/E     Dm7 F/C G         C/G G7
   Imagine all the people  sharing all the world. You!

   F        G         C        C E F         G              C     C E F
   You may say I'm a dreamer      but I'm not the only one.
                G            C       C E F       G              C
   I hope some day you'll join us     and the world will be as one.
```

M + T: John Lennon
© Copyright 1971 Lenono Music.
All Rights Reserved. International Copyright Secured.

# MANIC MONDAY

(BANGLES)

```
   D          Dsus4      G                    D     Dsus4 G
1. Six o' clock already, I was just in the middle of a dream.
        D           Dsus4      G                    D     Dsus4 G
   I was kissing Valentino by a crystal blue Italian stream.
            D         Dsus4          G                    D     Dsus4 G
   But I can't be late, cause then I guess I just won't get paid.
   D/A                       G/A                    D
   These are the days when you wish your bed was already made.
```

**Refrain:**
```
       A               D      G             D     G
   It's just another manic monday, I wish it was sunday.
                    D         G              D
   Because that's my fun day, my I don't have to run day.
       G/A               D
   It's just another manic monday.
```

```
   D             Dsus4       G                    D     Dsus4 G
2. Have to catch an early train, have to be to work by nine.
          D            Dsus4    G                 D     Dsus4 G
   And if I had an aeroplane, I still couldn't make it on time.
               D         Dsus4     G                  D     Dsus4 G
   Cause it takes me so long just to figure out what I'm gonna wear.
   D/A                              G/A                 D
   Blame it on the train, but the boss is already there.
```

Refrain

**Bridge:**
```
   Bm                                                     E7
   All of the nights, why did my lover have to pick last night to get down.
   G                         A                     Bm
   Doesn't it matter that I have to feed the both of us, employments down.
       G                    E7          A                             A7
   He tells me in his bedroom voice, c'mon honey, let's go make some noise.
```

Time it goes so fast, when you're having fun.

Refrain

M + T: Prince
© Copyright 1985 Controversy Music, USA.
Universal/MCA Music Limited. All rights in Germany
administered by Universal/MCA Music Publ. GmbH. All
Rights Reserved. International Copyright Secured.

# PAPERBACK WRITER

(THE BEATLES)

**Intro:**
```
C          G         Am7             Gsus4
Paperback writer, writer, writer.
```

```
          G
1. Dear Sir or Madam, will you read my book?
         G7                      G
It took me years to write, will you take a look.
         G
It's based on a novel by a man named Lear
       G7            G                    C
and I need a job so I want to be a paperback writer.
G   F   G
Paperback writer.
```

```
           G
2. It's a dirty story of a dirty man
        G7                  G
and his clinging wife doesn't understand.
         G
His son is working for the Daily Mail,
         G7           G                    C
it's a steady job but he wants to be a paperback writer.
G   F   G
Paperback writer.
```

Intro

```
             G
3. It's a thousand pages, give or take a few,
        G7           G
I'll be writing more in a week or two.
         G
I can make it longer if you like the style,
       G7              G                     C
I can change it round and I want to be a paperback writer.
G   F   G
Paperback writer.
```

```
            G
4. If you really like it you can have the rights,
        G7                  G
it could make a milion for you overnight.
         G
If you must return it you can send it here
        G7           G                      C
But I need a break and I want to be a paperback writer.
G   F   G
Paperback writer.
```

Intro

M + T: John Lennon & Paul McCartney
© Copyright 1966 Sony/ATV Music Publishing (UK) Limited.
All Rights Reserved. International Copyright Secured.

# NUR GETRÄUMT

(NENA)

**Intro:** G

```
     Am      Em    F Bb Am C D E Am       Em       F Bb Am E D C
1. Ich bin so allein.              Ich will bei dir sein.
Am        Em     F Bb Am C D E Am       Em       F Bb Am E D C
Ich seh' deine Hand,              hab' sie gleich erkannt.
Am    Em      F           Bb          Am C D E
Mein Kopf tut weh, mach die Augen zu.
Am          Em    F           C            D
Ich lieg' im grünen Gras und erzähl dir was.
```

Em C Am D Bm Em C Am D C D

**Refrain:**
```
G                            C                   D              G
Ich hab' heute nichts versäumt, denn ich hab' nur von dir geträumt.
G                              C                D               G
Wir haben uns lang nicht mehr gesehn, ich werd' mal zu dir rübergehn.
G                       C              D                 G
Alles, was ich and dir mag, ich mein das so wie ich es sag.
G                       C           D                        E
Ich bin total verwirrt, ich werd' verrückt, wenn's heut passiert.
```

```
     Am       Em    F Bb Am C D E Am        Em      F Bb Am E D C
2. Mir ist schon ganz heiß.         Ich geh' auf dich zu.
Am     Em      F         Bb          Am C D E Am      Em      F     C    D
Deine Blicke ärgern mich,            denken immer nur an dich.
```

Em C Am D C D

Refrain 2x

M: Jörn-Uwe Fahrenkrog-Petersen<br>
T: Nena Kerner / Rolf Brendel<br>
© Edition Hate. Mit freundlicher Genehmigung der EMI Songs Musikverlag GmbH.

# FIGHT FOR YOUR RIGHT

(BEASTIE BOYS)
[TRANSP. -1]

**Intro:** A5   7x |: A5 C5 D5 :| A5 C5 E5 A5

```
         A5                                      A5 C5 D5   A5 C5 D5
1. You wake up late for school, man, you don't wanna go.
      A5                                   A5 C5 D5   A5 C5 D5
You ask your mum please, but she still says "NO!"
      A5                              A5 C5 D5   A5 C5 D5
You missed two classes have no homework.
      A5                                     A5 C5 D5   A5
Your teacher preaches class like he's some kind of jerk.
```

**Refrain:**
```
                D5
You gotta fight
                D5
for your right
     A
to party!
```

Intro
```
         A5                                      A5 C5 D5   A5 C5 D5
2. Your pop caught you smoking and he said, "No way!"
      A5                         A5 C5 D5   A5 C5 D5
That hypocrite smokes two packs a day.
      A5                            A5 C5 D5   A5 C5 D5
Man, living at home is such a drag.
            A5                             A5 C5 D5   A5 C5 D5
Now your mom threw away your best porno mag. Bust it!
```

Refrain

```
          A5
3. Don't step out of this house
                                 A5 C5 D5   A5 C5 D5
if that's the clothes you're gonna wear
              A5                              A5 C5 D5   A5 C5 D5
I'll kick you out of my home, if you don't cut that hair
           A5                             A5 C5 D5   A5 C5 D5
Your mom busted in and said, "What's that noise?"
          A5                                A5 C5 D5   A5 C5 D5
Aw, mom, you're just jealous, it's the Beastie Boys!
```

Refrain

M + T: Adam Horovitz, Adam Yauch, Michael Diamond, Rick Rubin
© Copyright 1986 Brooklyn Dust Music USA/American Def Tunes,
USA/Universal Polygram International
Universal Music Publishing Limited/Universal/MCA Music Limited.
All Rights Reserved. International Copyright Secured.

# MOSKAU

(DSCHINGHIS KHAN)

```
   Em       C           G
1. Moskau, fremd und geheimnisvoll,
Am       Em            B7           Em
Türme aus rotem Gold, kalt wie das Eis.
Em       C            G
Moskau, doch wer dich wirklich kennt,
Am        Em            B7         Em
der weiß, ein Feuer brennt in dir so heiß.
```

**Bridge:**
```
Em        D      B7           Em
Kosaken, hey, he, he, hebt die Gläser.
Em        D     B7          Em
Natascha, ha, ha, ha, du bist schön.
Em         D      B7            Em
Tavarisch, hey, hey, hey, auf das Leben.
Em        C              Am        B7
Auf dein Wohl, Bruder, he Bruder, ho. Hey, hey, hey.
```

**Refrain 1:**
```
Em              C              G
Moskau, Moskau, wirf die Gläser an die Wand,
Am                    Em          Am       B   B7
Russland ist ein schönes Land, ho ho ho ho ho, hey.
Em              C           G
Moskau, Moskau, deine Seele ist so groß,
Am                 Em         B7         Em
nachts da ist der Teufel los, ha ha ha ha ha.
```

**Refrain 2:**
```
Moskau, Moskau, Liebe schmeckt wie Kaviar,
Mädchen sind zum küssen da, ho ho ho ho ho, hey.
Moskau, Moskau, komm, wir tanzen auf dem Tisch,
bis der Tisch zusammenbricht, ha ha ha ha ha.
```

```
2. Moskau, Tor zur Vergangenheit,
Spiegel der Zarenzeit, rot wie das Blut.
Mo Mo Mo Moskau, wer deine Seele kennt,
der weiß, die Liebe brennt, heiß wie die Glut.
```

Bridge    Refrain 1

Moskau la la la la la la, la la la la la, ho ho ho ho ho, hey
Moskau la la la la la la, la la la la la, ha ha ha ha ha

```
3. Moskau, Moskau, Wodka trinkt man pur und kalt,
das macht hundert Jahre alt, ho ho ho ho ho, hey.
Moskau, Moskau, Väterchen, dein Glas ist leer,
doch im Keller ist noch mehr, ha ha ha ha ha.
```

Bridge    Refrain 1    Refrain 2

M + T: Ralph Siegel, Bernd Meinunger
© Copyright 1979 Edition Meridian Ralph Siegel KG, Germany.
Warner/Chappell Overseas Holdings Limited, London.
Reproduced by permission of Faber Music Limited.
All Rights Reserved.

# PLEASE FORGIVE ME

(BRYAN ADAMS)

**Intro:** A  E  F#m  A/C#  D

```
            E                        A
1. It still feels like our first night together.
E                              F#m
Feels like the first kiss and it's getting better, baby.
C#m         D
No one can better this.
A                                     E
You're still holding on, you're still the one.
A                          C#
The first time our eyes met, same feeling I get.
F#m                         C#
Only it feels much stronger, I wanna love you longer.
A                       E
You still turn the fire on.
```

**Bridge:**
```
   A         F#m      A      D      E                       A
So if you're feeling lonely, don't. You're the only one I ever want.
       F#m     A      D   E                         F#m         D
I only wanna make it go. So if I love you a little more than I should.
```

**Refrain:**
```
           A
Please forgive me, I know not what I do.
           F#m
Please forgive me, I can't stop loving you.
           D
Don't deny me this pain I'm going through.
           A
Please forgive me, if I need you like I do.
           E
Please believe me, for what I say is true.
D          A           E
Please forgive me, I can't stop loving you.
```
**Solo:**  A  E  F#m  E

```
2. Still feels like our best time together,
feels like the first touch, we're still getting closer, baby.
Can't get close enough.
You're still holding on, you're still number one.
I remember the smell of your skin, I remember everything.
I remember all your moves, I remember you, yeah!
I remember the nights, you know I still do.
Bridge
Refrain
```

**Solo:**  F#m D  F#m E  F#m D  F#m A  D
```
E                      D A                       D E
One thing I'm sure of, is the way we made love.
                       D A                       D F#m
One thing I'm in pain now, is for us to stay strong.
                            D                         E
With every ride and every bus I'm prayin', that's why I'm saying
Refrain (1 Ton höher)
```

M + T: Bryan Adams & Robert John 'Mutt' Lange
© Copyright 1993 Badams Music Limited/Out Of Pocket Publishing Co.
Universal Music Publishing Limited/Sony/ATV Music Publishing.
All Rights Reserved. International Copyright Secured.

# MIT PFEFFERMINZ BIN ICH DEIN PRINZ
(WESTERNHAGEN)

```
   G
1. Draußen ist es grau, ich sitz mit dir hier, blau.
                               G7
Ob ich mir ein Küsschen klau? "Nun, lass das doch, du alte Sau!"
C                                             G
Liebling, lass uns tanzen, das tut dem Blutdruck gut.
D                          C                         G
Liebling, lass uns tanzen, denn tanzen darf ein jeder Jud.

   G                       G
2. Neger, die sind dunkel, im Dunkeln lässt sich's munkeln.
                         G7
An der Macht, da sind die Weißen, darauf reimt sich sch..sch...sch...
C                                        G
Liebling, lass uns tanzen, Sylvester gießen wir Blei.
D                                C                         G
Liebling, lass uns lauter singen, dann sind auch wir bald vogelfrei.

   G
3. Pippi ist kein Name und auch kein Getränk,
                           G7
und mancher muss schon rennen, wenn er nur an Pippi denkt.
C                                                  G
Liebling, lass uns tanzen, du wackelst ja wie Kleister, wie Kleister.
      D
Mein Hund heißt Fritz oder Franz oder so,
C                            G
und wenn man ihn tritt, dann beißt er.

   A
4. Glaubst du an den lieben Gott, oder an Guevara?
                           A7
Ich glaube an die Deutsche Bank, denn die zahlt aus in bar.
D                                         A
Liebling, lass uns tanzen, hast du noch 'nen Pfefferminz, 'nen
Pfefferminz.
E                  D                       A     C B Bb
So, und nun gib mir 'nen Kuss, mit Pfefferminz bin ich dein Prinz.
```

**Refrain:**
```
    A
Mit Pfefferminz bin ich dein Prinz.
    A
Mit Pfefferminz bin ich dein Prinz.
    D
Mit Pfefferminz bin ich dein Prinz.
    A
Mit Pfefferminz bin ich dein Prinz.
    E
Mit Pfefferminz, mit Pfefferminz,
    D                    A
mit Pfefferminz bin ich dein Prinz.
```

M + T: Marius Müller-Westernhagen
© 1978 Musik Unserer Zeit Verlag Edition
administered by Neue Welt Musikverlag GmbH,
Warner/Chappell Oversaes Holdings Ltd, London.
Reproduced by permission of Faber Music Limited.

# I FEEL LONELY

(SASHA)

**Refrain:**
```
      A                  F#m                       D
I feel lonely, lo lo lo lo lonely, you're the one and only
                         E
that makes me feel so blue.
      A                  F#m                       D
I feel lonely, lo lo lo lo lonely, you're the one and only
                         E
that makes my dreams come true.


      A              F#m                       D
1. All across the universe every boy and every girl
                                E
   is looking for this thing called love.
   A                     F#m                              D
   So why do all the other guys got pretty women by their side,
                                E
   some guys really can't complain.
   D                       E
   Every night I lay awake and cry,
   D                             E
   I'm missing someone to stand by my side.
```

Refrain

```
E     F#m    A F#m A  F#m     A F#m A
I feel lonely,      so lonely.
```

```
2. It's not easy to fall in love, so I pray to God above,
   Lord I need a helping hand.
   Hey Mr. DJ play this song, I felt lonely for so long,
   this is my SOS for love.
   All the time I got it on my mind,
   someone to hold me tight is hard to find.
```

Refrain

```
E     F#m    A F#m A  F#m     A F#m A
I feel lonely,      so lonely.

A                              F#m
I feel, I feel, I feel so low, I feel, I feel, I feel so low,
D                                      E
I feel, I feel, I feel so lonely girl.

A                              F#m
I feel, I feel, I feel so low, I feel, I feel, I feel so low,
D                                      E
I feel, I feel, I feel so lonely girl.
```

Refrain

M + T: Stephan Baader / Sascha Schmitz / Michael Kersting
© Edition Click II / BMG Rights Management GmbH / Ed. Hafenklang / Arabella Musikverlag GmbH.

# KRIMINAL TANGO

(HAZY OSTERWALD)

```
Cm         Fm              Cm
Kriminal Tango in der Taverne.
         Fm       G7        C
Dunkle Gestalten und rotes Licht.
```

```
                    C                          G7
1. Und sie tanzen einen Tango, Jacky Brown und Baby Miller.
                                                         C
Und er sagt ihr leise: "Baby, wenn ich austrink, machst du dicht."
                      C7                                F
Dann bestellt er zwei Manhattan, und dann kommt ein Herr mit Kneifer.
                      C
Jack trinkt aus und Baby zittert,
G7                            Cm
doch dann löscht sie schnell das Licht.
```

**Refrain:**
```
Cm         Fm              Cm
Kriminal Tango in der Taverne.
         Fm            Cm
Dunkle Gestalten, rote Laterne.
      C7                Fm
Abend für Abend lodert die Lunte,
         D7                G7
sprühende Spannung liegt in der Luft.
```

2. Und sie tanzen einen Tango, alle, die davon nichts ahnen.
Und sie fragten die Kapelle: "Hab'n Sie nicht was Heißes da?"
Denn sie können ja nicht wissen, was da zwischen Tag und Morgen
in der nächtlichen Taverne bei dem Tango schon geschah.

Kriminal Tango in der Taverne.
Dunkle Gestalten, rote Laterne.
Glühende Blicke, steigende Spannung.
Und in die Spannung, da fällt ein Schuss.

3. Und sie tanzen einen Tango, Jacky Brown und Baby Miller.
Und die Kripo kann nichts finden, was daran verdächtig wär.
Nur der Herr da mit dem Kneifer, dem der Schuss im Dunkeln galt,
könnt vielleicht noch etwas sagen, doch der Herr, der sagt nichts mehr.

Kriminal Tango in der Taverne.
Dunkle Gestalten, rote Laterne.
Abend für Abend immer das Gleiche,
denn dieser Tango geht nie vorbei.

Original Titel: ALLACCIA MOCCIA NEL TANGO
M:Piero Trombetta
Orig.T: Aldo Locatelli
Deutscher T: Kurt Feltz
© Copyright 1959 by Fortissimo S.a.r.L., Milano.
Für Deutschland, Österreich und die Schweiz: Edition
Rialto Hans Gerig KG, Bergisch Gladbach.

# A SPACEMAN CAME TRAVELLING

(CHRIS DE BURGH)

**Intro:** Dm C Bb Dm F C Bb (2x)

```
     Dm              F                  C              Dm
1. A spaceman came trav'ling on his ship from a-far,
        F             C              Bb                    C
   'twas light years of time since his mission did start
     Dm       Am           Bb           Dm
   and over a village he halted his craft,
             F         C          Bb          C Dm
   and it hung in the sky like a star, just like a star.
```

2. He followed a light and came down to a shed
where a mother and child were laying on a bed.
A bright light of silver shone round his head,
and he had the face of an angel and they were afraid.

3. Then the stranger spoke, he said "do not fear,
I come from a planet a long way from here
and I bring a message for mankind to hear,"
and suddenly the sweetest music filled the air.

**Refrain:**
```
Dm   Bb C    Dm        Am         Bb          Dm
And it went la la la la, la la la, la la la,
F         C            Bb C Dm        Am         Bb         Dm
la la la la, la la la,  la, la la la, la la la, la la la.
F            C             Bb              C     Dm      Bb C
Peace and good will to all men and love for the child.
Dm           Am         Bb          Dm   F        C         Bb   C
La la la la, la la la, la la la, la la la, la la la,
Dm           Am         Bb          Dm   F        C         Bb C Dm
la, la la la, la la la, la la la, la la la, la la la.
```

4. This lovely music went trembling through the ground
and many were wakened on hearing the sound.
And trav'lers on the road, the village were found
by the light of that ship in the sky which shone around.

5. And just before dawn at the paling of the sky
the stranger returned and said now I must fly.
When two thousand years of your time has gone by
the song will begin once again to a baby's cry.

Refrain

```
Dm            Bb                  C Am        Bb              Dm
Oh the whole world is waiting,  waiting to hear that song again.
F                  C                    Bb                 C
There are thousands standing on the edge of the world
Dm           Am                       Bb                Dm
and a star is moving somewhere,  the time is nearly here,
       F         C          Bb         C   Dm
this song will begin once again to a baby's cry.
```

M + T: Chris de Burgh
© Copyright 1975 (Renewed 1982) Chrysalis Music Limited.
All Rights Reserved. International Copyright Secured.

# PENNY LANE

(THE BEATLES)

```
           B              G#m7           C#m7        F#7
1. In Penny Lane there is a barber showing photographs.
           B              G#m7            Bm7
Of every head he's had the pleasure to know.
         G#m7b5             Gmaj7
And all the people that come and go
         F#7
stop and say hello.

           B          G#m7          C#m7       F#7
2. On the corner is a banker with a motor car.
             B              G#m7            Bm7
The little children laugh at him behind his back.
         G#m7b5             Gmaj7
And the banker never wears a mac
        F#7        E
in the pouring rain, very strange.

        A           A/C#         D
Penny Lane is in my ears and in my eyes.
A            A/C#          D            F#7
Wet beneath the blue suburban skies. I sit and meanwhile back
```

3. In Penny Lane there is a fireman with an hour glass.
And in his pocket is a portrait of the Queen.
He likes to keep his fire engine clean,
it's a clean machine.

```
        A           A/C#         D
Penny Lane is in my ears and in my eyes.
A          A/C#          D            F#7
A four of fish and finger pies in summer meanwhile back.
```

4. Behind the shelter in the middle of the roundabout,
the pretty nurse is selling poppies from a tray.
And though she feels as if she's in a play,
she is anyway.

5. In Penny Lane the barber shaves another customer.
We see the banker sitting, waiting for a trend.
And then the fireman rushes in
from the pouring rain, very strange.

```
        A           A/C#         D
Penny Lane is in my ears and in my eyes.
A            A/C#          D            F#7
Wet beneath the blue suburban skies. I sit and meanwhile back

        B           B/D#         E
Penny Lane is in my ears and in my eyes.
B             B/D#         E           B
Wet beneath the blue suburban skies. Penny Lane.
```

M + T: John Lennon & Paul McCartney
© Copyright 1967 Sony/ATV Music Publishing.
All Rights Reserved. International Copyright Secured

# GIRLS JUST WANT TO HAVE FUN

(CYNDI LAUPER)
[TRANSP. -1]

**Intro:** G Em C D (2x)

```
   G                                          Em
1. I come home in the morning light, my mother says:

"When you gonna live your life right?"
C
Oh mother dear, we're not the fortunate ones
     Em          D          C          Em         D            G Em C D
and girls, they want to have fu-un, oh girls just want to have fun.
   G                                             Em
2. The phone rings in the middle of the night, my father yells:

"What you gonna do with your life?"
C
Oh, daddy dear, you know you're still number one!
```

**Refrain:**
```
     Em          D          C          Em         D
But girls, they want to have fu-un, oh girls just want to have...
G                        Em             G
That's all they really want: some fun, when the working day is done,
     Em          D          C          Em         D            G Em C D
oh girls just want to have fun-un, oh girls just want to have fun.


      G
3. Some boys take a beautiful girl
      Em
and hide her away from the rest of the world.
C
I want to be the one to walk in the sun.
```

Refrain

```
G                  Em        C D G                    Em         C D
They just wanna, they just wanna.  They just wanna, they just wanna.
G      Em       C        D    G         Em       C       D     G
Girls, girls just want to have fu-un, oh girls just want to have fun.
```

M + T: Robert Hazard
© Copyright 1984 Heroic Music, USA.
Sony/ATV Music Publishing (UK) Limited.
All Rights Reserved. International Copyright Secured.

# CRYING IN THE RAIN

(A-HA)

```
      D    G/D    A/D     D
1. I'll never let you see
             G/D           A/D     D
   the way my broken heart is hurting me.
   D            G/D         F#          Bm           G
   I've got my pride and I know how to hide all my sorrows and pain.
   A                       Bm
   I'll do my crying in the rain.

      D    G/D    A/D     D
2. If I wait for stormy skies,
                G/D          A/D        D
   you will know the rain from the tears in my eyes,
   D           G/D         F#             Bm          G
   you'll never know that I still love you so only heartaches remain.
   A                       Bm
   I'll do my crying in the rain.

   G                Em           A                       D
   Raindrops falling from heaven could never take away my misery.
   Bm                            G
   Since we're not together I pray for stormy weather
      A
   to hide these tears, I hope you'll never see.

      D    G/D    A/D     D
3. Some day my crying's done.
              G/D          A/D        D
   I'm gonna wear a smile and walk in the sun.
      D         G/D         F#          Bm            G
   I may be a fool, but till then darling you'll never see me complain.
   A                       Bm
   I'll do my crying in the rain.

   A                       Bm
   I'll do my crying in the rain.
```

M + T: Howard Greenfield, Carole King
© Copyright 1961 Screen Gems-EMI Music Publishing Limited. Robert Mellin Musikverlag KG
Mit freundlicher Genehmigung von Bosworth Music GmbH.
All Rights Reserved. International Copyright Secured.

# HORIZONT

(UDO LINDENBERG)

**Intro:** C Am Dm G (2x)

```
      Am              G           Dm         C      G/B
1. Wir war'n zwei Detektive, die Hüte tief im Gesicht.
   Am              G              Dm          C     Bb
   Alle Straßen endlos, Barrikaden gab's für uns doch nicht.
   Am            C                D/F#                F   G
   Du und ich, das war einfach unschlagbar, ein Paar wie Blitz und Donner
   Am          G              F
   und immer nur auf brennend heißer Spur.

      Am              G            Dm            C       G/B
2. Wir war'n so richtig Freunde für die Ewigkeit, das war doch klar.
   Am              G             Dm         C     Bb
   Haben die Wolken nicht gesehen am Horizont bis es dunkel war.
   Am            C               D/F#
   Und dann war's passiert, hab es nicht kapiert, ging alles viel zu
   F    G  Am            G                F
   schnell, doch zwei wie wir, die dürfen sich nie verlier'n!
```

**Refrain:**
```
G        C            F          Dm       G
Hinterm Horizont geht's weiter, ein neuer Tag.
G        C/E          F          Dm              G
hinterm Horizont, immer weiter, zusammen sind wir stark!
        C                Am         Dm          G
Das mit uns ging so tief rein, das kann nie zu Ende sein,
        C/E             Am         Dm      F    G
so was Großes geht nicht einfach so vorbei!
```

Am G Dm C G/B Am G Dm C Bb

```
   Am            C                D/F#                F   G
   Du und ich, das war einfach unschlagbar, ein Paar wie Blitz und Donner.
   Am              G               F
   Zwei wie wir, die können sich nie verlier'n.
```

**Refrain:**
```
G        C            F          Dm       G
Hinterm Horizont geht's weiter, ein neuer Tag.
G        C            F          Dm              G
Hinterm Horizont, immer weiter, zusammen sind wir stark!
        C                Am         Dm          G
Das mit uns ging so tief rein, das kann nie zu Ende sein,
        C/E             Am          Dm      F
denn zwei wie wir, die können sich nie verlier'n.
G        C            F      Dm G C
Hinterm Horizont geht's weiter!
```

M + T: Lindenberg, Udo / Reszat, Bea
© PolyGram Songs Musikverlag GmbH / Universal Music Publishing GmbH.

# ADIEU, MEIN KLEINER GARDEOFFIZIER

(LIANE HAID)

```
      Ab        Eb          Abm6      Eb          Ab        Eb
1. Und eines Tages mit Sang und Klang, da zog ein Fähnrich zur Garde,
      Ab6         Bb7            Eb
ein Fähnrich jung und voll Leichtsinn und schlank,
         Ab6        Bb7          Eb
auf der Kappe die gold'ne Kokarde.
      Ab        Eb          Abm6    Eb          Ab  Eb Ab  Eb
Da stand die Mutter vor ihrem Sohn, hielt seine Hände umschlungen,
                        Ab6    Bb7        Eb
schenkt ihm ein kleines Me - dail - lon,
         F9       F7      Bb Bb7    Gm    Bb7
und sie sagt zu ihrem Jungen:
```

**Refrain:**
```
Ab Eb                                Ab Bb7 Bb+ Eb        Ab          Eb
Adieu, mein kleiner Gardeoffizier, adieu, adieu und vergiss mich nicht!
     Bb7          Eb
Und vergiss mich nicht!
Ab Eb                                Ab Bb7 Bb+ Eb        Ab          Eb
Adieu, mein kleiner Gardeoffizier, adieu, adieu, sei das Glück mit dir!
Bb7                Eb
Sei das Glück mit dir!
         Bb           Eb              Bb
Steh' gerade, kerzengrade, lache in den Sonnentag,
Eb   Bb       F7           Bb    Eb   Bb
was immer geschehen auch mag!
                              Eb
Hast du Sorgenmienen, fort mit ihnen!
Bb          Eb    Bb           F7      Bb  Ab Bb7
Tatata ratata! Für Trübsal sind andere da!
Bb+ Eb                               Ab Bb7 Bb+ Eb        Ab          Eb
Adieu, mein kleiner Gardeoffizier, adieu, adieu und vergiss mich nicht!
     Bb7          Eb
Und vergiss mich nicht!
```

2. Und eines Tages um neun Uhr früh, als er aus Träumen erwachte,
da stand auf dem Hauptplatz die ganze Kompanie,
und die wartet seit dreiviertel Achte.
Aus blauen Augen, so tief und schön, erstaunte Blicke ihn trafen,
er sagte: "Liebling, ich muss geh'n!" Da sagt' sie noch ganz verschlafen:

Refrain

3. Und eines Tages war alles aus, es ruhten endlich die Waffen;
man schickte alle Soldaten nach Haus, einen neuen Beruf sich zu schaffen.
Die alte Garde stand müd' und bleich um ihren Marschall im Kreise,
man blies den letzten Zapfenstreich und der Marschall sagte leise:

Refrain

```
Bb+    Ebmaj7     Bb+            Eb
Adieu, adieu, mein kleiner Gardeoffizier!
```

M: Robert Stolz
T: Walter Reisch
© Dreiklang-Dreimasken Bühnen- und Musikverlag GmbH (Universal Music Publishing Group).

# RHYTHM DIVINE

(ENRIQUE IGLESIAS)

**Intro:** G Dm F C G
```
G                   Dm            F C G
Escucha el ritmo de tu corazon.
```

```
              Am
1. From the coast of Ipanema to the island of Capri,
                                    G           F
all the way to Guadaloupe I will follow you wherever you may be.
           Am
From the moment I first saw you, knew my heart could not be free,
                                              G          F
have to hold you in my arms now, there can never be another for me.
```

**Refrain:**
```
         G            Dm
All I need is the rhythm divine,
F        C         G
lost in the music your heart will be mine.
         G            Dm
All I need is to look in your eyes,
F       C       G
viva la musica say you'll be mine.
```

```
              Am
2. Can you feel the heat of passion? Can you taste our love's sweet
                                                                wine?
                                      G              F
Join the dance and let it happen, put tomorrow cares right out of your
                                                                mind.
            Am
As the music draws you closer and you fall under my spell,
                                     G                  F
I will catch you in my arms now where the night can take us no one can
                                                                tell.
```
Refrain

```
Am
Gotta have this feeling forever, gotta live this moment together.
G       F            C
Nothing else matters, just you and the night.
Am
Follow on the wings of desire, now the rhythm's taking you higher,
G         F         Em
no one can stop us from having it all.
Dm             Am
You are my heart, you are my soul!
```

Refrain 2x

**Outro:**
```
G                        Dm
Can you feel the rhythm? Can you feel the rhythm?
F       C                G
Can you feel the rhythm? Burning through, burning through.
```

Outro 2x

M + T: Paul Barry, Mark Taylor
© PB Songs Limited / Universal Music Publishing Limited.
Universal Music Publishing Limited. All Rights Reserved.
International Copyright Secured.

# ROSE GARDEN

(LYNN ANDERSON)

**Refrain:**
```
C            Dm       G                       C
I beg your pardon, I never promised you a rose garden,
              Dm       G                   C
along with the sunshine, there's gotta be a little rain some time.
       F                                            Dm
When you take you gotta give, so live and let live and let go oh,
         G       G7                C
I beg your pardon, I never promised you a rose garden.
```

```
            C
1. I could promise you things like big diamond rings
                                            Dm
but you don't find roses growin' on stalks of clover,
                      G
so you better think it over.
      C
If sweet talking you could make it come true,
                                            Dm
I'd give you the world right now on a silver platter
                G
but what would it matter.

    Dm                   G
So smile for a while and let's be jolly,
Gm                 A
love shouldn't be so melancholy,
Dm                                          Fm  G
come along and share the good times while we can.
```

Refrain

```
           C
2. I could sing you a tune and promise you the moon
                                                Dm
but if that's what it takes to hold you, I'd just as soon let you go
                         G
but there's one thing I want you to know.
             C
You better look before you leap, still waters run deep
                                          Dm
and there won't always be someone there to pull you out
                   G
and you know what I'm talking about.

    Dm                   G
So smile for a while and let's be jolly,
Gm                 A
love shouldn't be so melancholy,
Dm                                          Fm  G
come along and share the good times while we can.
```

Refrain 2x

M + T: Joe South
© Copyright 1967 Sony/ATV Songs LLC, USA.
Sony/ATV Music Publishing (UK) Limited.
All Rights Reserved. International Copyright Secured.

# EL CONDOR PASA

(SIMON & GARFUNKEL)

```
         Em                       G
1. I'd rather be a sparrow than a snail.
D    G     D     G       B7    Em   B7 Em
Yes I would. If I could. I surely would.
     Em                     G
I'd rather be a hammer than a nail.
D    G     D        G       D     Em
Yes I would. If I only could. I surely would.


Refrain:
   C
Away, I'd rather sail away
          G         D         G
like a swan that's here and gone.
    C
A man gets tied up to the ground,
               G          D      G
he gives the world its saddest sound,
    B7      Em    D Em
its saddest sound.


         Em                      G
2. I'd rather be a forest than a street.
D    G     D     G       B7    Em
Yes I would. If I could. I surely would.
     Em                              G
I'd rather hear the earth beneath my feet.
D    G       D    G       D     Em
Yes I would. If I only could. I surely would.


Refrain
```

M: Jorge Milchberg & Daniel Robles
T: Paul Simon
Traditionell
© 2005 by Edition DUX, Manching

## SEE YOU LATER ALLIGATOR

(BILL HALEY)  
[TRANSP. +6]

```
                   A
1. Well, I saw my baby walking with another man today.
A7                       D7                       A
Well, I saw my baby walking with another man today.
                       E7        D7                  A
When I asked her what's the matter, this is what I heard her say:
```

**Refrain:**
```
                    A
See you later alligator after a while crocodile.
A7                 D7                    A
See you later alligator after a while crocodile.
                         E7
Don't you know you're in my way now,
D7                         A
can't you see you cramp my style?
```

2. When I thought of what she told me, nearly made me lose my head.

When I thought of what she told me, nearly made me lose my head.

But when she asked me what's the matter, reminded her of what she said:

Refrain

3. She said I'm sorry, pretty daddy, you know my love is just for you.

She said I'm sorry, pretty daddy, you know my love is just for you.

Won't you say that you'll forgive me and say your love for me is true.

Refrain

4. I said, wait a minute gator, I know you meant it just for play.

I said, wait a minute, gator, I know you meant it just for play.

Don't you know you really hurt me and this is what I have to say:

Refrain

M + T: Charles Robert Guidry  
© Copyright 1955-1956 by Arc Music Corp., New York.  
Für Deutschland, Österreich und die Schweiz:  
Musikverlage Hans Gerig KG, Bergisch Gladbach.

## DON'T THINK TWICE, IT'S ALL RIGHT
(BOB DYLAN)

**Intro:** C G Am F C G7 C

```
         C                  G7           Am
1. It ain't no use to sit and wonder why, babe,
F                 C    G7
if you don't know by now.
         C              G          Am
And it ain't no use to sit and wonder why babe,
D7              G   G7
it don't ever do somehow.

            C                       C7
When the rooster crows at the break of the dawn,
F                          D7/F#
look out of your window and I'll be gone.
C/G       G         Am           F
You're the reason I'm travelling on.
C/G          G7         C
Don't think twice it's all right.
```

2. It ain't no use in turning on your light babe,
the light I never knowed.
It ain't no use in turning on your light, babe,
I'm on the dark side of the road.

But I wish there was something you would do or say,
to try to me change my mind and stay.
But we never did too much talking anyway,
So don't think twice it's all right.


3. It ain't no use in calling out my name girl,
like you never done before.
It ain't no use in calling out my name girl,
I can't hear you anymore.

I'm a-thinking and wondering, walking down the road,
I once loved a woman, a child I am told.
I'd give her my heart, but she wanted my soul.
But don't think twice it's all right.


4. So long, honey babe.
Where I'm bound I can't tell.
Goodbye is too good a word, babe.
So I'll just say Fare-Thee-Well.

I ain't a-saying you treated me unkind,
you could have done better, but I don't mind.
You just kinda wasted my precious time,
But don't think twice it's all right.

M + T: Bob Dylan
© Copyright 1963 Warner Brothers Incorporated.
© Copyright Renewed 1991 Special Rider Music, USA.
All Rights Reserved. International Copyright Secured

# IT'S NOW OR NEVER

(ELVIS PRESLEY)
[TRANSP. +4]

**Refrain:**
```
         C                  Dm
It's now or never, come hold me tight.
        G7                 C
Kiss me, my darling, be mine tonight.
   Fm              Cm
Tomorrow will be too late.
C        G7              C
It's now or never, my love won't wait.
```

```
              C                    F
1. When I first saw you with your smile so tender,
           G7                   C
my heart was captured, my soul surrendered.
                                F
I've spent a lifetime waiting for the right time,
            C              G7      C
now that you're near the time is here at last.
```

Refrain

```
              C                    F
2. Just like a willow we would cry an ocean,
          G7                    C
if we lost true love and sweet devotion.
                                F
Your lips excite me, let your arms invite me,
            C              G7       C
for who knows when we'll meet again this way.
```

Refrain

M: E. di Capua
T: Giovanni Capurro
© Copyright 1960 Rachel's Own Music, USA.
Minder Music Limited.
All Rights Reserved. International Copyright Secured.

# ONE OF US

(ABBA)

```
       G            Gmaj7  Bm                    Em Em/D
1. They passed me by,    all of those great romances.
C            G/B          D/C         C          D
You were, I felt, robbing me of my rightful chances.
G            Gmaj7  Bm                    Em Em/D
My picture clear, everything seemed so easy
C         Bm
and so I dealt you the blow.
         Em
One of us had to go.
Am                 C/G          D
Now it's different, I want you to know.
```

**Refrain:**
```
D          G     Bm/F#       Em
One of us is crying, one of us is lying
G/D          C    E7  Am
in her lonely bed.
A7/G        D
Staring at the ceiling,
C             D7               G    Em  C
wishing she was somewhere else instead.
D          G     Bm/F#       Em
One of us is lonely, one of us is only
G/D          C    E7  Am
waiting for a call.
            A7/C#        G/D
Sorry for herself, feeling stupid feeling small,
D
wishing she had never left at all.
```

```
2. I saw myself as a concealed attraction,
I felt you kept me away from the heat and the action.
Just like a child, stubborn and misconceiving
that's how I started the show.
One of us had to go.
Now I've changed and I want you to know.

Refrain
            G   D7 G Bm/F# Em G/D C E7 Am
Never left at all.

Staring at the ceiling,
wishing she was somewhere else instead.
One of us is lonely, one of us is only
waiting for a call.
```

# DAY-O (BANANA BOAT SONG)

(HARRY BELAFONTE)

```
D     A       D
Day-o, day-ay-ay-o.
D                A        D
Daylight come and we wanna go home.
D
Day, me say day, me say day, me say day, me say day, me say day-ay-ay-o.
D                A        D
Daylight come and we wanna go home.

   D                                           A        D
1. Work all night on a drink of rum. Daylight come and we wanna go home.
D                                              A        D
Stack banana till thee morning come. Daylight come and we wanna go home.
```

**Refrain:**
```
D                          A
Come, Missa Tallyman, tally me banana.
D                A        D
Daylight come and we wanna go home.
D                          A
Come, Missa Tallyman, tally me banana.
D                A        D
Daylight come and we wanna go home.

2. It's six foot, seven foot, eight foot, bunch!
Daylight come and we wanna go home.
Six foot, seven foot, eight foot, bunch!
Daylight come and we wanna go home.

Day, me say day-ay-ay-o.
Daylight come and we wanna go home.
Day, me say day, me say day, me say day, me say day, me say day.
Daylight come and we wanna go home.

3. A beautiful bunch of ripe banana. Daylight come and we wanna go home.
Hide the deadly black tarantula. Daylight come and we wanna go home.

4. It's six foot, seven foot, eight foot, bunch!
Daylight come and we wanna go home.
Six foot, seven foot, eight foot, bunch!
Daylight come and we wanna go home.
```

Refrain

```
5. A clerk man a check, but him a check with caution.
Daylight come and we wanna go home.
My back just broke with bare exhaustion.
Daylight come and we wanna go home.

Day, me say day-ay-ay-o.
Daylight come and we wanna go home.
Day, me say day, me say day, me say day, me say day, me say day.
Daylight come and we wanna go home.
```

M + T: Irving Burgie und Williarn Attaway
© Lord Burgess Music Publishing , Music of 1091 /
BMG Rights Management GmbH

# THE BAD TOUCH

(BLOODHOUND GANG)

Haha! Well, now we call this the act of mating.
But there are several other very important differences
between human beings and animals that you should know about.
I'd appreciate your input.

```
      Cm                           Eb
1. Sweat, baby, sweat, baby, sex is a Texas drought me
         Bb                           Ab
and you do the kind of stuff that only Prince would sing about.
            Cm                        Eb
So put your hands down my pants and I'll bet you feel nuts.
         Bb                              Ab
Yes, I'm Siskel, yes, I'm Ebert and you're getting two thumbs up.
              Cm
You've had enough of two-hand touch,
             Eb
you want it rough you're out of bounds,
            Bb                                Ab
I want you smothered, want you covered like my Waffle House hashbrowns.
                        Cm
Come quicker than FedEx never reach an apex,
           Eb
like Coca-Cola stock you're inclined
            Bb                              Ab
to make me rise an hour early just like Daylight Savings Time.
```

**Refrain:**

```
Do it now!
Cm                         Eb
You and me, baby, ain't nothing but mammals,
         Bb                     Ab
so let's do it like they do on the Discovery Channel.

Do it again now!
Cm                         Eb
You and me, baby, ain't nothing but mammals,
         Bb                     Ab
so let's do it like they do on the Discovery Channel.
```

Gettin' horny now!

2. Love the kind you clean up with a mop and bucket
like the lost catacombs of Egypt only god knows where we stuck it.
Hieroglyphics? Let me be Pacific, I wanna be down in your South Seas
but I got this notion that the motion of your ocean
means "Small Craft Advisory".
So if I capsize on your thighs high tide B-5 you sunk my battleship.
Please turn me on I'm Mister Coffee with an automatic drip,
so show me yours I'll show you mine .
"Tool Time" you'll love it just like Lyle
and then we'll do it doggy style so we can both watch "X-Files".

Refrain 2x

M + T: Jimmy Pop
© Songs of PolyGram Int., Hey Rudy Music Publishing, The
Jimmy Franks Publishing. Universal Music Publishing Limited.
All Rights Reserved. International Copyright Secured.

# HEDONISM

(SKUNK ANANSIE)

**Intro:** Fm Eb/G (2x)

```
                    Fm
1. I hope you're feeling happy now,
         Eb/G                    Eb
I see you feel no pain at all it seems.
                Fm
I wonder what you're doin' now,
       Eb/G             Eb
I wonder if you think of me at all.
                  Fm
Do you still play the same moves now
              Eb/G                    Eb
or are those special moods for someone else?
                 Fm
I hope you're feeling happy now.
```

**Refrain:**
```
            Eb          Bb              Fm         Ab
Just because you feel good, doesn't make you right, oh no.
            Eb          Bb          Fm         Ab
Just because you feel good, still want you here tonight.
```

```
                      Fm
2. Does laughter still discover you?
          Eb/G                        Eb
I see through all the smiles that look so right.
                Fm
Do you still have the same friends now
           Eb/G              Eb
to smoke away your problems and your life?
               Fm
Oh how do you remember me,
           Eb/G                    Eb
the one that made you laugh until you cried?
                 Fm
I hope you're feeling happy now.
```

Refrain

```
                  Fm       Eb/G
I wonder what you're doing now.
                Fm       Eb/G
I hope you're feeling happy now.
                Fm       Eb/G
I hope you're feeling happy now.
```

M + T: Deborah Ann Dyer & Leonard Anthony Arran
© Copyright 1996 Chrysalis Music Limited.
All Rights Reserved. International Copyright Secured

## MORE THAN A FEELING

(BOSTON)

```
     D         Dsus4 D    C          G
1. I woke up this morning and the sun was gone,
 D          Dsus4 D  C       G
turned on some music to start my day.
     D      Dsus4 D    C         G
I lost myself in a familiar song,
    D         Dsus4 D    Cmaj7      G/B
I closed my eyes and I slipped away.
Am G D G C Em D G C Em D
```

**Refrain:**
```
        G          C          Em          D
It's more than a feeling, more than a feeling,
         G            C            Em    D
when I hear that old song they used to play (more than a feeling).
G       C        Em         D
I begin dreaming, more than a feeling,
         G          C             Eb
till I see Marianne walk away.
Em7       A             G    G F#m Em D
I see my Marianne walking away.
```

```
     D         Dsus4 D    C         G
2. So many people have come and gone,
         D       Dsus4 D    C         G
their faces fade as the years go by,
     D        Dsus4 D  C      G
yet I still recall as I wander on,
    D          Dsus4 D   Cmaj7     G/B
as clear as the sun in the summer sky.
Am G D G C Em D G C Em D
```

Refrain

```
     D         Dsus4 D    C         G
3. When I'm tired and thinking cold
     D        Dsus4 D  C      G
I hide in my music, forget the day
      D         Dsus4 D C       G
and dream of a girl I used to know.
    D         Dsus4 D    C         G    D C G D
I closed my eyes and she slipped away.
C     G      D
She slipped away.
Am G D G C Em D G C Em D
```

Refrain

M + T: Tom Scholz
© Copyright 1976 Pure Songs, USA. Sony/ATV Music Publishing (UK) Limited.
All Rights Reserved. International Copyright Secured.

# SUNDAY BLOODY SUNDAY

(U2)

**Intro:** Bm D G Bm D G

```
   Bm             D                    G
1. I can't believe the news today.
Bm             D                    G
Oh, I can't close my eyes and make it go away.
```

**Refrain:**
```
D          Em                              D          Em
How long? How long must we sing this song? How long, how long?
          Bm   D G                   Bm   D G
'Cause tonight we can be as one, tonight!
```

2. Broken bottles under children's feet.
Bodies strewn across the dead-end street.

3. But I won't heed the battle call.
It puts my back up against the wall.

```
Bm D        G         Bm D          G
Sunday, bloody Sunday. Sunday, bloody Sunday.
C  G        D         C  G          D
Sunday, bloody Sunday. Sunday, bloody Sunday.
```

Intro

4. And the battle's just begun.
There's many lost, but tell me who has won?
5. The trenches dug within our hearts.
And mother's children, brothers, sisters torn apart.

Sunday, bloody Sunday. Sunday, bloody Sunday.

Refrain

Wipe the tears from your eyes. Wipe your tears away.

Wipe your tears away. Wipe your bloodshot eyes.

Sunday, bloody Sunday. Sunday, bloody Sunday.

Intro

6. And it's true we are immune.
When fact is fiction and T.V. is reality.
7. And today the millions cry.
We eat and drink while tomorrow they die.
8. The real battle just begun.
To claim the victory Jesus won!

On Sunday, bloody Sunday. Sunday, bloody Sunday.

M + T: Larry Mullen, Adam Clayton, Dave Evans & Paul David Hewson
© Copyright 1983 Blue Mountain Music Limited (for the UK)/Mother Music (for the Republic of Ireland)/PolyGram International Music Publishing B.V (for the Rest of the World).
All Rights Reserved. International Copyright Secured.

# BREATHLESS

(THE CORRS)

Go on, go on leave me breathless!

**Intro:** B F# C#m G#m F#

```
     B                    F#
1. The daylight's fading slowly
C#m          G#m       F#        B
but time with you is standing still.
           F#
I'm waiting for you only,
C#m          G#m        F#       E
the slightest touch and I feel ill.
    F#      G#m      E     F#     B
I cannot lie. From you I cannot hide.
      E        F#       G#m       E              F#
I'm losing will to try. Can't hide it. Can't fight it.
```

**Refrain:**
```
     E          A          B
So go on, go on. Come on, leave me breathless.
     E         A            B
Have me, tease me, until I can't deny this
 E            A          B
loving feeling. Make me long for your kiss.
 E          A         B
Go on, go on, yeah, come on.
```

B F# C#m G#m F#

```
     B                    F#
2. And if there's no tomorrow
C#m          G#m        F#       B
and all we have is here and now
           F#
I'm happy just to have you,
C#m             G#m        F#    E
you're all the love I need somehow.
       F#       G#m      E           F#      B
It's like a dream.  Although I'm not asleep
    E       F#       G#m          E              F#
I never want to wakeup. Don't lose it. Don't leave it.
```

Refrain

B F# C#m G#m F# B F# C#m G#m F#

```
    E     F#      G#m         E       F#      B
And I can't lie. From you I cannot hide.
       E        F#       G#m        E              F#
I've lost my will to try. Can't hide it. Can't fight it.
```

Refrain 2x

M + T: Robert John Lange * / Andrea Corr / Sharon Corr / Caroline Corr / Jim Corr
© Copyright 2000 Beacon Communications Music Corporation/Out Of Pocket Productions
Limited/Universal-Songs Of PolyGram International Incorporated.
Universal Music Publishing Limited. All Rights Reserved. International Copyright Secured.

# I WILL LOVE AGAIN

(LARA FABIAN)

```
      Am           F         C/G              G
1. Did I ever tell you how you live in me.
Am            F         C/G            G
Every waking moment, even in my dreams.
         Am             F            C/G               G
And if all this talk is crazy and you don't know what I mean.
               Am        F       C/G           G
Does it really matter just as long as I believe?
```

**Refrain:**
```
        Am     F
I will love again!
C/G            G           Am         F            C/G G
Though my heart is breaking I will love again stronger than before.
         Am     F
I will love again!
C/G            G              Am          F           C/G
Even if it takes a lifetime to get over you, heaven only knows

G          Am
I will love again!
```

```
      Am          F         C/G             G
2. People never tell you the way they truly feel.
Am            F             C/G            G
I would die for you gladly if I knew it was for real.
        Am            F           C/G                G
So if all this talk sounds crazy and the words don't come out right.
               Am       F      C/G                G
Does it really matter if it gets me through this night?
```

Refrain

```
       F            Em           Dm                  Am
If I'm true to myself, nobody else can take the place of you.
       F            Em              G
But I got to hold on, tell me what else can I do.
```

Refrain

```
G      Am         F          C/G    G     Am          F C/G
I will love again! I will love again! I will love again!
G          Am          F C/G
One day I know, I will love again!
G                   Am              F                 C/G
You can't stop me from loving again, breathing again, feeling again.
G                  Am      F    C/G G Am
I know, one day, I'll love again!
```

M + T: Paul Barry, Mark Taylor
© PB Songs Limited / Universal Music Publishing Limited.
Universal Music Publishing Limited. All Rights Reserved.
International Copyright Secured.

# SIEBEN FÄSSER WEIN

(ROLAND KAISER)

```
              D           G         D    A      D
Intro:  La la la la, la la la la, lalalalala, la la la la la.
            D                             A
1. Sieben Fässer Wein können uns nicht gefährlich sein,
                            A7        D
   das wär doch gelacht, wer steht gerne auf einem Bein.
                    D7                G
   Wir machen durch, kommt, Freunde, seid bereit,
         D      A        D
   wie schön war doch die Junggesellenzeit.
```

2. Sieben Fässer Wein können uns nicht gefährlich sein,
   das haut uns nicht um, ja, das schaffen wir ganz allein.
   Heut feiern wir, auch wenn es traurig ist,
   dass man schon bald kein freier Mann mehr ist.

```
                      A                        D
Bridge: Ihr wisst, ich kenne tausend Fraun, doch ganz im Vertraun,
A                         D
dieses Mal hat es mich voll erwischt.
     A                   D
Das ist gefährlich, ganz ehrlich,
A              A7              D
jetzt bin ich dran, weil es kein Spaß mehr ist.
```

1. Strophe

3. Sieben Fässer Wein können uns nicht gefährlich sein,
   in den schwersten Stunden lasst mich bitte nicht allein.
   Denn es wird Zeit, wir müssen langsam gehn,
   sonst muß die Braut noch vor der Kirche stehn.

```
          D           G         D    A      D
La la la la, la la la la, lalalalala, la la la la la.
              A                      D
Bridge: Das muß ja wohl ein Irrtum sein, wir stehn hier allein,
A                      D
von der ganzen Hochzeit keine Spur.
       A                  D
Wo sind die Gäste, der Pfarrer,
       A                         D
und wo bleibt meine Braut, was mach ich nur?
```

(Gesprochen, Intro als Begleitung)
Guten Tag, mein Sohn! Du hier in der Kirche?
Und dann noch in diesem Zustand?
Wieso Hochzeit? Dein Termin war gestern!

4. Sieben Fässer Wein können manchmal die Rettung sein,
   wie das Leben spielt, vieles löst sich von ganz allein.
   Was soll's, jetzt geht's bei uns erst richtig rund,
   wir feiern, haben einen neuen Grund.
   Wir haben heute nichts mehr zu verliern,
   uns kann jetzt überhaupt nichts mehr passiern.

M: Norman Ascot
T: Renée Marcard
© 1977 by Edition Intro Meisel GmbH.

# MICHAEL ROW THE BOAT ASHORE

```
        C                     F  C
1. Michael row the boat ashore, Hallelujah.
     Em           Dm        C G7 C
Michael row the boat ashore, Hallelujah.

        C                       F  C
2. Michael's boat is a music boat, Hallelujah.
     Em            Dm          C G7 C
Michael's boat is a music boat, Hallelujah.

        C                       F  C
3. Sister, help to trim the sail, Hallelujah.
     Em           Dm           C G7 C
Sister, help to trim the sail, Hallelujah.

        C                         F  C
4. Jordan's river is deep and wide, Hallelujah.
     Em          Dm             C G7 C
Meet my mother on the other side, Hallelujah.

        C                          F  C
5. Jordan's river is chilly and cold, Hallelujah.
     Em          Dm             C G7 C
Kills a body but not the soul, Hallelujah.

        C                      F  C
6. Gabriel, blow the trumpet horn, Hallelujah.
     Em          Dm            C G7 C
Gabriel, blow the trumpet horn, Hallelujah.

        C                     F  C
7. Brother, lend a helping hand, Hallelujah.
     Em          Dm          C G7 C
Brother, lend a helping hand, Hallelujah.

        C                         F  C
8. Boasting talk will sink your soul, Hallelujah.
     Em           Dm            C G7 C
Boasting talk will sink your soul, Hallelujah.

        C                        F  C
9. Jesus stood on the other side, Hallelujah.
     Em          Dm            C G7 C
Jesus stood on the other side, Hallelujah.

        C                       F  C
10. River run and darkness come, Hallelujah.
      Em         Dm            C G7 C
River run and darkness come, Hallelujah.

        C                        F  C
11. Sinner, row to save your soul, Hallelujah.
      Em          Dm            C G7 C
Sinner, row to save your soul, Hallelujah.
```

Traditionell
© 2005 by Edition DUX, Manching

# CARBONARA

(SPLIFF)

```
Intro: Em D/E (4x)
         Em                D/E         Em                D/E
1. Io voglio viaggiare in Italia in paese dei limoni.
Em              D/E        Em                       D/E
Brigade Rosse e la Mafia cacciano sulla Strada del Sol.
G                    F/A    G                F/A
Distruzione della Lira Gelati Motta con brio,
G                   F/A         G                      F/A
Tecco mecco con ragazza ecco la mamma de amore mio.
        Em              D/E       Em              D/E
Sentimento grandioso per Italia baciato da sole calda
Em           D/E           Em                       D/E
borsellino e vuoto totale percio mangio sempre solo.
```

```
Refrain:
          Am7  G/B  C      G D   G D
Spaghetti Carbonara e una Coca Cola,
Am7  G/B  C      G D   G D
Carbonara e una Coca Cola,
Am7  G/B  C      G D   G D
Carbonara e una Coca Cola
Am7  G/B  C      G D   G D Em
Carbonara e una Coca Cola
```

```
    Em                        D/E
2. Scusi, Senorina, willst du auch'n Spliff?
      Em                      D/E
Oder stehst du nur auf Männer mit Schlips?
Em                          D/E
Ich hab sonst nichts was ich dir geben kann,
      Em                      D/E
aber blond bin ich, is das vielleicht nix?
G             F/A          G                    F/A
Amaretto ist ein geiles Zeug, ich bin schon lull und lall,
G                      F/A
hab keine Ahnung ob du mich verstehst,
            G                         F/A
doch du lächelst und mein Herz tut 'n Knall.
            Em                    D/E
Belladonna, ich lad dich jetzt zum Essen ein,
Em                  D/E
mangiare, tu capito? andiamo!
     Em                     D/E
Asti Spumante wird es nicht gerade sein.
       Em                  D/E
Aber dafür gibt's schon wieder mal
```

Refrain

M + T: Reinhold Heil
© Edition Spliff.
Mit freundlicher Genehmigung der EMI Songs Musikverlag GmbH.

# WITH OR WITHOUT YOU

(U2)

**Intro:** D A Bm7 G (2x)

```
D          A              Bm7            G              D
See the stone set in your eyes. See the thorn twist in your side.
      A        Bm7 G
I'll wait for you.
D           A              Bm7            G              D
Sleight of hand and twist of fate. On a bed of nails she makes me wait.
      A      Bm7    G
And I wait without you.

             D          A        Bm7        G
With or without you. With or without you.

D         A               Bm7          G              D
Through the storm we reach the shore. You give it all but I want more.
      A       Bm7 G
And I'm waiting for you.

             D          A        Bm7        G
With or without you. With or without you.
             D     A      Bm7    G
I can't live. With or without you.
         D             A          Bm7           G
And you give yourself away. And you give yourself away.
         D             A          Bm7           G
And you give, and you give, and you give yourself away.

      D        A   Bm7      G                      D
My hands are tied. My body bruised she got me with
         A       Bm7             G
nothing to win and nothing left to lose.
         D             A          Bm7           G
And you give yourself away. And you give yourself away.
         D             A          Bm7           G
And you give, and you give, and you give yourself away.
             D          A        Bm7        G
With or without you. With or without you.

             D     A      Bm7    G
I can't live. With or without you.
             D          A        Bm7        G
With or without you. With or without you.
             D     A      Bm7    G
I can't live. With or without you.
             D     A Bm7 G
With or without you.
```

M + T: Larry Mullen, Adam Clayton, Dave Evans & Paul David Hewson
© Copyright 1987 Blue Mountain Music Limited/Mother Music/Taiyo Music Incorporated/PolyGram International Music Publishing Limited.
All Rights Reserved. International Copyright Secured.

# BIENE MAJA

(KAREL GOTT)

```
   D                  A      G                    D
1. In einem unbekannten Land, vor gar nicht allzu langer Zeit,
             A          G                        D
   war eine Biene sehr bekannt, von der sprach alles weit und breit.
```

**Refrain:**
```
A   G/A A  D                                Em
Und diese Biene, die ich meine, nennt sich Maja,
A              A7           D
kleine, freche, schlaue Biene Maja.
                  A       A7                     D
Maja fliegt durch ihre Welt, zeigt uns das, was ihr gefällt.
A   G/A A  D                            Em
Wir treffen heute unsre Freundin, Biene Maja,
A               A7           Bm    E7
diese kleine, freche Biene Maja.
D/A           G  E7
Maja, alle lieben Maja!
D/A                            A7             D
Maja! (Maja!) Maja! (Maja!) Maja! Erzähle uns von dir!
```

```
   D                   A      G                      D
2. Wenn ich an einem schönen Tag durch eine Blumenwiese geh,
                  A         G                        D
   und kleine Bienen fliegen seh, denk ich an eine, die ich mag.
```

Refrain

```
D/A           G  E7
Maja, alle lieben Maja!
D/A                            A7             D
Maja! (Maja!) Maja! (Maja!) Maja! Erzähle uns von dir!
```

M + T: Karel Svoboda, Florian Cusano
© Copyright by Filmkunst-Musikverlag Edition FKM-Junior, München.
Originalverlag: ProVox Music Publishing.
All Rights Reserved. International Copyright Secured

# NO SON OF MINE

(GENESIS)

```
         Em            C/E         D/E            Esus2
1. Well, the key to my survival was never in much doubt,
    Em             D/E                                  C/E
the question was how I could keep sane trying to find a way out.
Em         C/E              D/E              Esus2
Things were never easy for me, peace of mind was hard to find
       D/E              A/E         C/E                        Em7
and I needed a place where I could hide somewhere I could call mine.

     Em              C              D                      Bsus4
2. I didn't think much about it till it started happening all the time.
Em                    D              Bm                C
Soon I was living with the fear everyday of what might happen at night.
Em                C                       D                 Bsus4
I couldn't stand to hear the crying of my mother and I remember when
         D                              A             C
I swore that, that would be the last they'd see me and I never went home
 G
again.
```

**Bridge:**
```
D/E               E             D/E             E
They say time is a healer and now my wounds are not the same,
D/E                    E                D/E                   E
I rang the bell with my heart in my mouth I had to hear what he'd say.
C/G                  G           D/A                   Am7
He sat me down to talk to me, he looked me straight in the eyes, he said
```

**Refrain:**
```
G/D   Am/D         Bm/D     Am/D
You're no son, you're no son of mine.
G/D   Am/D         Bm/D     Am/D
You're no son, you're no son of mine.
 G   D/G         C/G
You walked out, you left us behind
 G         D/G           C/G     D/G G D/G C/G G D/G
and you're no son, you're no son of mine.
         C/G                    D/G        Em7    D/E C/D D C
Oh his words how they hurt me, I'll never forget it
          D/C          C     D/C          Em7
and as the time, it went by, I lived to regret it.
                           C               D
You're no son, you're no son of mine,
                         C/D        Em7
but where should I go and what should I do.
                           C           D
You're no son, you're no son of mine
                          C/D           Em
but I came here for help, I came here for you.
```

3. Well the years they passed so slowly I thought about him everyday.
What would I do if we passed on the street, would I keep running away?
In and out of hiding places soon I'd have to face the facts.
We'd have to sit down and talk it over and that would mean going back.
Bridge
Refrain

M + T: Michael Rutherford, Phil Collins & Anthony Banks
© Copyright 1991 Philip Collins Limited/Michael Rutherford Music Limited.
Imagem Music. All Rights Reserved. International Copyright Secured.

# STAN

(EMINEM FEAT. DIDO)

**Refrain:**
```
  Em7           C              D         G       D/F#    Em7
My tea's gone cold I'm wondering why I got out of bed at all,
              C              D         G       D/F#    Em7
the morning rain clouds up my window, and I can't see at all.
       C -           D                  G        D/F#    Em7
And even if I could it'll all be gray, but your picture on my wall
     C                C#°               C                    Em7
it reminds me, that it's not so bad, it's not so bad, so bad.
```
Refrain
```
     Em7          C
1. Dear Slim, I wrote you but you still ain't callin',
D                               G                D/F#
I left my cell, my pager, and my home phone at the bottom.
Em7                             C
I sent two letters back in autumn, you must not have got them,
D                              G              D/F#
there probably was a problem at the post office or something.
Em7                             C
Sometimes I scribble addresses too sloppy when I jot them,
     D                          G                 D/F#
but anyways, fuck it, what's been up? Man how's your daughter?
Em7                             C
My girlfriend's pregnant too, I'm about to be a father,
         C#°                    C                           Em7
if I have a daughter, guess what I'm a call her? I'm a name her Bonnie.
```

2. I read about your Uncle Ronnie too I'm sorry,
I had a friend kill himself over some bitch who didn't want him.
I know you probably hear this every day, but I'm your biggest fan,
I even got the underground shit that you did with Scam.
I got a room full of your posters and your pictures man,
I like the shit you did with Ruckus too, that shit was fat.
Anyways, I hope you get this man, hit me back,
just to chat, truly yours, your biggest fan. This is Stan.

Refrain

3. Dear Slim, you still ain't called or wrote, I hope you have a chance,
I ain't mad. I just think it's fucked up you don't answer fans.
If you didn't wanna talk to me outside your concert,
you didn't have to, but you coulda signed an autograph for Matthew.
That's my little brother man, he's only six years old,
we waited in the blistering cold for you,
four hours and you just said, "No."
That's pretty shitty man, you're like his fucking idol.
He wants to be just like you, man, he likes you more than I do.
4. I ain't that mad though, I just don't like being lied to,
remember when we met in Denver, you said if I'd write you,
you would write back, see, I'm just like you in a way.
I never knew my father neither. He used to always cheat on my mom and
beat her. I can relate to what you're saying in your songs,
so when I have a shitty day, I drift away and put 'em on, cause
I don't really got shit else so that shit helps when I'm depressed.
I even got a tattoo of your name across the chest.

5. Sometimes I even cut myself to see how much it bleeds,
it's like adrenaline, the pain is such a sudden rush for me.

See everything you say is real, and I respect you cause you tell it.
My girlfriend's jealous cause I talk about you 24/7,
but she don't know you like I know you Slim, no one does.
She don't know what it was like for people like us growin up,
you gotta call me man, I'll be the biggest fan you'll ever lose.
Sincerely yours, Stan. P.S. We should be together, too.
Refrain
**6.** Dear Mister-I'm-Too-Good-To-Call-Or-Write-My-Fans,
this'll be the last package I ever send your ass.
It's been six months and still no word. I don't deserve it?
I know you got my last two letters, I wrote the addresses on 'em perfect
So this is my cassette I'm sending you, I hope you hear it.
I'm in the car right now, I'm doing 90 on the freeway.
Hey Slim, I drank a fifth of vodka, you dare me to drive?
You know the song by Phil Collins, "In the Air of the Night"
**7.** About that guy who could have saved that other guy from drowning,
but didn't, then Phil saw it all, then at a show he found him?
That's kinda how this is, you coulda rescued me from drowning,
now it's too late - I'm on a 1000 downers now, I'm drowsy,
and all I wanted was a lousy letter or a call.
I hope you know I ripped ALL of your pictures off the wall.
I love you Slim, we coulda been together, think about it,
you ruined it now, I hope you can't sleep and you dream about it.
**8.** And when you dream I hope you can't sleep and you scream about it,
I hope your conscience eats at you and you can't breathe without me.
See Slim. Shut up bitch! I'm tryin to talk!
Hey Slim, that's my girlfriend screamin in the trunk.
But I didn't slit her throat, I just tied her up, see I ain't like you,
cause if she suffocates she'll suffer more, and then she'll die, too.
Well, gotta go, I'm almost at the bridge now,
oh shit, I forgot, how'm I supposed to send this shit out?
Em C Em C Em C Em C
Refrain
**9.** Dear Stan, I meant to write you sooner but I just been busy.
You said your girlfriend's pregnant now, how far along is she?
Look, I'm really flattered you would call your daughter that
and here's an autograph for your brother, I wrote it on the starter cap.
I'm sorry I didn't see you at the show, I musta missed you.
Don't think I did that shit intentionally just to diss you.
But what's this shit you said about you like to cut your wrists too?
I say that shit just clownin dogg, c'mon - how fucked up is you?
**10.** You got some issues Stan, I think you need some counselling,
to help your ass from bouncing off the walls when you get down some.
And what's this shit about us meant to be together?
That type of shit'll make me not want us to meet each other!
I really think you and your girlfriend need each other,
or maybe you just need to treat her better.
I hope you get to read this letter, I just hope it reaches you in time,
before you hurt yourself, I think that you'll be doin' just fine
**11.** If you relax a little, I'm glad I inspire you, but Stan,
why are you so mad? Try to understand, that I do want you as a fan,
I just don't want you to do some crazy shit.
I seen this one shit on the news a couple weeks ago that made me sick,
some dude was drunk and drove his car over a bridge,
and had his girlfriend in the trunk, and she was pregnant with his kid.
And in the car they found a tape, but they didn't say who it was to.
Come to think about, his name was.... it was you.     Damn!

M + T: Dido Armstrong, Paul Herman and Marshall Mathers
© Copyright 2000 Eight Mile Style/Ensign Music Corporation/Champion Music Ltd.
Warner/Chappell Music Limited, London, W6 8BS, Cheeky Music Limited.
All Rights Reserved. International Copyright Secured.

# ALL YOU NEED IS LOVE

(THE BEATLES)

```
Intro: G D G C D7
G     D/F#   Em    G     D/F#   Em    Am    G     D/F# Em D D/C G/B D7
Love, Love, Love. Love, Love, Love. Love, Love, Love.

      G                    D/F#               Em
1. There's nothing you can do that can't be done.
   G                D/F#              Em
Nothing you can sing that can't be sung.
Am             G               D/F#                       Em
Nothing you can say but you can learn how to play the game.
        D    D/C G/B D7
It's easy.

      G                    D/F#                Em
2. Nothing you can make that can't be made.
   G              D/F#              Em
No one you can save that can't be saved.
Am             G              D/F#                      Em
Nothing you can do but you can learn how to be you in time.
        D    D/C G/B D7
It's easy.


Refrain:
G      A7     D7    G      A7     D7
All you need is love. All you need is love.
G      B7     Em    G/D
All you need is love, love.
C        D7          G
Love is all you need.


Refrain

      G                    D/F#              Em
3. Nothing you can know that isn't known.
   G              D/F#             Em
Nothing you can see that isn't shown.
Am             G              D/F#                  Em
Nowhere you can be that isn't where you're meant to be.
        D    D/C G/B D7
It's easy.


Refrain 2x


G       G/D
Love is all you need.

She loves you, yeah yeah yeah.

She loves you, yeah yeah yeah.
```

M + T: John Lennon & Paul McCartney
© Copyright 1967 Sony/ATV Music Publishing.
All Rights Reserved. International Copyright Secured.

# MA BAKER

(BONEY M.)

Freeze! I'm Ma Baker - put your hands in the air, gimme all your money!
**Intro:** D C# C C# D
```
D              C           Bb           A           D       C#
This is the story of Ma Baker, the meanest cat from old Chicago town.
C C# D C Bb A
Dm C Am Dm   Dm C Am Dm   C Dm C Dm   Dm C Am Dm   Dm C Am Dm   C Dm C Dm
```

```
           Dm              C           Am      Dm
1. She was the meanest cat, in old Chicago town,
                     C              Am            Dm
   she was the meanest cat, she really mowed them down.
           C      Dm          C       Dm
   She had no heart at all, no no no heart at all.
```

2. She was the meanest cat, oh she was really tough,
   she left her husband flat, he wasn't tough enough.
   She took her boys along, cause they were mean and strong.

**Refrain:**
```
Dm           C              Bb              Am
Ma Ma Ma Ma Ma Baker, she taught her four sons,
     Dm      C           Bb          Am
Ma Ma Ma Ma Ma Baker, to handle their guns.
     Dm      C           Bb          Am
Ma Ma Ma Ma Ma Baker, she never could cry,
     Dm      C              Am            Dm
Ma Ma Ma Ma Ma Baker, but she knew how to die!
```

3. They left a trail of crime across the U.S.A.
   And when one boy was killed, she really made them pay.
   She had no heart at all, no no no heart at all.

Refrain

4. She met a man she liked, she thought she'd stay with him,
   one day he fought with them, they did away with him.
   She didn't care at all, just didn't care at all.

[Dm C Dm Bb A   Dm C Dm Bb A]
" Here is a special bulletin:
Ma Baker is the FBI's most wanted woman.
Her photo is hanging on every post office wall.
If you have any information about this woman,
please contact the nearest police station..."
[Dm C Am Dm   Dm C Am Dm   C Dm C Dm]
Don't anybody move! The money or your lives!

5. One day they robbed a bank, it was their last foray,
   the cops appeared too soon, they couldn't get away.
   And all the loot they had, it made them mighty mad.

6. And so they shot it out, Ma Baker and her sons.
   They didn't want to hang, they died with blazing guns.
   and so the story ends, of one who left no friends

Refrain 2x

M + T: Frank Farian / George Reyam / Fred Jay
© Far Musikverlag GmbH.
Mit freundlicher Genehmigung von Far Musikverlag GmbH & Co. KG.

# WORDS

(F. R. DAVID)

**Refrain:**
```
C          Am         Dm        G
Words don't come easy to me,
G          Gm    A              Dm     G
how can I find a way to make you see I love you?
                    C      F G
Words don't come easy.
```

**Refrain 2:**
```
C          Am         Dm        G
Words don't come easy to me,
G          Gm    A              Dm     G
this is the only way for me to say I love you.
                    C
Words don't come easy.
```

```
    C         G              C
1. Well, I'm just a music man,
       G                  C
melodies are for my best friend,
          Am              Em
but my words are coming out wrong, girl.
F            G
I reveal my heart to you and
Fm             G
hope that you believe it's true cause:
```

Refrain

```
    C         G              C
2. This is just a simple song
            G              C
that I've made for you on my own.
           Am                Em
There's no hidden meaning you know when I,
F              G
when I say I love you, honey!
Fm             G
Please believe I really do cause:
```

Refrain

```
Am E/G# C/G D/F#
        F                      G
It isn't easy, words don't come easy.
```

Refrain

Refrain 2

M + T: R.Fitoussi, S.Yaguda & M.Kuppersmith
© Cezame Argile S A. Universal Music Publishing Limited.
All Rights Reserved. International Copyright Secured.

# BABICKA

(KAREL GOTT)

```
   Gm
1. Als wir Kinder waren, sind wir oft gefahren
Bb
oben auf dem Wagen mit dem Heu
Cm          A7     D
und bei uns war immer Babicka.
   Gm
Herrliche Geschichten konnte sie berichten
Bb
und für uns war's immer wieder neu.
Cm          A7     D
Alle Kinder liebten Babicka.
```

**Refrain:**
```
G                                                  D
Singen, kochen, tanzen, lachen, glücklich machen. Das war Babicka.
                                           G6     G
Pferde stehlen, Äpfel schälen und erzählen. Das war Babicka.
G7                                  C              A7
Sie hat uns getröstet in der Nacht und gut ins Bett gebracht.
      G                        D           G
Wir liebten sie und spielten gern mit uns'rer Babicka.
```

```
2. Löcher in den Strümpfen, oh was konnt' sie schimpfen,
doch wir wussten, dass sie's nicht so meint.
Denn wir kannten uns're Babicka.
Wenn wir sie besuchten, roch es schon nach Kuchen,
wir probierten heimlich Erdbeerwein
und dann wurde uns so schlecht davon.
```

Refrain

```
3. Ich seh's noch wie heute. Hör' die Glocken läuten
in der kleinen Kirche gleich beim Haus.
Alle weinten wir um Babicka.
Sie hat für ein Leben nie klein beigegeben,
einer nur war stärker noch als sie
und der holte uns're Babicka.
```

Refrain

M + T: Ralph Siegel, Bernd Meinunger
© 1979 Edition Meridian Ralph Siegel KG, Germany
Warner/Chappell Overseas Holdings Limited, London.
Reproduced by permission of Faber Music Limited.
All Rights Reserved.

# FOREVER YOUNG

(ALPHAVILLE)

```
      C              G                     Am
1. Let's dance in style, let's dance for a while,
        F                             G
heaven can wait, we're only watching the skies.
              Dm               F
Hoping for the best but expecting the worst,
                      Am          G6 C
are you gonna drop the bomb or not?
```

```
2. Let us die young or let us live forever,
we don't have the power, but we never say never.
Sitting in the sandpit, life is a short trip,
the music's for the sad man.
```

```
3. Can you imagine when this race is won?
turn our golden faces into the sun.
Praising our leaders, we're getting in tune,
the music's played by the madmen.
```

**Refrain:**
```
C         G              Am           F
Forever young, I want to be forever young.
G                   Am
Do you really want to live forever?
F        G
Forever, you'll never...
C         G              Am           F
Forever young, I want to be forever young.
G                   Am           F G
Do you really want to live forever?
G        C
Forever young.
```

```
4. Some are like water, some are like the heat,
some are a melody and some are the beat.
Sooner or later they all will be gone.
Why don't they stay young?
```

```
5. It's so hard to get old without a cause,
I don't want to perish like a fading horse.
Youth's like diamonds in the sun
and diamonds are forever.
```

```
6. So many adventures couldn't happen today,
so many songs we forgot to play.
So many dreams swinging out of the blue,
we'll let it come true.
```

Refrain 2x

M: Gold, Marian / Lloyd, Bernhard / Mertens, Frank
T: Gold, Marian
© 1984 Rolf Budde Musikverlag GmbH, Berlin.

# WHEN I COME AROUND

(GREEN DAY)
[TRANSP. -1]

```
   G D            Em C G     D          Em C
1. I heard you crying loud all the way across town.
         G                 D         Em           C
You've been searching for that someone and it's me out on the prowl.
      G    D         Em        C
As you sit around feeling sorry for yourself.

G    D          Em C G    D             Em C
Well, don't get lonely now. And dry your whining eyes.
           G              D        Em              C
I'm just roaming for the moment sleazing my back yard so don't get
    G            D            Em        C
so uptight you been thinking about ditching me.
```

**Refrain:**
```
A                      C
No time to search the world around.
A                      C
Cause you know where I'll be found.
             G D Em C
When I come around.

   G D          Em C G    D             Em   C
2. I heard it all before. So don't knock on my door.
        G         D        Em          C
I'm a loser and a user, so I don't need no accuser
    G            D          Em          C
to try and slag me down because I know you're right.

G  D           Em C G    D              Em C
So go do what you like. Make sure you do it wise.
            G                D         Em              C
You may find out that your self doubt means nothing was ever there.
     G            D          Em          C
You can't go forcing something if it's just not right.
```

Refrain

M + T: Billie Joe Armstrong, Frank E. Wright, Mike Pritchard
© 1994 Green Daze Music,
Warner/Chappell North America, London.
Reproduced by permission of Faber Music Limited.
All Rights Reserved.

# SYLVIA'S MOTHER

(DR. HOOK & THE MEDICINE SHOW)

```
       A
1. Sylvia's mother says "Sylvia's busy,
                   E
too busy to come to the phone."

Sylvia's mother says "Sylvia's trying
                          A
to start a new life of her own"
D                      A
Sylvia's mother says "Sylvia's happy,
    E              A
so why don't you leave her alone?"
```

**Refrain:**
```
          E
And the operator says "40 cents more for the next 3 minutes."
    D                    A
Ple-ease Mrs. Avery, I just gotta talk to her,
E                         A
I'll only keep her a while.
D                   A                 E
Please Mrs. Avery, I just wanna tell 'er goodbye.
```

2. Sylvia's mother says "Sylvia's packing,
she's gonna be leaving today."
Sylvia's mother says "Sylvia's marrying
a fellow down Galveston way."
Sylvia's mother says "please don't say nothing
to make her start crying and stay."

Refrain

3. Sylvia's mother says "Sylvia's hurrying,
she's catching the nine o'clock train."
Sylvia's mother says "take your umbrella,
cause Sylvie, it's starting to rain."
And Sylvia's mother says "thank you for calling,
and Sir, won't you call back again?"

Refrain

M + T: Shel Silverstein<br>© Evil Eye Music Inc.

## KUMBAYA

```
      D            G    D
1. Kumbaya, my Lord, kumbaya.
      Bm7          G    A
Kumbaya, my Lord, kumbaya.
      D            G    D
Kumbaya, my Lord, kumbaya.
G  D     A    D
Oh, Lord, kumbaya.

            D            G    D
2. Someone's crying, Lord, kumbaya.
            Bm7          G    A
Someone's crying, Lord, kumbaya.
            D            G    D
Someone's crying, Lord, kumbaya.
G  D     A    D
Oh, Lord, kumbaya.

            D            G    D
3. Someone's singing, Lord, kumbaya.
            Bm7          G    A
Someone's singing, Lord, kumbaya.
            D            G    D
Someone's singing, Lord, kumbaya.
G  D     A    D
Oh, Lord, kumbaya.

            D            G    D
4. Someone's praying, Lord, kumbaya.
            Bm7          G    A
Someone's praying, Lord, kumbaya.
            D            G    D
Someone's praying, Lord, kumbaya.
G  D     A    D
Oh, Lord, kumbaya.

      D            G    D
5. Kumbaya, my Lord, kumbaya.
      Bm7          G    A
Kumbaya, my Lord, kumbaya.
      D            G    D
Kumbaya, my Lord, kumbaya.
G  D     A    D
Oh, Lord, kumbaya.
```

Traditionell
© 2005 by Edition DUX, Manching

# TRULY MADLY DEEPLY

(SAVAGE GARDEN)

```
      C                             G
1. I'll be your dream, I'll be your wish, I'll be your fantasy.
   F                            G                            C
   I'll be your hope, I'll be your love, be everything that you need.
                                G
   I love you more with every breath truly, madly, deeply do.
   F                                            G
   I will be strong, I will be faithful cause I'm counting on
     Am             G                 F              G
   a new beginning. A reason for living. A deeper meaning, yeah.
```

**Refrain:**
```
              C                   G
   I want to stand with you on a mountain.
              F                    G
   I want to bathe with you in the sea.
              C                  G
   I want to lay like this forever.
              F                G
   Until the sky falls down on me...
```

```
2. And when the stars are shining brightly in the velvet sky,
   I'll make a wish, send it to heaven then make you want to cry.
   The tears of joy for all the pleasure and the certainty.
   That we're surrounded by the comfort and protection of
   the highest power. In lonely hours. The tears devour you.
```

Refrain

```
Fmaj7       G
Oh can't you see it baby?
Fmaj7                                      G
You don't have to close your eyes cause it's standing right before you.
Fmaj7        G              C
All that you need will surely come.
```

```
C                                G
I'll be your dream, I'll be your wish, I'll be your fantasy.
F                            G                            C
I'll be your hope, I'll be your love, be everything that you need.
                              G
I'll love you more with every breath truly, madly, deeply do.
```

Refrain 2x

M + T: Craig Stevens, Sean Flowerdew & Graeme Flowerdew
© Copyright 1997 Sony/ATV Music Publishing (UK) Limited.
All Rights Reserved. International Copyright Secured.

# YOU NEVER CAN TELL

(EMMYLOU HARRIS)

```
        C
1. It was a teenage wedding and the old folks wished them well,
                                         G
you could see that Pierre did truly love the mademoiselle.
And now the young monsier and madame have rung the chapel bell.
                                                            C
C'est la vie say the old folks. It goes to show you never can tell.


          C
2. They furnished off an apartment with a two room Roebuck sale,
                                          G
the coolerator was crammed with TV dinners and ginger ale.
But when Pierre found work the little money coming worked out well.
                                                            C
C'est la vie say the old folks. It goes to show you never can tell.


         C
3. They had a hifi phono, boy did they let it blast,
                                     G
seven hundred little records all rock rhythm and jazz.
But when the sun went down the rapid tempo of the music fell.
                                                            C
C'est la vie say the old folks. It goes to show you never can tell.


             C
4. They bought a souped up jitney t'was a cherry red fiftythree,
                                             G
they drove it down to New Orleans to celebrate their anniversary.
It was there that Pierre was wedded to the lovely mademoiselle.
                                                            C
C'est la vie say the old folks. It goes to show you never can tell.


        C
1. It was a teenage wedding and the old folks wished them well,
                                         G
you could see that Pierre did truly love the mademoiselle.
And now the young monsier and madame have rung the chapel bell.
                                                            C
C'est la vie say the old folks. It goes to show you never can tell.
```

M + T: Chuck Berry
© Copyright 1964 by Arc Music Corp., New-York.
Good Tunes Music AG, Genf, für Deutschland, Österreich und Schweiz.

## IM OSTEN

(NIEMANN)

```
   E                            A
1. Die eingefleischten Kenner wissen, dass die Männer im Osten besser
küssen,
         E                        A
dass die Mädchen im Osten schöner sind, weiß heutzutage jedes Kind.
      A            B
Dass die Mauern im Osten besser halten,
         E                             A
dass die meisten hier meistens etwas schneller schalten,
A                    B                    E
dass eigentlich fast alles etwas besser ist als im Westen.
```

2. Jeder wird mal die Erfahrung machen, dass die Kinder im Osten öfter lachen.
Dass sie sich auch über kleine Sachen freuen
und, wenn sie böse war'n, das später auch bereuen.
Dass die Omis im Osten viel lieber sind
und jeder Spinner hier eigentlich nur halb so viel spinnt,
dass eigentlich fast alles etwas besser ist als im Westen.

**Refrain:**
```
E                  A          B
Trotzdem sind wir (mir sind ja so schön!)
            E         E             C#m
viel zu bescheiden (Junge, sind mir schön!)
   A              B                   E
Trotzdem kann uns immer noch nicht jeder leiden.

(mir sind ja so schön!)
         A          B
Wir sind (mir sind ja so schön!)
            E         E             C#m
viel zu bescheiden, (Junge, sind mir schön!)
   A                B                    E
dass wir irgendwann die Sieger sind, lässt sich nicht vermeiden.
```

3. Jeder weiß, dass wir hier immer unser Bestes gaben
und dass die Ossis den Golf erfunden haben,
dass die Zeit hier nicht so schnell vergeht,
weil sich die Erde etwas langsamer dreht.
Dass die Butter hier mehr nach Butter schmeckt
und der Sekt auch etwas mehr nach Sekt,
dass eigentlich fast alles etwas besser ist als im Westen.

Refrain (mit doll statt schön)

4. Jeder weiß, dass die Sonne im Osten erwacht
und um den Westen meistens einen großen Bogen macht.
Und dass der Wind von Osten meistens etwas frischer weht
und dass die Semperoper nicht in Düsseldorf steht.
Dass Martin Luther auch schon ein Ossi war,
und dass im Osten überhaupt alles wunderbar
und eigentlich auch alles etwas besser ist als im Westen.

Refrain (mit cool statt schön)

M + T: Kai Niemann
© Hanseatic Musikverlag GmbH & Co KG / Edition Revi Songs. Warner/Chappell Overseas Holdings Ltd, London (for Germany). Warner/Chappell Overseas Holdings Ltd, London (for Austria and Switzerland). Reproduced by permission of Faber Music Ltd. All Rights Reserved.

# THE JET SET

(ALPHAVILLE)

```
   G
1. This is the time, now gimme that beat,
D
feel how the rhythm grips your feet.
A                              C
Ah Kitty Baby, take my hand, she's like a devil: heaven sent.
   G                              D
I'm in her arms and she's in mine, maybe we'll make the film on time.
A                       C
Sitting in the 15th row, Oh Baby Baby, I love you so.

              G         D             A
Refrain: We are the jet set society, we are the jet set
                 C
and that means liberty.
         G         D             A
We are the jet set society, we are the jet set
                 C
and that means liberty.

   G
2. We're on the run, we know where to go,
D
we've got the tickets for the midnight show.
A                                    C
These nights are burning out so fast, hop on the beam, you won't be
last.
G                              D
The Russians seem to be that way, we love 'em like we love D. Kaye.
A
We need no money, we got it free,
              C
we are the high high high high high society.

Refrain

G                 D             G                 D
We are the jet set, hop on the beam, we are the jet set, hop on the beam

          G    D              C
Bridge: Shine on society, shine on liberty,
G    D            C      G D C
shine on luxury, shine on society

   G                                         D
3. Streets are full of love and fear, this could be the final year.
A                        C
Enrico's dead but still ok, we dance the streets, feeling well.
   G                              D
If she's a liar, I'm her lover, if she's a priestess, I'm her cover.
   A                            C
If she's a lady, I'm her man, if she's a man, I'll do what I can.

Refrain  Bridge  Refrain
```

M: Gold, Marian / Lloyd, Bernhard / Mertens, Frank
T: Gold, Marian
© 1984 Rolf Budde Musikverlag GmbH, Berlin.

# EASY DAY

(BANANAFISHBONES)

**Intro:** E D Bm D (2x)

```
     E                   D                    Bm                 D
1. Every day I get up, put my black plastic security suit on my gasmask,
                        E
leave the cellar and go to work.
              D                        Bm
Afraid to be poisoned or trampelled by this huge machinery
       D                 E           D
and I think to myself what fuck above do I have to thank.
       Bm                D                         E
That I'm here to live in this shit I don't wanna complain about
      D                 Bm                   D
the acid rain 'cause it's nice compared to this poison air.
        E            D              Bm              D
And I wish I could just once see the moon, oh, one gorgeous show.
     E                    D                           Bm
So I take it off, yeah, that's feeling good though I'm deeply sick
      D
right away.
```

**Refrain:**
```
                             A                      G
It's like dancing in the sun, having trouble having fun,
                        Bm
having anything you wish to come.
D                A         G            F#
Then it finally smiles your way and you have an easy day.
G                          Bm
It's time to have an easy day.
G                          Bm
It's time to have an easy day.
G                          Bm
It's time to have an easy day.
Intro
       E                    D
2. What the hell, this must be an antique supermarket!
Bm                   D                         E
What am I doing here, god these people drinking milk!

But the clothes they wear look rather cool to me.
Bm                  D
I wear the same, what am I doing here?
E                 D
Excuse me sir, can you help me out?
Bm                    D
I wanna bake a cake but I don't know how.
E                    D
No, I don't but I'm sure I will.
        Bm                 D
So what do we need for your bakery?
```

Refrain

Every working morning tired, yawn too often I got fired.
Wondered if there is a god searching for a fishingrod with hooks
that sting right through our hearts, forcing us onto new starts.
Love and knowledge are the way, try to have an easy day.

M + T: Peter Horn Jr., Sebastian Horn, Forian Rein
© Edition Base Two Music, Chrysalis Music Holdings.
Mit freundlicher Genehigung von Chrysalis Music Holdings GmbH.

# RAMONA

**Intro:** F                                                                 (THE BLUE DIAMONDS)

```
       F                              C
1. Ramona, zum Abschied sag ich dir "goodbye".
   C7                              F
Ramona, ein Jahr geht doch so schnell vorbei.
                                C
Verzag' nicht und frag' nicht, denn in Gedanken bin ich bei dir,
                         F
bei Tag bringt die Sonne, bei Nacht der Mond die Grüße von mir.


       F                        C
2. Ramona, denk' jeden Tag einmal daran.
   C7                         D7
Ramona, dass nichts vergeht, was so begann.
     Bb   Bbm      F       E7      Eb7     D7
Nach einem Jahr steh ich mit Blumen vor der Tür,
    Gm7        C7        F   C7
Ramona, dann bleib ich bei dir.


       F                              C
1. Ramona, zum Abschied sag ich dir "goodbye".
   C7                              F
Ramona, ein Jahr geht doch so schnell vorbei.
                                C
Verzag' nicht und frag' nicht, denn in Gedanken bin ich bei dir,
                         F
bei Tag bringt die Sonne, bei Nacht der Mond die Grüße von mir.


       F                        C
2. Ramona, denk' jeden Tag einmal daran.
   C7                         D7
Ramona, dass nichts vergeht, was so begann.
     Bb   Bbm      F       E7      Eb7     D7
Nach einem Jahr steh ich mit Blumen vor der Tür,
    Gm7        C7        F
Ramona, dann bleib ich bei dir.
```

M: Mabel Wayne
T: Wolke Gilbert
© Copyright 1927 Feist Leo Incorporated.
EMI United Partnership Limited.
All Rights Reserved. International Copyright Secured.

# LA CUCARACHA

**Refrain:**
```
       F                              C7
La cucaracha, la cucaracha, ya no puede caminar;
                                           F
Porque no tiene, porque le falta Marihuana que fumar
```

**Refrain 2:**
```
       F                              C7
La cucaracha, la cucaracha, ya no quiere caminar;
                                          F
Porque no tiene, porque le falta dinero para gastar
```

```
                                      C7
1. Ya murió la cucaracha, ya la llevan a enterrar,
                                    F
   Entre cuatro zopilotes y un ratón de sacristán
```

2. Pobre de la cucaracha, se queja con decepción,
   De no usar ropa planchada, por la escasez de carbón.

3. Con las barbas de carranza, voy a hacer una toquilla,
   Pa' ponérsela al sombrero de su padre Pancho Villa.

4. Ya se van los carrancistas, ya se van por el alambre,
   Porque dicen los villistas, que se están muriendo de hambre.

5. Un panadero fue a misa, no encontrando que rezar,
   Le pidió a la Virgen pura, Marihuana pa' fumar

6. Una cosa me da risa: Pancho Villa sin camisa;
   Ya se van los carrancistas porque vienen los villistas

7. Una cosa me da risa: Pancho Villa sin camisa,
   Otra cosa me da horror, al vil Huerta en camisón.

8. Para sarapes, Saltillo; Chihuahua para soldados;
   Para mujeres, Jalisco; Para amar, toditos lados.

9. Mi vecina de enfrente se llamaba Doña Clara,
   Y si no había muerto es probable se llamara.

10. Las muchachas de Las Vegas son muy altas y delgaditas,
    Pero son más pedigueñas que las ánimas benditas.

11. Las muchachas de la villa no saben ni dar un beso,
    Cuando las de Albuquerque hasta estiran el pescuezo.

12. Las muchachas mexicanas son lindas como una flor,
    Y hablan tan dulcemente que encantan de amor.

13. Necesita automóvil par' hacer la caminata
    Al lugar a donde mandó la convención zapata.

14. Cuando uno quiere a una y esta una no lo quiere,
    Es lo mismo que si un calvo en calle encuetr' un peine.

**15.** Las muchachas son de oro; las casadas son de plata;
Las viudas son de cobre, y las viejas hoja de lata.

**16.** Pobrecito de Madero, casi todos le han fallado,
Huerta el ebrio bandolero, es un buey para el arado.

**17.** La ropa sin almidón, se pone todos los días;
Y sin esas boberías, se me figura melón.

**18.** Con las barbas de Forey, voy a hacer un vaquerillo,
Pa' ponérselo al caballo del valiente don Porfirio.

**19.** El que persevera alcanza, dice un dicho verdadero,
Yo lo que quiero es venganza, por la muerte de Madero.

**20.** Un panadero fue a misa, no teniendo que rezar,
Le pidió a la virgen pura, a la nieta de don Juan.

**21.** Todos se pelean la silla que les deja mucha plata;
en el Norte Pancho Villa y en el Sur Viva Zapata!

**22.** Ahora come su ensalada, verdolaga y quintonil,
Porque no tiene dinero para comprar melapil.

**23.** También suprimió el candil de petróleo que tenía,
Y todo va suprimiendo por la horrible carestía.

**24.** Antes tan solo a Gambrinus se le miraba llegar,
Mas ora que esta repobre a la piquera va a dar.

**25.** En la mina todo brilla debido a sus minerales,
Ya murió Francisco Villa: General de generales.

**26.** Una guacamaya pinta le dijo a una colorada,
Quien se meta con mi patria, se lo carga la ....

**27.** Hay unos que roban mucho, y luego huyen muy lejos,
Validos de fuero y mando y de que nos creen penitentes.

**28.** Hay otros que nos saquen y con sus deudas nos parte,
Debido a que con su raza todo el botín se reparten.

**29.** Que bonitas soldaderas cuando bailan el fandango.
Viva Panfilo Natera, el orgullo de Durango.

Traditionell
© 2005 by Edition DUX, Manching

# IF YOU COULD READ MY MIND

(GORDON LIGHTFOOT)

**Intro:** G Gsus2 G Gsus2

```
        G                                    F
1. If you could read my mind, love. What a tale my thoughts could tell.
   G                                F
Just like an old time movie. Bout a ghost from a wishing well.
G           G7          C                D               Em
In a castle dark or a fortress strong, with chains upon my feet.
      C                G
You know that ghost is me.
     C             G/B
And I will never be set free
    Am7          D                    G Gsus2
as long as I'm a ghost that you can't see.
```

2. If I could read your mind, love. What a tale your thoughts could tell.
Just like a paper back novel, the kind the drugstores sell.
When you reach the part where the heartaches come, the hero would be me.
But heros often fail.
And you won't read that book again
because the ending's just too hard to take!

```
G         G7         C               D                     Em
I'd walk away like a movie star who gets burned in a threeway script.
C          G     C             G/B
Enter number two: A movie queen to play the scene
   Am7          D             Em
of bringing all the good things out in me.
           C                 G
But for now love, let's be real.
    C                   G/B
I never thought I could act this way
          Am7               D
and I've got to say that I just don't get it.
C                     G/B
I don't know where we went wrong
          Am7                D                G     Gsus2 G Gsus2
but the feeling's gone and I just can't get it back.
```

3. If you could read my mind, love. What a tale my thoughts could tell.
Just like an old time movie. Bout a ghost from a wishing well.
In a castle dark or a fortress strong, with chains upon my feet.
But stories always end.
```
             C                G/B                 Am7
And if you read between the lines you'd know that I'm just
D         Em         C                    G
trying to understand the feelings that you lack.
    C                   G/B
I never thought I could feel this way
          Am7               D
and I've got to say that I just don't get it.
C                     G/B                      Am7
I don't know where we went wrong but the feeling's gone
      D                  G       F G
and I just can't get it back!
```

M + T: by Gordon Lightfoot
© Early Morning Music. Universal Music Publishing Limited. All Rights Reserved. International Copyright Secured.

## TAKE MY BREATH AWAY

(BERLIN)
[TRANSP. -4]

**Intro:**   C   G/B   Am   G

```
        C                  G/B                 Am     G
1. Watching every motion. In my foolish lover's game.
   C                  G/B                Am       G
On this endless ocean. Finally lovers know no shame.
Dm                       C                      G
Turning and returning. To some secret place inside.
C                        G/B                  F    G
Watching in slow motion. As you turn around and say.
```

**Refrain:**
```
G              C    G/B F G
Take my breath away.
G              C    G F G
Take my breath away
```

```
        C                 G/B                  Am     G
2. Watching I keep waiting. Still anticipating love.
   C                G/B              Am    G
Never hesitating. To become the fated ones.
Dm                       C                      G
Turning and returning. To some secret place to hide.
C                        G/B                F    G
Watching in slow motion. As you turn to me and say.
```

Refrain

```
Dm                   G              F               C
Through the hourglass I saw you. In time you slipped away.
Dm                         G            F                 C
When the mirror crashed I called you. And turned to hear you say.
                 Dm           G
If only for today. I am unafraid.
```

Refrain

```
        C                  G/B                  Am     G
3. Watching every motion. In this foolish lover's game.
   C                 G/B                     Am    G
Haunted by the notion. Somewhere there's a love in flames.
Dm                       C                      G
Turning and returning. To some secret place inside.
C                        G/B                 F    G
Watching in slow motion. As you turn my way and say.
```

Refrain

M: Giorgio Moroder
T: Tom Whitlock
© 1986 Jastian Music / Famous Music Corp.
Warner/Chappell Music North America Ltd, London /
Sony/ATV Harmony (UK) Limited.
All Rights Reserved. International Copyright Secured.

## YOU'RE THE ONE THAT I WANT

(OLIVIA NEWTON-JOHN & JOHN TRAVOLTA)

```
        Am                            F            C
1. I got chills, they're multiplying, and I'm losing control
      E              Am
cause the power you're supplying, it's electrifying.
            C            Em          Am                    F
You better shape up, cause I need a man, and my heart is set on you.
            C             Em           Am               F
You better shape up, you better understand, to my heart I must be true.

Nothing left, nothing left for me to do.
```

**Refrain:**
```
              C                                          F
You're the one that I want (you are the one I want), ooh ooh ooh, honey.
    C                                                F
The one that I want (you are the one I want), ooh ooh ooh, honey.
    C                                            F
The one that I want (you are the one I want), ooh ooh ooh,
              G                                          Am
the one I need (the one I need), oh yes indeed (yes indeed).
```

```
            Am                       F           C
2. If you're filled with affection, 'n you're too shy to convey,
      E       Am
meditate my direction, feel your way.
               C          Em
I better shape up, cause you need a man,
Am                      F
I need a man, who can keep me satisfied.
               C        Em
I better shape up, if I'm gonna prove,
Am                               F
you better prove that my fate is justified.

Are you sure? Yes I'm sure down deep inside.
```

Refrain

M + T: John Farrar
© Copyright 1978 Ensign Music Corporation, USA.
Sony/ATV Harmony (UK) Limited.
All Rights Reserved. International Copyright Secured.

# I'M OUTTA LOVE

(ANASTACIA)

**Intro:**   Bbm F Ab Eb Bbm F Ab Eb

```
      Bbm              F                 Ab                    Eb              Bbm
1. Now baby come on, don't claim that love you never let me feel.
            F/A           Ab                     Eb
I should have known cause you've brought nothing real.
              Bbm              F
Come on, be a man about it, you won't die.
   Gb                Ebm       Ab
I ain't got no more tears to cry
            Bbm            F
and I can't take this no more.
            Gb         F
You know I gotta let it go

and you know
```

**Refrain:**
```
          Bbm           F             Ab             Eb
I'm outta love. Set me free and let me out this misery.
                Bbm             F
Just show me the way to get my life again
     Ab          Eb
cause you can't handle me.
                Bbm             F
I said I'm outta love, can't you see,
           Gb          F             Bbm
baby, that you gotta set me free. I'm outta love. Yeah!
```

```
   Bbm           F        Ab              Eb            Bbm
2. Said how many times have I tried to turn this love around?
         F/A   Ab              Eb
But every time you just let me down.
              Bbm            F
Come on, be a man about it, you'll survive.
Gb                  Ebm     Ab
True that you can work it out all right.
           Bbm          F
Tell me, yesterday did you know?
            Gb         F
I'd be the one to let you go?

And you know

Refrain

Gbmaj7                      F7
Let me get over you, the way you've gotten over me too, yeah.
Ebm7                          Cm7b5             F
Seems like my time has come and now I'm moving on.

I'll be stronger.

Refrain 2x
```

M + T: Anastacia, Sam Watters & Louis Biancaniello
© Copyright 2000 EMI April Music Incorporated, USA/Poho Productions/Universal Music Corporation, USA/Breakthrough Creations/S.M.Y. Publishing/Sony-ATV Tunes LLC.Universal Music Publishing Limited/Sony/ATV Music Publishing/EMI Music Publishing/Universal/MCA Music Limited.
All Rights Reserved. International Copyright Secured.

# LIFE FOR RENT

(DIDO)
[TRANSP. +3]

```
      Am                                         F
1. I haven't really ever found a place that I call home.
      Am                                   F
I never stick around quite long enough to make it.
      Am                                F
I apologise that once again I'm not in love.
                      Am                              F
But it's not as if I mind that your heart ain't exactly breaking.
           Dm           G7
It's just a thought, only a thought.
```

**Refrain:**
```
             C G      F
But if my life is for rent
         C      G       F   G
and I don't learn to buy.
             C             G        F      G
Well, I deserve nothing more than I get
             C G           F
cause nothing I have is truly mine.
```

```
      Am                                              F/A
2. I've always thought that I would love to live by the sea.
      Am                       F/A
To travel the world alone and live more simply.
      Am                      F/A
I have no idea what's happened to that dream.
             Am                            F
Cause there's really nothing left here to stop me.
           Dm           G7
It's just a thought, only a thought.
```

Refrain 2x

```
            C           G          Dm           G
While my heart is a shield and I won't let it down.
            C           G              Dm         G
While I am so afraid to fail, so I won't even try.
             Dm         G7
Well, how can I say I'm alive?
```

Refrain 2x

```
         C G          F
Nothing I have is truly mine.
         C G          F
Nothing I have is truly mine.
             C G           F
Cause nothing I have is truly mine.
```

M: Rollo Armstrong
T: Dido Armstrong & Rollo Armstrong
© 2003 Warner/Chappell Music Ltd / Universal Music Publishing MGB International Limited. Warner Chappell Music Limited, London / Universal Music Publishing Limited. Reproduced by permission of Faber Music Ltd. All Rights Reserved. International Copyright Secured.

# SAD LISA

(CAT STEVENS)

```
         Em                        D   C
1. She hangs her head and cries in my shirt,
       D       Em        D   G
she must be hurt very badly.
                    D       Em  A
Tell me what's making you sadly?
Em          A          D           C
Open your door, don't hide in the dark,
     D            Em        D         G
you've lost in the dark, you can trust me
                    D        Em   A
'cause you know that's how it must be.
Em        A       B       Em  D Em
Lisa, Lisa, sad Lisa, Lisa.


         Em                        D   C
2. Her eyes like windows trickling rain,
D       Em              D   G
upon her pain getting deeper.
                 D       Em   A
Tho' my love wants to relieve her.
    Em     A           D        C
She walks alone from wall to wall,
D         Em              D     G
lost in a hall, she can't hear me,
                  D        Em   A
tho' I know she likes to be near me.
Em        A       B       Em  D Em
Lisa, Lisa, sad Lisa, Lisa.


         Em                        D   C
3. She sits in a corner by the door.
        D        Em         D    G
There must be more I can tell her,
                  D       Em   A
if she really wants me to help her,
        Em        A        D          C
I'll do what I can to show her the way.
D         Em         D    G
And maybe I will free her,
                D        Em   A
tho' I know no one can see her.
Em        A       B       Em  D Em
Lisa, Lisa, sad Lisa, Lisa.
```

M + T: Cat Stevens
© Copyright 1970 Salafa Limited. All Rights Reserved. International Copyright Secured.
All Rights Reserved. International Copyright Secured.

# ODE TO MY FAMILY

(THE CRANBERRIES)
[TRANSP. +2]

```
              C           Am            Em            F         G
Intro: Dub du dub du, dub du dub du, dub du dub du, dub du dub du. (2x)

         C     Am            Em           F      G      C
1. Understand the things I say, don't turn away from me,
               Am              Em          F       G      C
cause I spent half my life out there, you wouldn't disagree.
                Am              Em
D' you see me, d' you see, do you like me,
     F      G        C
do you like me standing there.
                Am               Em
D' you notice, d' you know, do you see me,
     F       G
do you see me, does anyone care.
```

**Refrain:**
```
C            Am              Em
Unhappiness, where's when I was young,
    F     G      C
and we didn't give a damn.
              Am          Em            F      G     C
Cause we were raised, to see life as fun and take it if we can.
             Am              Em
My mother, my mother, she'd hold me,
       F       G      C
she'd hold me, when I was out there.
             Am          Em
My father, my father, he liked me,
       F             G           C Am Em F G
oh, he liked me, does anyone care.

         C      Am            Em       F      G    C
2. Understand what I've become, it wasn't my design,
C           Am             Em        F      G      C
and people everywhere think something better than I am.
C              Am           Em
But I miss you, I miss, 'cause I liked it,
         F           G           C
'cause I liked it, when I was out there.
C              Am                Em
D' you know this, d' you know, you did not find me,
            F        G      C
you did not find, does anyone care.
```

Refrain

```
C              Am              Em             F         G     C
Does anyone care, does anyone care, does anyone care, does anyone care?
              Am              Em             F      G
Does anyone care, does anyone care, does anyone care?
       C           Am            Em           F       G
Dub du dub du, dub du dub du, dub du dub du, dub du dub du. (3x)
```

M + T: Dolores O'Riordan & Noel Hogan
© Copyright 1994 Island Music Limited. Universal/Island Music Limited.
All rights in Germany administered by Universal Music Publ. GmbH.
All Rights Reserved. International Copyright Secured.

# SWEET DREAMS

(EURYTHMICS)
[TRANSP. -4]

**Intro:** Em C B (4x)   C B Em Am   C B

```
   Em            C       B
1. Sweet dreams are made of this.
Em           C   B
Who am I to disagree?
   Em                    C       B
I traveled the world and the seven seas.
Em              C         B
Everybody's looking for something.
```

**Bridge:**
```
Em                     C       B
Some of them want to use you.
Em                    C       B
Some of them want to get used by you.
Em                   C       B
Some of them want to abuse you.
Em               C       B    C B Em Am   C B   Em C B Em C B
Some of them want to be abused.
```

```
   Em            C       B
1. Sweet dreams are made of this.
Em           C   B
Who am I to disagree?
   Em                    C       B
I traveled the world and the seven seas.
Em              C         B
Everybody's looking for something.
```

C B Em Am C B

**Refrain:**
```
Em                    D
Hold your head up. Keep your head up moving on.
Em                              D
Hold your head up moving on. Keep your head up moving on.
Em                    D
Hold your head up. Keep your head up moving on.
Em                              D
Hold your head up moving on. Keep your head up moving on.
```

Bridge

Refrain

M + T: Annie Lennox & David A. Stewart
© Copyright 1983 BMG Music Publishing Limited.
Universal Music Publishing MGB Limited.
All Rights Reserved. International Copyright Secured.

# BECAUSE I GOT HIGH

(AFROMAN)

```
   G                            C
1. I was gonna clean my room until I got high.
        D                             G
I gonna get up and find the broom but then I got high.
   G                            C
My room is still messed up and I know why.
             G                D              G
Because I got high, because I got high, because I got high!

2. I was gonna go to class before I got high.
I coulda cheated and I coulda passed but I got high.
I am taking it next semester and I know why.
Because I got high, because I got high, because I got high!

3. I was gonna go to work but then I got high.
I just got a new promotion but I got high.
Now I'm selling dope and I know why.
Because I got high, because I got high, because I got high!

4. I was gonna go to court before I got high.
I was gonna pay my child support but then I got high.
They took my whole paycheck and I know why.
Because I got high, because I got high, because I got high!

5. I wasn't gonna run from the cops, but I was high.
I was gonna pull right over and stop, but I was high.
Now I am a paraplegic and I know why.
Because I got high, because I got high, because I got high!

6. I was gonna pay my car note until I got high.
I was gonna gamble on the boat but then I got high.
Now the tow truck is pulling away and I know why.
Because I got high, because I got high, because I got high!

7. I was gonna make love to you, but then I got high.
I was gonna eat yo pussy too, but then I got high.
Now I'm jacking off and I know why.
Because I got high, because I got high, because I got high!

8. I messed up my entire life because I got high.
I lost my kids and wife because I got high.
Now I'm sleeping on the sidewalk and I know why.
Because I got high, because I got high, because I got high!

9. I'm gonna stop singing this song because I'm high.
I'm singing this whole thing wrong because I'm high.
And if I don't sell one copy I know why.
Because I'm high, because I'm high, because I'm high!
```

M + T: Joseph Foreman
© Copyright 2001 Universal/MCA Music Limited. All rights in Germany administered by Universal/MCA Music Publ. GmbH.
All Rights Reserved. International Copyright Secured.

# SUPERGIRL

(REAMONN)
[TRANSP. +2]

**Intro:** Em Bm Am C Em Bm Am C

```
          Em                            Bm
1. You can tell by the way, she walks that she's my girl,
         Am                          C
you can tell by the way, she talks she rules the world.
           Em                        Bm
You can see in her eyes that no one is her chain,
       Am           C
she's my girl, my supergirl.
```

**Refrain:**
```
                 G                          D
And then she'd say, "It's ok, I got lost on the way,
              Em                         C
but I'm a supergirl, and supergirls don't cry."
                 G                            D
And then she'd say, "It's alright, I got home late last night
              Em                      C
but I'm a supergirl and supergirls just fly."

                     Em                        Bm
2. And then she'd say that nothing can go wrong.
            Am              C
When you're in love, what can be wrong?
                 Em                         Bm
And then she'd laugh the night time into day,
            Am              C
pushing her fear further along.

                 G                          D
And then she'd say, "It's ok, I got lost on the way,
              Em                         C
but I'm a supergirl, and supergirls don't cry."
                 G                            D
And then she'd say, "It's alright, I got home late last night
              Em                      C
but I'm a supergirl and supergirls just fly."

                 G                              D
And then she'd shout down the line, tell me she's got no more time,
                    Em                         C
cause she's a supergirl and supergirls don't cry.
                 G                                 D
And then she'd scream in my face, tell me to leave, leave this place,
                    Em                      C
cause she's a supergirl and supergirls just fly.

              G              D
Yes, she's a supergirl, a supergirl,
              Em
she's sowing seeds, she's burning trees,
         C
she's sowing seeds, she's burning trees.
              G              D              Em            C   Em
Yes, she's a supergirl, a supergirl, a supergirl,  my supergirl.
```

M + T: Michael Raymond Garvey / Sebastian Padotzke / Uwe Bossert / Mike Gommeringer / Phillip Rauenbusch
© B612 Publishing GmbH & Co. KG.
Administriert durch Rudi Schedler Musikverlag GmbH.

# AN DER NORDSEEKÜSTE

(KLAUS UND KLAUS)

```
   D                          G
1. Damals vor unendlich langer Zeit,
   D              A            D
da machten wir Friesen am Wasser uns breit.
      D                          G
Die Jahre vergingen wie Saus und wie Braus,
    D           A              D
aber breit sehn wir Friesen auch heute noch aus.
```

**Refrain:**
```
         A                D                G
An der Nordseeküste, x x x      am plattdeutschen Strand,
        D       G       A        D
sind die Fische im Wasser und selten an Land.
```

```
      D                            G
2. Nach Flut kommt die Ebbe, nach Ebbe die Flut,
      D         A                   D
   die Deiche, sie halten mal schlecht und mal gut.
                                          G
   Die Dünen sie wandern am Strand hin und her,
      D         A                          D
   von Grönland nach Flandern, jedenfalls ungefähr.
```

Refrain

```
         D                    G
3. Die Seehunde singen ein Klagelied,
         D           A                            D
   weil sie nicht mit dem Schwanz wedeln können, so'n Schiet!
         D                              G
   Die Schafe, sie blöken wie blöd auf dem Deich,
         D              A                       D
   und mit schwarzgrünen Kugeln garnier'n sie ihn gleich.
```

Refrain 2x

M + T: W. Oertel, R. Mol, T. de Reede, B. van Hil & T. Buchner
© Nanada CNR Music – c/o Nanada Music BV.

# LIES

(ALPHAVILLE)

```
      G                D                       Em
1. Baby, baby, what do I do? Playing my tune for you,
                            C
playing my tune for you, just to get you in the mood.
                    G                             D
Everybody's going to Hollywood, you're driving me mad,
                        Em
but I'm smiling to the crowd instead.
 C                                           G
A lot of money is at stake, this is hit and that's a fake.

                          D
2. This is what you mean to me, this is what they all should see,
Em                      C7
make a makeup in a foolish style, telling the truth by making a big?
    G
Lie when I come, I come but nothing's at ease,
D
breaking up the whole is a modern disease,
Em
maybe you think tomorrow's just a joke.
      C7
It's a joke after joke after joke after joke.
```

**Refrain:**
```
      G                    D
My love, everything's an interview
                      Em                          C7
and nothing's really new and everybody's looking for clues.
                                     G
And you know what to do with a clue, my love.
                 D                             Em
I get ready for the show, they're waiting and they will never go.
                    C              G     D Em C7
This night is just to goooo, and it's only for show.

      G
3. Dig that deal and be a millionaire,
D
drinking cocktails in the stratosphere,
Em
getting jetlagged with my business friends
C7
in these supersonic wonderlands.
G
There's a shadow on the graphic display,
D
first he's smiling then he's fading away.
Em
Maybe he thinks tomorrow's just a joke,
         C7
it's a joke after joke after joke after joke.
```

Refrain

M: Gold, Marian / Lloyd, Bernhard / Mertens, Frank
T: Gold, Marian
© 1984 Rolf Budde Musikverlag GmbH, Berlin.

# A HARD DAY'S NIGHT

(THE BEATLES)

**Intro:** G7sus4

```
              C      F7    C                Bb7                  C
1. It's been a hard day's night and I've been working like a dog.
           F7        C                Bb7                C
It's been a hard day's night I should be sleeping like a log.
           F7                            G7
But when I get home to you I find the things that you do,
               C    F7  C
will make me feel alright.


              C      F7    C                Bb7                  C
2. You know I work all day to get you money to buy you things.
                             F7          C
And it's worth it just to hear you say,
          Bb7               C
you're gonna give me everything.
           F7                                 G7
So why on earth should I moan, cause when I get you alone,
              C    F7  C
you know I'll be okay.
```

**Refrain:**

```
         Em7    Am7                       Em7
When I'm home, everything seems to be right,
           C    Am7                   F6      G7
When I'm home, feeling you holding me tight, tight, yeah.


              C      F7    C                Bb7                  C
1. It's been a hard day's night and I've been working like a dog.
           F7        C                Bb7                C
It's been a hard day's night I should be sleeping like a log.
           F7                            G7
But when I get home to you I find the things that you do,
               C    F7  C
will make me feel alright.
            F7   C
You know I feel all right.
            C    F7  C
You know I feel all right.
```

M + T: John Lennon & Paul McCartney
© Copyright 1964 Sony/ATV Music Publishing (UK) Limited.
All Rights Reserved. International Copyright Secured.

# NIEMALS GEHT MAN SO GANZ

(TRUDE HERR)

**Intro:** Dm F Am G Dm F Am G

```
          F                         G
1. Wenn man Abschied nimmt, geht nach unbestimmt
       C              G/B
mit dem Wind, wie Blätter wehn.
       Am                    C
Singt met Abschiedsleed, dat sich om Fernweh dreht,
     F                    G
om Horizonte, Salz un Teer.
```

2. Wer singe Püngel schnürt söök wo'e hinjehührt,
hätt wie ne Zochvuel nit nur ei Zohuss.
Man lässt vieles hier, Freund ich danke dir
für den Kuss den letzten Gruß.

```
Dm                     F
Ich will weitergehn, keine Tränen sehn,
      Am                   G     C
so ein Abschied ist lang noch kein Tod.
```

**Refrain:**
```
F             G           C         G/B    F     C/E
Niemals geht man so ganz, irgendwas von mir bleibt hier,
Dm              G            Am
es hat seinen Platz immer bei dir.
```

3. Wenn't och noch su sticht, stutz die Flüjel nit,
dämm dae in de Käld kein Zokunft sieht.
Mach 'nem Vagabund doch et Hätz nit wund,
fleech e Stöck met op singem Wääsch.

Doch dann lass' mich los, sieh, die Welt ist groß,
ohne Freiheit bin ich fast schon wie tot.

Refrain 2x

4. Ich verspreche hier, bin zurück bei dir,
wenn der Wind von Süden weht.
Ich saach nit "Lebwohl", dat Wort, dat klingt wie Hohn,
völlig hohl, mach et joot.

Sieh, ich weine auch, Tränen sind wie Rauch,
sie vergehn, dieser Käfig macht mich tot.

Refrain 2x

Nie verlässt man sich ganz, irgendwas von dir geht mit,
es hat seinen Platz immer bei mir.

M: Jürgen Fritz
T: Trude Herr
© 1987 MIAU MUSIKVERLAG GMBH.

# LENINGRAD

(BILLY JOEL)

```
   D         Em/D   G/D       A/D D      Em/D G/D     A
1. Victor was born in spring of '44 and never saw his father anymore,
D/C      G/B       D/A       E/G#
a child of sacrifice, a child of war,
D/A     A#°      Bm        G      A     D
another son who never had a father after Leningrad.

   D         Em/D   G/D        A/D
2. He went off to school and learned to serve the state.
D          Em/D   G/D          A/D
He followed the rules and drank his vodka straight.
D/C      G/B        D/A          E/G#
The only way to live was to drown the hate,
D/A     A#°      Bm            G      A    D
a Russian life was very sad and such was life in Leningrad.

Dm                     Am
I was born in '49, a cold war kid in McCarthy time,
Gsus4           G           Asus4          A
stop em at the 38th Parallel, blast those yellow reds to hell.
Dsus4                 Dm
And cold war kids were hard to kill
Asus4              Am
under their desk in an air raid drill.
Gsus4             G            Asus4             A
Haven't they heard we won the war. What do they keep on fighting for?

   D         Em/D  G/D       A/D
3. Victor was sent to some Red Army town,
D           Em/D   G/D      A/D
served out his time, became a circus clown.
D/C      G/B       D/A      E/G#  D/A      A#°              Bm
The greatest happiness he'd ever found was making Russian children glad
              G     A    D
and children lived in Leningrad.

Dm                                Am
But children lived in Levitown, hid their shelters underground.
Gsus4                         G
When the Soviets turned their ships around
Asus4           A
and tore the Cuban missiles down.
Dsus4                 Dm            Asus4               Am
And in that bright October sun, we knew our childhood days where done.
Gsus4                      G
And I watched my friends go off to war.
Asus4           A
What do they keep on fighting for?
   D         Em/D    G/D      A/D
4. And so my child and I came to this place
D          Em/D   G/D      A/D
to meet him eye to eye and face to face.
D/C      G/B          D/A       E/G#
He made my daughter laugh. Then we embraced:
D/A     A#°           Bm           G     A    D
We never knew what friends we had until we came to Leningrad.
```

M + T: Billy Joel
© Copyright 1989 Joelsongs.
Rondor Music International.
All Rights Reserved. International Copyright Secured.

# A KIND OF MAGIC

(QUEEN)

```
           A                    B9
1. One dream, one soul, one prize, one goal.
      Dmaj7            A
One golden glance of what should be.
      A                 B9
One shaft of light that shows the way.
     Dmaj7         A
No mortal man can win this day.
     A                 B9
The bell that rings inside your mind
     Dmaj7           A
is challenging the doors of time.
     F#m           D
The waiting seems eternity,
     F#m            E
the day will dawn of sanity.
```

**Refrain:**
```
    D           A         D          A
Is this a kind of magic? There can be only one.
    E         G      D                         E
This rage that lasts a thousand years will soon be gone.
```

```
           A              B9
2. This flame that burns inside of me.
      Dmaj7        A
I'm hearing secret harmonies.
     A                 B9
The bell that rings inside your mind
     Dmaj7           A
is challenging the doors of time.
D A
   It's a kind of magic.
D A
   It's a kind of magic.
      E       G        D
This rage that lasts a thousand years will soon be,
                             E
Will soon be, will soon be done.
```

**Refrain:**
```
    D           A         D          A
This is a kind of magic? There can be only one.
    E         G      D                         E
This rage that lasts a thousand years will soon be gone.
D A
   It's a kind of magic.
D A
   It's a kind of magic.
```

M + T: Roger Taylor
© Copyright 1986 Queen Music Limited.
Reproduced by permission of International Music Publications Limited
(a trading name of Faber Music Ltd).
All Rights Reserved.

# WANTED DEAD OR ALIVE

(BON JOVI)

**Intro:** Dm

```
          D           Dsus4 Dsus2 D C              G
1. It's all the same,           only the names will change.
C        G                C      F      D
Everyday it seems we're wasting away
   D          Dsus4 Dsus2 D         C              G
Another place             where the faces are so cold.
     C        G              C    F    D
I'd drive all night just to get back home.
```

**Refrain:**
```
      C       G      F           D
I'm a cowboy, on a steel horse I ride.
   C      G C    D   F D
I'm wanted   dead or alive.
C    G C    D  F D
Wanted  dead or alive.
```

```
           D          Dsus4 Dsus2 D  C              G
2. Sometimes I sleep,         sometimes it's not for days
     C          G       C       F       D
and people I meet always go their separate ways.
   D                    Dsus4 Dsus2 D      C             G
Sometimes you tell the day          by the bottle that you drink
     C                   G     C      F      D
and times when you're all alone all you do is think.
```

Refrain 2x

```
        D              Dsus4 Dsus2 D       C            G
3. I walk these streets,        a loaded six string on my back,
    C        G      C       F      D
I play for keeps cause I might not make it back.
            D       Dsus4 Dsus2 D         C           G
I've been everywhere,           still I'm standing tall,
    C           G              C       F      D
I've seen a million faces and I've rocked them all.
```

```
      C       G      F           D
I'm a cowboy, on a steel horse I ride.
   C      G C    D   F D
I'm wanted   dead or alive.
      C       G     F           D
I'm a cowboy, I got the night on my side.
   C      G C    D   F D
I'm wanted   dead or alive.
C    G C    D  F D
Wanted  dead or alive.
```

M + T: Jon Bon Jovi & Richie Sambora
© Copyright 1995 Bon Jovi Publishing/Aggressive Music, USA.
Sony/ATV Music Publishing (UK) Limited / Kobalt Music
Limited. All Rights Reserved. International Copyright Secured.

# LADY MADONNA

(THE BEATLES)

```
A      D    A              D
Lady Madonna, children at your feet,
A           D     A/E F   G    A
wonder how you manage to  make ends meet.
A           D    A             D
Who finds the money when you pay the rent,
A              D    A/E F  G    A
did you think that money was heaven sent.

    Dm                              G7
1. Friday night arrives without a suitcase,
C                               Am
Sunday morning creep in like a nun,
Dm                              G7
Monday's child has learnt to tie his bootlace.
C   Bm7     E7sus4 E7
See how they run!

A      D    A           D
Lady Madonna, baby at your breast,
A           D     A/E F   G    A
wonder how you manage to  feed the rest.

2. Instrumental: Dm G7 C Am Dm G7
C   Bm7     E7sus4 E7
See how they run!

A      D    A             D
Lady Madonna, lying on the bed,
A           D     A/E     F   G    A
listen to the music playing in your head.

    Dm                           G7
3. Tuesday afternoon is never ending,
C                               Am
Wednesday morning papers didn't come,
Dm                              G7
Thursday night your stockings needed mending.
C   Bm7     E7sus4 E7
See how they run!

A      D    A              D
Lady Madonna, children at your feet,
A           D     A/E F   G    A
wonder how you manage to  make ends meet.
```

M + T: John Lennon & Paul McCartney
© Copyright 1968 Sony/ATV Music Publishing.
All Rights Reserved. International Copyright Secured.

## EIN BISSCHEN FRIEDEN

(NICOLE)

```
      C                  G
1. Wie eine Blume am Winterbeginn
      G7              C
und so wie ein Feuer im eisigen Wind,
C7                          F
wie eine Puppe, die keiner mehr mag,
     G                 C
fühl ich mich an manchem Tag.

           C                      G
2. Dann seh ich die Wolken, die über uns sind
      G7                       C
und höre die Schreie der Vögel im Wind,
C7                            F
ich singe aus Angst vor dem Dunkel mein Lied
     G                       C
und hoffe, dass nichts geschieht.
```

**Refrain:**
```
               C                     G
Ein bisschen Frieden, ein bisschen Sonne,
         G7                C
für diese Erde, auf der wir wohnen,
               C                     G
ein bisschen Frieden, ein bisschen Freude,
               G7                C
ein bisschen Wärme, das wünsch ich mir.
               C                     G
Ein bisschen Frieden, ein bisschen träumen,
         G7                        C
und dass die Menschen nicht so oft weinen,
               C                     G
ein bisschen Frieden, ein bisschen Liebe,
         G7                        C
dass ich die Hoffnung nie mehr verlier.
```

```
           C                          G
3. Ich weiß, meine Lieder, die ändern nicht viel,
       G7                            C
ich bin nur ein Mädchen, das sagt, was es fühlt.
   C7                        F
Allein bin ich hilflos, ein Vogel im Wind,
      G                          C
der spürt, dass der Sturm beginnt.
```

Refrain

```
C        G      G7       C           G      G7       C
Sing mit mir ein kleines Lied, dass die Welt in Frieden lebt.
C        G      G7       C           G      G7       C
Sing mit mir ein kleines Lied, dass die Welt in Frieden lebt!
```

M + T: Ralph Siegel, Bernd Meinunger
© Copyright 1982 Edition Meridian Ralph Siegel KG, Germany.
Warner/Chappell Overseas Holdings Limited, London. Reproduced by permission of Faber Music Limited. All Rights Reserved.

# THANK YOU

(DIDO)
[TRANSP. +4]

**Intro:** Em Cmaj7 (8x)

```
      Em           Cmaj7              D            G       G/F#      Em
1. My tea's gone cold, I'm wondering why  I got out of bed at all.
            Cmaj7         D          G       G/F#     Em
The morning rain clouds up my window and I can't see at all.
            Cmaj7           D              G       G/F#     Em
And even if I could it'd all be grey but your picture on my wall,
      Cmaj7          Em              Cmaj7
it reminds me that it's not so bad, it's not so bad.
```

Em Cmaj7 (2x)

```
      Em           Cmaj7              D
2. I drank too much last night, got bills to pay,
      G       G/F#     Em
my head just feels in pain.
            Cmaj7            D              G       G/F#     Em
I missed the bus and there'll be hell today, I'm late for work again.
            Cmaj7         D              G         G/F#     Em
And even if I'm there, they'll all imply that I might not last the day.
            Cmaj7           Em                  Cmaj7
And then you call me and it's not so bad, it's not so bad and…
```

**Refrain:**
```
G           C                         G            C
I want to thank you for giving me the best day of my life.
G           C                       Bm            Am
Oh, just to be with you is having the best day of my life.
```

```
G                    C                   D             G
Push the door, I'm home at last and I'm soaking through and through.
              C                      G
Then you hand me a towel and all I see is you.
                       C                           Bm
And even if my house falls down, I wouldn't have a clue.
              Am
Because you're near me and
```

Refrain 2x

**Outro:** Am

M + T: Dido Armstrong & Paul Herman
© 1997 Warner/Chappell Music Limited / Submarine Music Limited. Warner/Chappell Music Ltd, London / Peermusic (UK) Limited. Reproduced by permission of Faber Music Ltd. All Rights Reserved.
All Rights Reserved. International Copyright Secured.

# EASY

(FAITH NO MORE)
(LIONEL RICHIE)
[TRANSP. +1]

```
        G             Bm                    Am              D
1. Know it sounds funny but I just can't stand the pain.
   G        Bm             Am      D
   Girl, I'm leaving you tomorrow.
   G           Bm                     Am        D
   Seems to me girl you know I've done all I can.
   G          Bm                 Am         D
   You see I begged, stole, and I borrowed! Yeah.
```

**Refrain:**
```
   D                   G    Bm Am
   Ooh that's why I'm easy.
          D              G    Bm Am
   I'm easy like Sunday morning.
   D                  G    Bm Am
   That's why I'm easy.
          D              F   C/E   C/D G
   I'm easy like Sunday mor---------ning!


             F     C/E Dm
   I wanna be high, so high.
       C/E F                  Em        C/E Dm
   I wanna be free to know the things I do are right.
         C/E F      C/E Dm   Bb    F   Dm   C
   I wanna be free. Just me! Whoa, oh! Babe!


G Bm Am D  4x


        G            Bm                    Am             D
2. Why in the world would anybody put chains on me?
   G       Bm               Am      D
   I've paid my dues to make it.
   G          Bm                     Am           D
   Everybody wants me to be what they want me to be.
   G           Bm                Am         D
   I'm not happy when I try to fake it! no!
```

Refrain 2x

M + T: Lionel Richie
© Jobete Music Co. Inc.
Subverlag: EMI Songs Musikverlag GmbH.

# WELCOME TO HEARTLIGHT

(KENNY LOGGINS)

```
     Am                    G
1. I like the love and I like the peaceful.
      Am                  F              Em
I wish everyone I know could stand in the heartlight.
Am                 G
I hold the hand, I walk with the teacher,
    Am                   F        Em     G
we welcome in the morning singing together.
```

**Refrain:**
```
Am              F                   G
Can you feel the love that's in my heart,
                E                Am
can you see the flame we got to start
             F              G
burning like a beacon in the night?
                       Am
O welcome to heartlight.
    F       G        E      Am
Oh, oh heartlight. Oh, oh heartlight.
    F       G        E      Am
Oh, oh heartlight. Oh, oh heartlight.
    F       G        E      Am
Oh, oh heartlight. Oh, oh heartlight.
    F       G        E           Am
Oh, oh heartlight. Oh welcome to heartlight.
```

```
     Am                       G
2. I'm like the rain. Cause I like your thunder.
           Am                  F            Em
I know we've learned to live together here in the heartlight.
Am                 G
Stand in the dark, I'll light the candle
                  Am                  F         G
and then we'll dance it in the moonlight until the sunrise.
```

Refrain 2x

M + T: Kenneth Loggins
© Copyright 1983 Milk Money Music, USA.
Universal/MCA Music Publishing GmbH.
All Rights Reserved. International Copyright Secured.

# IT'S ALL COMING BACK TO ME NOW

(CELINE DION)

```
            C            Em           F
1. There were nights when the wind was so cold
         Dm          Em
that my body froze in bed
              Am             Dm            F    C G
if I just listened to it right outside the window.

            C            Em          F
2. There were days when the sun was so cruel
         Dm              Em
that all the tears turned to dust
                Am              Dm          F    C G
and I just knew my eyes were drying up forever.

Em        Am       F       G       C
I finished crying in the instant that you left
       Em         Am            G
and I can't remember where or when or how
    Em          Am          F    G    F   G
and I banished every memory you and I had ever made.

                C                   G/B
But when you touch me like this and you hold me like that
         Am       Dm          F          G
I just have to admit that it's all coming back to me.
           C                  G/B
When I touch you like this and I hold you like that
           Am         Dm         F         G
it's so hard to believe but it's all coming back to me.
       C                        F         F   G
It's all coming back, it's all coming back to me now.

             Am       F                Em         F
There were moments of gold and there were flashes of light,
              Am                F
there were things I'd never do again
               Em           F
but then they'd always seemed right.
              Am                   Em         Am        F       Dm
There were nights of endless pleasure it was more than any laws allow.
G
Baby, baby.

          C                    G/B
If I kiss you like this and if you whisper like that
        Am         Dm        F           G
it was lost long ago but it's all coming back to me.
           C                  G/B
If you want me like this and if you need me like that
        Am         Dm        F           G
it was dead long ago but it's all coming back to me.
            Am       Dm       F         G
It's so hard to resist and it's all coming back to me.
         Am       Dm          F         G       Am G/B F/C
I can barely recall but it's all coming back to me now.
Em                  Am G/B F Dm
But it's all coming back.
```

**3.** There were those empty threats and hollow lies
and whenever you tried to hurt me
I just hurt you even worse and so much deeper.

**4.** There were hours that just went on for days
when alone at last we'd count up all the chances
that were lost to us forever.

But you were history with the slamming of the door
and I made myself so strong again somehow
and I never wasted any of my time on you since then.

But if I touch you like this and if you kiss me like that
it was so long ago but it's all coming back to me.
If you touch me like this and if I kiss you like that
it was gone with the wind but it's all coming back to me.
It's all coming back, it's all coming back to me now.

There were moments of gold and there were flashes of light,
there were things we'd never do again
but then they'd always seemed right.
There were nights of endless pleasure,
it was more than all your laws allow.
Baby, baby, baby.

When you touch me like this and when you hold me like that
it was gone with the wind but it's all coming back to me.
When you see me like this and when I see you like that
then we see what we want to see all coming back to me.
The flesh and the fantasies all coming back to me.
I can barely recall but it's all coming back to me now.

If you forgive me all this if I forgive you all that,
we forgive and forget and it's all coming back to me.
When you see me like this and when I see you like that
we see just what we want to see all coming back to me.
The flesh and the fantasies all coming back to me.
I can barely recall but it's all coming back to me now.

It's all coming back to me now.
And when you kiss me like this it's all coming back to me now.
And when I touch you like that it's all coming back to me now.
If you do it like this it's all coming back to me now.
And be free.

M + T: Jim Steinman
© Copyright 1996 Lost Boys Music/Songs Of PolyGram International, USA.
Universal Music Publishing Limited.
All rights in Germany administered by Universal Music Publ. GmbH.
All Rights Reserved. International Copyright Secured.

## ALWAYS ON MY MIND
(ELVIS PRESLEY)

```
       G           D/F#       Em       G/D         C         C D
1. Maybe I didn't treat you quite as good as I should have.
   G           D/F#       Em         G/D         A/C#      A
Maybe I didn't love you quite as often as I should have.
C                       G/B
Little things I should have said and done
C       G/B         Am    C/G C/E
I just never took the time.

D      Em7    D7/F# G           Am    G7/B   C
You were always on my mind, you were always on my mind,
C         D7          G    C D
you were always on my mind.

       G           D/F#       Em       G/D           C    C D
2. Maybe I didn't hold you all those lonely, lonely times.
   G              D/F#       Em       G/D         A/C# A
And I guess I never told you I'm so happy that you're mine.
C                      G/B
If I made you feel the second best,
C        G/B          Am    C/G C/E
girl, I'm so sorry, I was blind.

D      Em7    D7/F# G           Am    G7/B   C
You were always on my mind, you were always on my mind,
C         D7          G    C D
you were always on my mind.

G D/F# Em G/D C           G/B           Am     D7
Tell   me,  tell me that your sweet love hasn't died.
G D/F# Em G/D     C             G/B           Am     D7    G
Give   me, give me one more chance to keep you satisfied, satisfied.

C                        G/B
Little things I should have said and done
C       G/B         Am    C/G C/E
I just never took the time.

D      Em7    D7/F# G           Am    G7/B   C
You were always on my mind, you were always on my mind,
C              D7
you were always on my mind

Solo: G D/F# Em G/D C G/B Am D7
                        G
You were always on my mind.
```

M + T: Christopher, Johnny / James, Mark & Wayne Carson Thompson
© 1971 Budde Songs, Inc / Screen Gems-EMI Music Inc.
Für D/A/CH: Rolf Budde Musikverlag GmbH, Berlin.
EMI Music Publishing Germany GmbH.

# TWIST AND SHOUT

(THE BEATLES)

**Refrain:**
```
A    A7         D         G         A
Well, shake it up baby now. Shake it up baby.
A7         D      G       A
Twist and shout. Twist and shout.
       A7                      D        G       A
Come on, come on, come on, come on baby, now. Come on baby.
     A7                D    G         A
Come on and work it on out. Work it on out.
```

```
          A7         D    G       A
1. Well, work it on out. Work it on out.
       A7         D         G        A
You know you look so good. Look so good.
       A7         D         G        A
You know you got me going now. Got me going.
       A7             D         G              A
Just like I knew you would. Like I knew you would.
```

Refrain

```
          A7              D          G           A
2. You know you twist, little girl. Twist little girl.
       A7            D       G       A
You know you twist so fine. Twist so fine.
      A7                    D          G              A
Come on and twist a little closer now. Twist a little closer.
       A7                 D         G          A
And let me know that you're mine. Let me know you're mine.
```

D G A G   D G A G   D G A G   D G A G

```
A
Ah, ah, ah, ah, yeah.
```

Refrain

```
          A7              D          G           A
2. You know you twist, little girl. Twist little girl.
       A7            D       G       A
You know you twist so fine. Twist so fine.
      A7                    D          G              A
Come on and twist a little closer now. Twist a little closer.
       A7                 D         G          A
And let me know that you're mine. Let me know you're mine.
      A7                               D         G           A
Well shake it, shake it, shake it, baby now. Shake it up baby.
      A7                               D         G           A
Well shake it, shake it, shake it, baby now. Shake it up baby.
      A7                               D         G           A
Well shake it, shake it, shake it, baby now. Shake it up baby.
```

```
A           D
Ah, ah, ah, ah.
```

M + T: Bert Russell, Phil Medley
© Robert Mellin Inc. / Robert Mellin Musikverlag KG.
Mit freundlicher Genehmigung der Bosworth Music GmbH, Berlin.

# GOD SHUFFLED HIS FEET

(CRASH TEST DUMMIES)

```
      D           Bm         G             D      A
1. After seven days he was quite tired, so God said:
   D             Bm           G            Bm        G
   "Let there be a day just for picnics, with wine and bread."
   A                  D             G
   He gathered up some people he had made,
   Em                   D              G
   created blankets and laid back in the shade.

           D              Bm                G
2. The people sipped their wine and what with God there,
             D      A
   they asked him questions
            D            Bm                 G             Bm G
   Like: do you have to eat or get your hair cut in heaven?
   A                  D              G
   And if your eye got poked out in this life
   Em                     D              G
   would it be waiting up in heaven with your wife?
```

**Refrain:**
```
A              E                A           D
God shuffled his feet and glanced around at them.
     A              E                        A      D G
The people cleared their throats and stared right back at him.

   G           D             Bm       G          D      A
3. So he said: "Once there was a boy who woke up with blue hair.
      D         Bm         G            Bm       G
   To him it was a joy until he ran out into the warm air.
   A              D                    G
   He thougt of how his friends would come to see
   Em                     D              G
   and would they laugh or had he got some strange disease?"
```

Refrain

```
         D          Bm              G            D  A
4. The people sat waiting out on their blankets in the garden
      D              Bm          G               Bm G
   but God said nothing, so someone asked him, "I beg your pardon:
   A                 D              G
   I'm not quite clear about what you just spoke.
   Em                    D             G
   Was that a parable or a very subtle joke?"
```

Refrain

M + T: Brad Roberts
© Copyright 1993 Dummies Productions Incorporated, Canada.
Universal Music Publishing Limited.
All Rights Reserved. International Copyright Secured.

# SUPREME

(ROBBIE WILLIAMS)

```
     Dm                  Gm
1. Oh, it seemed forever stopped today,
         C                        F
all the lonely hearts in London caught a plane and flew away
         Dm7                              E
and all the best women are married, all the handsome men are gay,
           Asus4
you feel deprived.

     Dm              Gm
2. Yeah, are you questioning your size?
           C                      F
Is there a tumor in your humor, are there bags under your eyes?
           Dm7                            E
Do you leave dents where you sit, are you getting on a bit?
           Asus4         A7
Will you survive? You must survive!
```

**Refrain:**
```
                Dm         Bb
When there's no love in town
             F                    A
this new century keeps bringing you down.
             Dm           Bb
All the places you have been
      F              A          Dm
trying to find a love supreme. A love supreme.
```

3. Oh, what are you really looking for?
Another partner in your life to abuse and to adore?
Is it lovey dovey stuff, do you need a bit of rough?
Get on your knees.

4. Yeah, turn down the love songs that you hear
cause you can't avoid the sentiment that echoes in your ear
saying love will stop the pain, saying love will kill the fear.
Do you believe? You must believe!

Refrain

5. I spy with my little eye something beginning with. I got my back up
and now she's screaming, so I've got to turn the track up,
sit back and watch the royalities stack up.
I know this girl, she likes to switch teams
and I'm a fiend, but I'm living for a love supreme

Refrain

```
      Dm              Bb
|: Come and live a love supreme.
              F                         A
Don't let it get you down, everybody lives for love. :|
```

M + T: Robert Williams, Guy Chambers, Dino Fekaris, Frederick Perren and Francois De Roubaix
© Polygram Int. publishing Inc, Perren Vibes Music Inc, Kobalt Music Publishing Ltd, Sido Music B Liechti et Cie. EMI Virgin Music Ltd., London, Universal Music publishing Group, Sido Music B. Liechti et Cie. Sidomusic Germany. Reproduced by permission of International Music Publications Ltd (a trading name of Faber Music Ltd) All Rights Reserved.

## DER ALBATROS

(KARAT)

```
      Em                              D
1. Es gibt einen Vogel, den haben Matrosen zum Herrscher gekrönt,
   Em                                D
   er fliegt um die Erde vom Südpol nach Norden, kein Ziel ist zu weit:
         C              Bm   Em
   Der Albatros kennt keine Grenzen.

       Em                           D
2. Er segelt mit Würde, durchwandert die Lüfte als wär er ein Gott,
   Em                                                       D
   er folgt ihren Schiffen auf Hochsee durch Klippen, berauschend sein
   Flug.
       C                Bm   Em
   Er sucht ihren Weg durch die See.

        D             Am    G D
   Und krachen die Stürme mit rauer Gewalt
                    C    G     D
   auf den Ozeanen so unendlich weit,
                          Am            Em   Bm       Em Bm Em
   dann fliegt er mit Feuer und steigt ungeheuer zur Freiheit der Meere.
```

3. Doch wenn er gefangen mit armdicken Schlingen, mit Tücke und List,
dann brechen die Schwingen, es trauert das Meer,
das den Herrscher vermisst.
Gefangen sein heißt für ihn Tod

4. Die Sklaven der Erde verhöhnt und geschunden, sie teilten sein Los,
wenn er liegt gefesselt, verblutend am Ufer, gebrochen sein Flug.
Der Albatros ist ihr Symbol.

Doch ruft ihn die Weite, die endlose Macht,
dann stürmt er ins Freie mit maßloser Kraft,
er schwingt seine Flügel, sprengt Schlösser und Riegel der Fesseln und
Ketten.

5. Und türmen sich Wände und greifen ihn Zwingen aus Wolken wie Blei
und schlagen ihn Blitze, er kämpft mit den Schwingen das Hindernis frei.
Er findet den Weg auch im Orkan.

Und krachen die Stürme mit rauer Gewalt
auf den Ozeanen so unendlich weit,
dann fliegt er mit Feuer und steigt ungeheuer zur Freiheit der Meere.

M: Ulrich Swillms
T: Norbert Kaiser
© Copyright 1980 by Harth Musik Verlag GmbH, Bergisch Gladbach.

# HALLELUJAH

(JEFF BUCKLEY)
(LEONARD COHEN)

```
         C                        Am
1. Now I've heard there was a secret chord,
   C                        Am
that David played, and it pleased the Lord.
   F             G           C       G
But you don't really care for music, do you?
   C                F            G
It goes like this: The fourth, the fifth,
  Am                F
the minor fall, the major lift.
   G              E             Am
The baffled king composing Hallelujah.
```

**Refrain:**
```
    F           Am         F          C G C    Am C Am
Hallelujah, Hallelujah, Hallelujah, Hallelu--jah.
```

```
         C                        Am
2. Your faith was strong, but you needed proof,
   C                 Am
you saw her bathing on the roof.
   F                    G   C          G
Her beauty and the moonlight overthrew you.
   C              F        G
She tied you to a kitchen chair,
  Am                              F
she broke your throne and she cut your hair
   G                  E             Am
and from your lips she drew the Hallelujah.
Refrain
```

3. Baby, I've been here before,
I've seen this room and I've walked this floor.
I used to live alone before I knew you.
I've seen your flag on the marble arch
our love is not a victory march,
it's a cold and it's a broken Hallelujah.
Refrain

4. Well, there was a time when you let me know
what's really going on below
but now you never show that to me, do you?
But remember when I moved in you
and the holy dove was moving, too
and every breath we drew was Hallelujah.
Refrain

5. Well, maybe there's a God above
but all I've ever learned from love
was how to shoot somebody who outdrew you.
It's not a cry that you hear at night,
it's not somebody who's seen the light,
it's a cold and it's a broken Hallelujah.
Refrain 2x

M + T: Leonard Cohen
© Copyright 1984 Sony/ATV Music Publishing.
All Rights Reserved. International Copyright Secured.

# I STILL HAVEN'T FOUND WHAT I'M LOOKING FOR

(U2)

```
         D
1. I have climbed highest mountains.

I have run through the fields,
        G                D
only to be with you, only to be with you.

I have run, I have crawled. I have sealed these city walls,
          G              D            Dsus4 D
these city walls. Only to be with you.

             A        G           D          Dsus4 D
Refrain: But I still haven't found what I'm looking for.
         A          G            D         Dsus4 D
But I still haven't found what I'm looking for.


         D
2. I have kissed honey lips,

felt that healing finger tips.
             G                  D
It burned like fire, this burning desire.

I have spoke with the tongue of angels.

I have held the hand of the devil.
                       G              D     Dsus4 D
It was warm in the night. I was cold as a stone.

Refrain


         D
3. I believe in the kingdom come,
                                            G
then all the colors will bleed into one, bleed into one.
                    D
But yes, I'm still running.

You broke the bonds, and you loose the chains,
                                   G
carry the cross of my shame, of my shame.
                     D     Dsus4 D
You know I believe it.

Refrain
```

M + T: Larry Mullen, Adam Clayton, Dave Evans & Paul David Hewson
© Copyright 1987 Blue Mountain Music Limited
All Rights Reserved. International Copyright Secured.

## THE UNFORGIVEN

(METALLICA)

**Intro:** Am C G Em Am C G E Am

```
      Am                   Em          D            Am
1. New blood joins this earth and quickly he's subdued.
                     Em          D              Am
Through constant pain disgraced, the young boy learns their rules.
                     Em           D             Am
With time the child draws in, this whipping boy done wrong.
                 Em            D              Am
Deprived of all his thoughts, the young man struggles on and on.
            C                G         Am
He's known a vow unto his own, that never from this day
     C               G    E
his will they'll take away. Yeah.
```

**Refrain:**
```
Am         C                G             Em                       Am
What I've felt, what I've known never shined through in what I've shown.
       C          G         E               Am
Never be. Never see. Won't see what might have been.
        C               G
What I've felt, what I've known,
     Em                    Am
never shined through in what I've shown.
       C          G       E           Am
Never free. Never me. So I dub thee unforgiven.
```

```
         Am          Em        D          Am
2. They dedicate their lives to running all of his,
                   Em          D         Am
he tries to please them all, this bitter man he is.
                     Em           D            Am
Throughout his life's the same, he's battled constantly.
                    Em         D            Am
This fight he cannot win. A tired man they see no longer cares.
       C             G        Am
The old man then prepares to die regretfully.
       C           G   E
That old man here is me. Yeah.
```

Refrain 2x

M + T: James Hetfield, Lars Ulrich & Kirk Hammett
© Copyright 1991 Creeping Death Music, USA.
Universal Music Publishing Limited.
All Rights Reserved. International Copyright Secured.

# ATLANTIS

(DONOVAN)

**Intro:** C D Fmaj7 C G
Gesprochen:
```
C                                            D
The continent of Atlantis was an island which lay before the great flood
               Fmaj7                     C                         G
in the area we now call the Atlantic Ocean. So great an area of land,
                            C
that from her western shores those beautiful sailors journeyed
         D
to the South and the North Americas with ease,
          Fmaj7                   C G
in their ships with painted sails.

             C                                  D
To the East, Africa was a neighbour, across a short strait of sea miles.
Fmaj7                                           C                  G
The great Egyptian age is but a remnant of the Atlantian culture.
              C
The antediluvian kings colonised the world,
         D
all the Gods who play in the mythological dramas
                        Fmaj7                      C G
in all legends from all lands were from far Atlantis.

C                                                              D
Knowing her fate Atlantis sent out ships to all corners of the Earth.
                         Fmaj7
On board were the Twelve: The poet, the physician,
                             C
the farmer, the scientist, the magician and the other
         G                        C
so called Gods of our legends. Though Gods they were
                           D
and as the elders of our time choose to remain blind
                    Fmaj7
let us rejoice and let us sing and dance and ring in the new.
C       G
Hail Atlantis!

       C              D      F           C           G
Way down below the ocean where I wanna be she may be,
       C              D      F           C           G
way down below the ocean where I wanna be she may be,
       C              D      F           C           G
way down below the ocean where I wanna be she may be.
       C              D      F           C           G
Way down below the ocean where I wanna be she may be,
       C              D      F           C           G
way down below the ocean where I wanna be she may be.
```

M + T: Donovan Leitch
© Copyright 1968 Donovan (Music) Limited.
All Rights Reserved. International Copyright Secured.

# THE BALLAD OF CHASEY LAIN

(BLOODHOUND GANG)

Intro: C#m E A G# C#m E A G#

```
         C#m                   E                    A    G#
1. Dear Chasey Lain I wrote to explain I'm your biggest fan.
             C#m                  E
   I just wanted to ask could I eat your ass?
                            A    G#
   Write back as soon as you can.
```

**Refrain:**
```
        C#m              E
You've had a lotta dick, had a lotta dick.
     A                   G#
I've had a lotta time, had a lotta time.
        C#m             G#                       C#   G#
You've had a lotta dick Chasey, but you ain't had mine.
```

```
             C#m                 E                  A   G#
2. Dear Chasey Lain I wrote to complain ya never wrote me back.
               C#m                  E
   How could I ever eat your ass when ya treat
                         A    G#
   your biggest fan like that?
```

Refrain

```
              C#m                E                    A    G#
3. Dear Chasey Lain I wrote to constrain this letter is my last.
                C#m           E              A    G#
   As your biggest fan I must demand you let me eat your ass.
```

Refrain

```
     B                                C#m
P.S. Mom and Dad this is Chasey, Chasey this is my mom and dad.
            E                           B       F#
Now show 'em them titties, now show 'em them titties.
     B                                C#m
P.S. Mom and Dad this is Chasey, Chasey this is my mom and dad.
            E                           B       F#
Now show 'em them titties, now show 'em them titties.

Would ya fuck me for blow?

C#m E A G# C#m E A G#
```

M + T: Jimmy Pop Ali
© Songs of PolyGram Int., Hey Rudy Music Publishing,
The Jimmy Franks Publishing. Universal Music Publishing Limited.
All Rights Reserved. International Copyright Secured.

# INDIANER

(PUR)

```
D                      G
Wo sind all die Indianer hin,
D                    G         A      D G A G  D G A G
wann verlor das große Ziel den Sinn?
             D              G
1. Dieses alte Bild aus der Kinderzeit
      A            G             D      G A G  D G A G
zeigt alle Brüder vom Stamm der Gerechtigkeit.
           D                   G
Wir waren bunt bemalt und mit wildem Schrei
     A           G             D      G A G  D G A G
stand jeder stolze Krieger den Schwachen bei.
         A             G           A            G
Unser Ehrenwort war heilig, nur ein Bleichgesicht betrog,
       A          G           Em          A
und es waren gute Jahre bis der erste sich belog.
```

**Refrain:**
```
D              G        D             G       A
Wo sind all die Indianer hin? Wann verlor das große Ziel den Sinn?
D        Em              A
So wie Chingachgook für das Gute stehn,
   Bm           Em         G      A    D      G A G  D G A G
als letzter Mohikaner unter Geiern nach dem Rechten sehn.

           D               G
2. Der "Kleine Büffel" spielt heute Boss,
      A          G              D      G A G  D G A G
er zog mit Papi's Firma das große Los.
   D                    G
"Geschmeidige Natter" sortiert die Post
      A          G             D      G A G  D G A G
und in seiner Freizeit sagt er meistens "Prost".
           A          G              A        G
Und die Friedenspfeife baumelt über'm Videogerät,
         A         G           Em           A
wieviel Träume dürfen platzen, ohne dass man sich verrät?
```

Refrain

```
    Dm7            G/D         D            A/D
Es gibt noch ein paar wenige vom Stamme der Schoschonen,
     F              G              D
die finden sich, erkennen sich am Blick.
        Dm7         G/D          D            A/C#
Und deren gute Taten kann man nur durch Freundschaft belohnen,
     G/B         G       A     D
sie nehmen ein Versprechen nie zurück.
           A          G              A        G
Und die Friedenspfeife baumelt über'm Videogerät,
         A         G           Em           A
wieviel Träume dürfen platzen, ohne dass man sich verrät?
```

Refrain 2x

M + T: Hartmut Engler / Ingo Reidl
© EMI Nobile Musikverlag GmbH.
Mit freundlicher Genehmigung der EMI Nobile Musikverlag GmbH.

# WONDERWALL

(OASIS)

**Intro:** F#m7 A Esus4 B7sus4  (4x)

```
      F#m7       A                          Esus4                 B7sus4
1. Today is gonna be the day that they're gonna throw it back to you.
By now you should've somehow realized what you gotta do.
I don't believe that anybody feels the way I do
about you now.   Dadd9 Esus4 B7sus4

2. Backbeat the word is on the street that the fire in your heart is out
I'm sure you've heard it all before but you never really had a doubt.
I don't believe that anybody feels the way I do
about you now.
```
**Bridge:**
```
     Dadd9           Esus4              F#m7
And all the roads we have to walk are winding.
     Dadd9          Esus4             F#m7
And all the lights that lead us there are blinding.
Dadd9         Esus4          A        Esus4/G# F#m7
There are many things that I would like to say to you
     Esus4      B7sus4
but I don't know how.
```

**Refrain:**
```
     Dadd9 F#m7 A
Cause maybe
     F#m7                    Dadd9      F#m7 A
you're gonna be the one that saves me?
    F#m7   Dadd9 F#m7
And after all
A       F#m7   Dadd9 F#m7 A F#m7
you're my wonderwall.

3. Today was gonna be the day but they'll never throw it back to you.
By now you should've somehow realized what you're not to do.
I don't believe that anybody feels the way I do
about you now.

And all the roads that lead you there are winding.
And all the lights that light the way are blinding.
There are many things that I would like to say to you
but I don't know how.

I said maybe
you're gonna be the one who saves me?
And after all
you're my wonderwall.

I said maybe
you're gonna be the one who saves me?
And after all
you're my wonderwall.

I said maybe
you're gonna be the one who saves me?
You're gonna be the one who saves me?
You're gonna be the one who saves me?
```

```
| Chords used
| (capo on 2nd)
|
| 022033 - F#m7
| 320033 - A
| X00233 - Esus4
| X02233 - B7sus4
| X32033 - Dadd9
```

M + T: Noel Gallagher
© Copyright 1995 Creation Songs Limited/
Oasis Music (GB). Sony/ATV Music Publishing.
All Rights Reserved. International Copyright Secured.

# PASSENGER

(IGGY POP)

gesamtes Lied: Am F C G/B    Am F C E/B

I am the passenger and I ride and I ride.
I ride through the city's backsides, I see the stars come out of the sky,
yeah the bright and hollow sky. You know it looks so good tonight.

I am the passenger, I stay under glass,
I look through my window so bright, I see the stars come out tonight,
I see the bright and hollow sky over the city's ripped backsides
and everything looks good tonight.
Singing la la la la lalalala, la la la la lalalala
la la la la lalalala la la.

We get into the car. We'll be the passenger,
we'll ride through the city tonight, we'll see the city's ripped backside,
we'll see the bright and hollow sky, we'll see the stars that shine so bright.
Stars made for us tonight.

Oh, the passenger, oh, how he rides,
oh, the passenger, he rides and he rides,
he looks through his window. What does he see?
He sees the bright and hollow sky, he sees the stars come out tonight,
he sees the city's ripped backsides, he sees the winding ocean drive
and everything was made for you and me, all of it was made for you and me
'cause it just belongs to you and me, so let's take a ride and see what's mine.
Singing la la la la lalalala, la la la la lalalala,
la la la la lalalala la la.

Oh, the passenger, he rides and he rides,
he sees things from under glass, he looks through his window side,
he sees the things he knows are his, he sees the bright and hollow sky,
he sees the city sleep at night, he sees the stars are out tonight
and all of it is yours and mine and all of it is yours and mine.
So let's ride and ride and ride and ride.
Singing la la la la lalalala, la la la la lalalala,
la la la la lalalala la la.

M + T: James Osterberg and Ricky Gardiner
© Copyright 1977 James Osterberg Music / Ricky Gardiner Songs Limited / EMI Music Publishing Limied. BMG Rights Management GmbH / EMI Music Publishing Limited.
All Rights Reserved. International Copyright Secured.

# RUSSIANS

(STING)
[TRANSP. +3]

```
         Am      Em/G   Fmaj7  Em/G       Dm       C/E         F      G
1. In Europe and   America there's a growing feeling of hysteria.
         Am      Em/G     Fmaj7    Em/G
Conditioned to respond to all the threats
         G#+         Am            Am/E  E
in the rhetorical speeches of the Soviets.
         C                   G#+
Mr. Krushchev said we will bury you,
      Am                          E
I don't subscribe to this point of view.
             Am      Em/G     Fmaj7     Em/G
It would be such an ignorant thing to do
         Dm                   G         Am
if the Russians love their children too.


         Am      Em/G   Fmaj7  Em/G       Dm       C/E         F      G
2. How can I save my little boy from Oppenheimer's deadly toy.
         Am      Em/G     Fmaj7    Em/G
There is no monopoly of common sense
     G#+      Am             Am/E     E
on either side of the political fence.
     C                 E           Am                E
We share the same biology, regardless of ideology.
      Am      Em/G    Fmaj7    Em/G
Believe me when I say to you,
     Dm       C/E      F              G          Am
I hope the Russians love their children too.


3. There is no historical precedent,
to put the words in the mouth of the president.
There's no such thing as a winnable war,
it's a lie we don't believe anymore.
Mr. Reagan says we will protect you,
I don't subscribe to this point of view.
Believe me when I say to you,
I hope the Russians love their children too.


We share the same biology, regardless of ideology.
What might save us, me and you,
is if the Russians love their children too.
```

M + T: Sting
© Copyright 1985 Magnetic Publishing Limited/EMI Music Publishing Limited.
All Rights Reserved. International Copyright Secured.

## CENTERFOLD

(J. GEILS BAND)

```
      G                F              C                   F    C
1. Does she walk? Does she talk? Does she come complete?
      G                  F             C                F    C
My homeroom, homeroom angel always pulled me from my seat.
  G              F             C                  F      C
She was pure like snowflakes, no one could ever stain.
      G              F            C
The memory of my angel could never cause me pain.
    Em                              Am              C      D
The years go by, I'm looking through a girly magazine
   Em                              Am              C      D
and there's my homeroom angel on the pages in between.
```

**Refrain:**
```
       G              F            C
My blood runs cold, my memory has just been sold,
       G           F            C
my angel is the centerfold, angel is the centerfold.
       G              F            C                   G F
My blood runs cold, my memory has just been sold.
C
Angel in the centerfold.
```

```
       G              F            C                   F        C
2. Slipped me notes, under the desk while I was thinking about her dress
    G           F          C                    F  C
I was shy, I turned away, before she caught my eye.
    G              F             C                  F      C
I was shakin' in my shoes whenever she flashed those baby blues.
   G              F             C
Something had a hold on me when angel passed close by.
       Em                           Am           C    D
Those soft, fuzzy sweaters, too magical to touch.
      Em                       Am          C    D
To see her in that neglige is really just too much.
```

Refrain
```
      G              F            C
Nah nah nah nah nah nah. Nah nah nah nah nah nah nah nah. (3x)
```

```
        G              F              C                 F     C
3. It's okay, I understand this ain't no never-never land.
  G                  F             C                    F          C
I hope that when this issue's gone I'll see you when your clothes are on
   G           F              C                  F      C
Take your car, yes we will, we'll take your car and drive it.
   G           F            C
Take it to a motel room, and take 'em off in private.
    Em                              Am              C     D
A part of me has just been wrecked. The pages from my mind are stripped.
  Em                      Am          C       D
Oh no, I can't deny it. Oh yeah, I guess I got to buy it.
```

Refrain

M + T: Seth Justman
© 1981 Center City Music / Pal Park Music. Rondor Music International.

# HELP

(THE BEATLES)
[TRANSP. +2]

```
Am                              F
Help! I need somebody. Help! Not just anybody.
D7                          G
Help! You know I need someone. Help!

      G                            Bm
1. When I was younger, so much younger than today,
Em                          C      F    G
I never needed anybody's help in any way.
                                  Bm
But now these days are gone, I'm not so self-assured,
Em                                C       F        G
now I find I've changed my mind, I've opened up the door.
```

**Refrain:**
```
Am
Help me if you can I'm feeling down
      F
and I do appreciate you being 'round.
D7
Help me get my feet back on the ground,
             G
won't you please, please help me.

      G                            Bm
2. And now my life has changed in oh, so many ways,
Em                    C      F       G
my independence seemed to vanish in the haze.
                       Bm
But every now and then I feel so insecure,
Em                                C      F        G
I know that I just need you like I've never done before.
```

Refrain

```
      G                            Bm
1. When I was younger, so much younger than today,
Em                          C      F    G
I never needed anybody's help in any way.
                                  Bm
But now these days are gone, I'm not so self-assured,
Em                                C       F        G
Now I find I've changed my mind, I've opened up the door.
```

**Refrain:**
```
Am
Help me if you can I'm feeling down
      F
and I do appreciate you being 'round.
D7
Help me get my feet back on the ground,
             G                     Em              G      G6
won't you please, please help me, help me, help me, oo.
```

M + T: John Lennon & Paul McCartney
© Copyright 1965 Sony/ATV Music Publishing.
All Rights Reserved. International Copyright Secured.

# SAY YOU SAY ME

(LIONEL RICHIE)
[TRANSP. +1]

**Refrain:**
```
G    D/F#      Em   G/D       C     C/D
Say you, say me, say it for always,
                  G
that's the way it should be.
      D/F#      Em    G/D       C     C/D    G    D
Say you, say me, say it together naturally!
```

```
    G       D/F#          Em         G/D
1. I had a dream, I had an awesome dream.
Am                   F                    D
People in the park playing games in the dark.
G          D/F#        Em       G/D
And what they played was a masquerade.
        Am                    F                       D
From behind the walls of doubt a voice was crying out!
```

Refrain

```
    G       D/F#        Em             G/D
2. As we go down life's lonesome highway.
          Am                F                       D
Seems the hardest thing to do is to find a friend or two.
G          D/F#              Em        G/D
That helping hand, someone who understands
        Am                                    F
when you feel you've lost your way, you've got someone there to say
  D
I'll show you! Ooh, ooh!
```

Refrain

**Bridge:**
```
G      Bb              F       C    G
So you think you know the answer. Oh, no!
            Bb                 F
Well, the whole world's got ya dancing,
              C#+       Dm
that's right I'm telling you.
      Bb           F          C    G
It's time to start believing. Oh, yes!
    Bb                C                    D
Believe in who you are: You are a shining star!
```

Refrain
```
        C              G
Say it together naturally!
```

M + T: Lionel Richie
© Copyright 1985 Brockman Music, USA/Brenda Richie Publishing. Imagem Music/Kobalt Music Limited.
All Rights Reserved. International Copyright Secured.

# LUKA

(SUZANNE VEGA)  
[TRANSP. -1]

```
      G       D      C          D
1. My name is Luka, I live on the second floor.
   G        D              C                    D
   I live upstairs from you, yes, I think you've seen me before.
   Em          D                Em
   If you hear something late at night,
                    D                  C
   some kind of trouble, some kind of fight.

             D                C          D
   Just don't ask me what it was. Just don't ask me what it was.
   C         D                 G
   Just don't ask me what it was.

      G          D              C              D
2. I think it's because I'm clumsy, I try not to talk too loud.
   G           D              C           D
   Maybe it's because I'm crazy, I try not to act too proud.
   Em          D        Em
   They only hit until you cry
                D                C
   and after that you don't ask why.

              D              C              D
   You just don't argue anymore. You just don't argue anymore.
   C         D              G
   You just don't argue anymore.


       G      D            C              D
3. Yes I think I'm okay, I walked into the door again.
   G          D                  C                     D
   Well, if you ask that's what I'll say and it's not your business anyway.
   Em         D
   I guess I'd like to be alone
   Em          D               C
   with nothing broken, nothing thrown.

             D             C           D
   Just don't ask me how I am. Just don't ask me how I am.
   C         D             G
   Just don't ask me how I am.
```

M + T: Suzanne Vega  
© 1987 WB Music Corp and Waifersongs Ltd,  
Warner/Chappell North America Limited, London.  
Reproduced by permission of Faber Music Limited  
All Rights Reserved.

# WHEN I WAS YOUNG

(ERIC BURDON)

```
          Em              D
1. The rooms were so much colder then,
      Em              D
my father was a soldier then
      Em              D
and times were very hard.
                Em          D      Em
When I was young. When I was young.

          Em              D
2. I smoked my first cigarette at ten
Em              D
and for girls I had a bad yen,
Em            D
I had quite a ball.
                Em      D  Em
When I was young.

          G                  Em
When I was young it was more important.
                                            D
Pain more pain but I laughed so much louder, yeah.
                Em          D      Em
When I was young. When I was young.

          Em              D
3. I met my first love at thirteen.
Em                D
She was brown and I was pretty green.
      Em              D
And I learned quite a lot.
                Em          D      Em
When I was young. When I was young.

Gm F (3x) Gm

          Bb                 Gm
When I was young it was more important.
                                            F
Pain more pain though I laughed so much louder, yeah.
                Gm      F   Gm
When I was young. When I was young.

          Gm              F
4. My faith was so much stronger then.
Gm              F
I believed in fellow men.
      Gm              F
And I was so much older then.
                Gm      F   Gm      F   Gm      F   Gm
When I was young. When I was young. When I was young. When I was young.
```

M + T: Eric Burdon, Victor Briggs, Barry Jenkins, Danny McCullock, John Weider
© 1967 Anim Music Ltd, Slamina Music Inc and Carlin Music Corp.
Warner/Chappell Music Ltd, London.
Reproduced by permission of Faber Music Ltd. All Rights Reserved.

# KNOWING ME, KNOWING YOU

(ABBA)

```
   C    Dm       Am7        Em7  C   Dm       Am7      Em7
1. No more carefree laughter. Silence ever after.
Am                                                  G
Walking through an empty house, tears in my eyes.
F                                          Em/A  Am
This is where the story ends, this is goodbye.
```

**Refrain:**
```
            F          G
Knowing me, knowing you (ah-haa),
                        C
there is nothing we can do.
            F          G
Knowing me, knowing you (ah-haa),
                        C        F      G
we just have to face it, this time we're through.
C          Em        F          G      C    F  G
Breaking up is never easy, I know but I have to go.
           C         F          G         C
Knowing me, knowing you, it's the best I can do.

   Em  F  G      C   Em  F   G

   C    Dm       Am7       Em7
2. Mem'ries, good days, bad days,
   C    Dm       Am7  Em7
they'll be, with me always.
Am                                           G
In these old familiar rooms children would play,
F                                     Em/A Am
now there's only emptiness, nothing to say.
```

Refrain 2x

M + T: Benny Andersson, Bjorn Ulvaeus & Stig Anderson  
© Copyright 1976 Universal/Union Songs Musikforlag AB.  
Universal Music Publishing Limited.  
All Rights Reserved. International Copyright Secured.

# WITH A LITTLE HELP FROM MY FRIENDS

(THE BEATLES)
[TRANSP. +4]

```
   C             G          Dm
1. What would you do if I sang out of tune
                   G7          C
would you stand up and walk out on me?
             G             Dm
Lend me your ears and I'll sing you a song
                  G7         C
and I'll try not to sing out of key. Oh...
```

**Refrain:**
```
       Bb              F              C
I get by with a little help from my friends.
         Bb             F            C
Mm, I get high with a little help from my friends.
              Bb            F         C        G7
Mm, I'm gonna try with a little help from my friends.
```

```
   C           G        Dm
2. What do I do when my love is away,
                G7      C
does it worry you to be alone?
         G            Dm
How do I feel by the end of the day,
                 G7           C
are you sad because you're on your own? No..
```

Refrain

**Bridge:**
```
C      Am7    D7      C         Bb     F
Do you need anybody? I need somebody to love.
       Am7   D7       C         Bb     F
Could it be anybody? I want somebody to love.
```

```
   C             G           Dm
3. Would you believe in a love at first sight?
                       G7              C
Yes, I'm certain that it happens all the time.
             G              Dm
What do you see when you turn out the light?
               G7              C
I can't tell you but I know it's mine. Oh..
```

Refrain

M + T: John Lennon & Paul McCartney
© Copyright 1967 Sony/ATV Music Publishing.
All Rights Reserved. International Copyright Secured.

# COUNTRY HOUSE

(BLUR)

**Intro:** A E Bm Bm D F#m C#
C#
And so the story begins.
```
      A                         E
1. City dweller, successful fella
Bm
thought to himself, "Oops, I've got a lot of money",
D         F#m            C#
caught in a rat race terminally.
        A                     E
I'm a professional cynic but my heart's not in it,
    Bm
I'm paying the price of living life at the limit.
D         F#m          C#          E
Caught in the century's anxiety. Yes it preys on him. He's getting thin.
```

**Refrain:**
```
    A                                 E
He lives in a house, a very big house in the country.
Eb       D                                        A
Watching afternoon repeats and the food he eats in the country.
                                                          E
He takes all manner of pills and piles up analyst bills in the country.
         Eb         D                             A
Oh, it's like an animal farm, lots of rural charm in the country.
```

2. He's got morning glory and life's a different story,
everything's going jackanorry.
Touched with his own mortality.
He's reading Balzac and knocking back Prozac,
it's a helping hand that makes you feel wonderfully bland.
Oh, it's the century's remedy. For the faint at heart. A new start.

**Refrain 2:**
He lives in a house, a very big house in the country.
He's got a frog in his chest, so he needs a lot of rest in the country.
He doesn't drink, smoke, laugh, takes herbal baths in the country.
But you'll come to no harm on the animal farm in the country.
```
        E
In the country. In the country. In the country!
A            E          D              A
Blow, blow me out I am so sad I don't know why. (2x)
```

Refrain
Refrain 2

M + T: Damon Albarn, Graham Coxon, Alex James & David Rowntree
© 1995 EMI Music Publishing Ltd, London, W8 5SW. Reproduced by
permission of International Music Publications Ltd (a trading name of
faber Music Ltd). All Rights Reserved.

# TWENTYFIRST CENTURY DIGITAL BOY

(BAD RELIGION)

```
         D     F  G  Bb A
I can't believe it,
      D      F       G     Bb
the way you look sometimes,
A    D      F        C     G
like a trampled flag on a city street,
    D   F   A
oh yeah.

          D      F  G  Bb A
And I don't want it,
      D            F         G  Bb A
the things you're offering me,
D             F          C       G
symbolized bar code, quick i.d.,
    D   F   A
oh yeah.
```

**Refrain:**
```
     D       Bb      F         C
I'm a 21st century digital boy,
     D            Bb         F            C
I don't know how to live, but I've got a lot of toys,
     D          Bb         F           G
my daddy is a lazy middle class intellectual,
     D          Bb          F       G     A
my mommy's on valium, she's so ineffectual,

ain't life a mystery?

D  F  G  Bb A  D  F  A
```

```
I can't explain it,
the things they're saying to me,
it's going yayayayayayaya,
oh yeah.

I'm a 21st century digital boy,
I don't know how to read, but I've got a lot of toys,
my daddy is a lazy middle class intellectual,
my mommy's on valium, she's so ineffectual,
ain't life a mystery?

C
I tried to tell you about no control
G
but now I really don't know
Bb                              F
and then you told me how bad you had to suffer,
A
is that really all you have to offer?
```

Refrain

M + T: Brett Gurewitz
© Westbeach Music.
Universal Music Publishing Limited. All Rights Reserved.
International Copyright Secured.

# SEX BOMB

(TOM JONES)
[TRANSP. +4]

```
     Em                    Am
1. Spy on me baby, you're a satellite,
Em                        B7
if you're apt to see me move through the night.
Em              Am              Em           B7         Em
Ain't gonna fire, shoot me right, I'm gonna like the way you fight.
       Em              Am
Now you found the secret code I use,
Em             B7
to wash away my lonely blues,
Em                         Am          Em           B7        Em
so I can't deny, all lie, 'cause you're there, only want to make me fly.
```

**Refrain:**
```
    Em          Am
Sexbomb, sexbomb, you're a sexbomb,
Em                      B7
you can give it to me when I need to come along.
    Em          Am
Sexbomb, sexbomb, you're my sexbomb,
    Em       B7      Em
and baby you can turn me on.
```

```
         Em                           Am
2. Now don't get me wrong, ain't gonna do you no harm,
       Em                B7
this bomb's for loving, you can shoot it far.
Em                      Am
I'm your main target, come on, help me ignite,
Em          B7          Em
love struck me holding you tight.
Em                     Am
Make me explode although you know,
    Em             B7
the route to go to sex me slow,
          Em              Am
And, yes, I must react to claims of those,
       Em          B7      Em
who say that you are not all that.
```

Refrain 2x

```
Em                              Am
You can give me more and more, counting up the score,
Em                      B7
you can turn me upside down and inside out.
Em                   Am
You can make me feel the real deal,
Em              Am          Em                  B7
and I can give it to you when you tell me, 'cause you're mine.
```

Refrain
```
    Em          B7      Em              B7          Em
and baby, you can turn me on, and baby, you can turn me on,
                B7      Em
and baby, you can turn me on.
```

M + T: Guendogdu, Mustafa / Rennalls, Errol
© Edition Merg Music/Rondor Musikverlag GmbH.

## SOUNDS LIKE A MELODY

(ALPHAVILLE)

**Intro:** Am Em Bm D (2x)

                           Am                                             Em
1. It's a trick of my mind, two faces bathing in the screenlight.
      Bm              D
She's so soft and warm in my arms.
                  Am                                     Em
I tune it into the scene, my hands are resting on her shoulders
         Bm            D
when we're dancing away for a while.
    Am                     Em
Oh, we're moving, we're falling, we step into the fire,
    Bm              D
by the hour of the wolf in my dreams.
               Am
There's no reason to hurry,
    Em                                 Bm
just start that brand new story and set it alight.
                        D
We're head over heels in love. Head over heels.

**Refrain:**
Am                               Em
The ringing of your laughter, it sounds like a melody
Bm                        D
to once forbidden places we'll go for a while.
Am                               Em
The ringing of your laughter, it sounds like a melody
Bm                        D
to once forbidden places we'll go for a while.

Am Em Bm D

                         Am                                            Em
2. It's the definite show, our shadows resting in the moonlight.
      Bm                    D
It's so clear and bright in your eyes.
                      Am                                Em
It's the touch of your sighs, my lips are resting on your shoulders
              Bm            D
when we're moving so soft and slow.
                  Am                     Em
We need the extasy, the jealousy, the comedy of love
    Bm                        D
like Cary Grants and Kellys once before.
              Am                      Em
Gimme more tragedy, more harmony and fantasy, my dear
               Bm                          D
and set it alight, just starting that satellite.

Refrain

M: Gold, Marian / Lloyd, Bernhard/ Mertens, Frank
T: Gold, Marian
© 1984 Rolf Budde Musikverlag GmbH, Berlin.

# I HEARD IT THROUGH THE GRAPEVINE

(MARVIN GAYE)

```
    Dm7
1. Bet you're wondering how I knew
         A7                G7
'bout you're plans to make me blue
              Dm7
with some other guy that you knew before.
                  A7                  G7
Between the two of us guys you know I love you more.
               Bm           G7
It took me by surprise I must say,
     Dm7           G7
when I found out yesterday. Ooh.
```

**Refrain:**
```
    Dm7
I heard it through the grapevine,
         G7
not much longer would you be mine.
        Dm7
Ooh, I heard it through the grapevine
       G7                              Dm
and I'm just about to lose my mind. Honey, honey, yeah.
```

```
                Dm7
2. I know that a man ain't supposed to cry
         A7              G
but these tears I can't hold inside.
     Dm7
Losin' you would end my life you see
             A7        G
cause you mean that much to me.
              Bm         G
You could have told me yourself
        Dm7            G
that you found someone else. Instead.
```

Refrain

```
              Dm7
3. People say believe half of what you see,
         A7            G
son, and none of what you hear.
       Dm7
I can't help bein' confused
       A7                G
if it's true please tell me dear?
        Bm        G
Do you plan to let me go
           Dm7              G
for the other guy that you knew before?
```

Refrain

M + T: Norman Whitfield & Barrett Strong
© Stone Agate Music
Subverlag: EMI Songs Musikverlag GmbH.

# WANNABE

(SPICE GIRLS)

```
       B                      D
I'll tell you what I want, what I really really want.
     E                        A                    Bb
So tell me what you want, what you really really want.
```

**Refrain:**
```
       B                      D
I'll tell you what I want, what I really really want.
     E                        A                    Bb
So tell me what you want, what you really really want.
         B                 D
I wanna huh, I wanna huh, I wanna huh, I wanna huh
         E                    A              Bb
I wanna really, really, really wanna zigazig, ahh!
```

```
      F#         G#m      E       B
1. If you want my future forget my past.
F#           G#m         E            B
If you wanna get with me better make it fast.
F#          G#m        E        B
Now don't go wasting my precious time.
F#         G#m           E        B
Get your act together we could be just fine.
```

Refrain

2. If you wanna be my lover you gotta get with my friends.
Make it last forever friendship never ends.
If you wanna be my lover you have got to give.
Taking is too easy but that's the way it is.

3. What d'you think about that, now you know how I feel?
Say you can handle my love, are you for real?
I won't be hasty, I'll give you a try.
If you really bug me then I'll say goodbye!

Refrain
2. Strophe

4. So... Here's the story from A to Z.
You wanna get with me, you gotta listen carefully.
We've got 'M' in the place who likes it in her face.
You got 'G' lock MC who likes it on a...
Easy V doesn't come for free, she's a real lady
and as for me, ha you'll see!

```
B                      D
Slam me body down and wind it all around.
B                      D
Slam me body down and wind it all around.
```

2. Strophe

```
F#                   G#m
If you wanna be my lover.
```

M + T: Matthew Rowbottom, Richard Stannard, Melanie Brown,
Victoria Adams, Geri Halliwell, Emma Bunton & Melanie Chisholm
© Copyright 1996 EMI Music Publishing (WP) Limited/PolyGram
Music Publishing Limited (GB).
Universal Music Publishing Limited/EMI Music Publishing Limited.
All Rights Reserved. International Copyright Secured.

## ICH WOLLT ICH WÄR EIN HUHN

(COMEDIAN HARMONISTS)

```
    C6          G+    C6              G+    C6       F7        C
1. Der Mann hat's auf der Welt nicht leicht, das Kämpfen ist sein Zweck,
B+    E6      B+      E6         B+      E6      F7         E
und hat er endlich was erreicht, nimmt's eine Frau ihm weg!
   F     F#    G    Ab    A   Bb    B     C   C#       D   Eb  E   Eb
Er lebt, wenn's hoch kommt, hundert Jahr und bringts bei gutem Start,
D   C#    C    B   Bb    A   Ab    G    D7  D+     D         G
und nur wenn er sehr fleißig war, zu einem Rauschebart!
```

**Refrain:**
```
G+    C         G+       C                   C#°       G7
Ich wollt, ich wär ein Huhn! Ich hätt' nicht viel zu tun!
                                              G+   C
Ich legte vormittags ein Ei und nachmittags wär ich frei!
G+   C         G+       C                   C#°      G7
Mich lockte auf der Welt kein Ruhm mehr und kein Geld,
                                              G+ C6
und fände ich das große Los, dann fräße ich es bloß!
           F7          C6           D7            G7
Ich brauchte niemehr ins Büro, ich wäre dämlich aber froh,

drum hab ich mir gedacht:
G+   C         G+       C                   C#°      G7
Ich wollt, ich wär ein Huhn, ich hätt' nicht viel zu tun,
                                         G+    C6    Bb7 C6
ich legte täglich nur ein Ei und Sonntags auch mal zwei! Juchhei!


    G+  C6                      G+    C6        F6       C
2. Die Eier werden manchmal rar, sie stehn auch gut im Preis,
B+    E6     B+      E6         B+   E6      F7         E
drum ist das Huhn ein großer Star, den man zu schätzen weiß.
   F    F#    G    Ab    A   Bb   B     C   C# D     Eb    E    Eb
Und hab' ich manchmal keine Lust, ein kluger Mensch zu sein,
D   C#    C    B     Bb  A   Ab    G     D7  D+     G         G
erwacht ein Wunsch in meiner Brust und ich gestehe ein!
```

Refrain

M: Peter Kreuder
T: Hans-Fritz Beckmann
© Dreiklang- Dreimasken Bühnen- Musikverlag GmbH
(Universal Music Publ. Group).

# THE LAST UNICORN

(AMERICA)

```
         Cm
1. When the last eagle flies
       Abmaj7        Bb/Ab
over the last crumbling mountain,
         Cm
and the last lion roars
       Abmaj7    Bb/Ab
at the last dusty fountain.
```

**Refrain:**
```
        Cm           Eb/G
In the shadow of the forest,
       Abmaj7          Eb/G
though she may be all and one,
        Fm7        Gm7
they would stare unbelieving
       Abmaj7  Bbsus4 Bb
at the last unicorn.
```

2. When the first breath of winter
through their flowers it's icing,
and you look to the north
and the pale moon is rising.

**Refrain:**
And it seems like all is dying
and would leave the world to more.
In the distance hear the laughter
of the last unicorn:

```
     Eb Cm      Ab Bb Cm
I'm alive! I'm alive!
```

3. When the last moon is cast
over the last star of morning,
and the future has passed
without even a last desperate warning.

**Refrain:**
Then look into the sky where through
the clouds of pact is born.
Look and see her how she sparkles:
She's the last unicorn.

I'm alive! I'm alive!

M + T: Jimmy Webb
© Copyright 1993 Sony ATV Tunes LLC.
Sony/ATV Music Publishing.
All Rights Reserved. International Copyright Secured.

# WEISS DER GEIER

(WOLFGANG PETRY)
[TRANSP. +1]

**Intro:** G Em C D (2x)

```
   G                    Em              C              D
1. Jetzt ist Schluss mit lustig. Ich will dich wiedersehn.
   G                    Em              C              D
Bis gestern warn wir Freunde. Jetzt hab ich ein Problem.

       D                                    Em
2. Die letzte Nacht hat alles verdreht, du hast mich einfach flachgelegt
      C                              D
Ich mach für dich den Hampelmann, du wirfst mich aus der Bahn!
```

**Refrain:**
```
         G              D          C               G
Weiß der Geier oder weiß er nicht. Ganz egal, ich liebe dich!
     C                G               Am                D
Du kannst alles von mir haben, doch es läuft nichts ohne mich.
         G              D          C               G
Weiß der Geier oder weiß er nicht. Ganz egal, ich liebe dich!
     C                G           Am           D   G
Du kannst alles von mir haben, doch es läuft nichts ohne mich.

   G                Em           C                D
3. Mein Leben ist im Eimer, steh völlig auf dem Schlauch.
   G                Em       C              D
Der Tag ist fast am Ende, und ich bin's langsam auch.

       D                                    Em
4. Die letzte Nacht hat alles verdreht, du hast mich einfach flachgelegt
      C                              D
Ich mach für dich den Hampelmann, du wirfst mich aus der Bahn!
```

Refrain 2x

M: Valance, Jean-Pierre / Buschjan, Michael
T: Obenaus, Holger / Zucker, Norbert / Newman, Cynthia
© Gothic Musikverlag GmbH / PickUp Music Thomas Hauptmann
Mit freundlicher Genehmigung der Rolf Budde Musikverlag GmbH, Berlin.

# AN ENGLISHMAN IN NEW YORK

(STING)

```
       Em           A           Bm            A
1. I don't drink coffee, I take tea my dear,
   Em          A               Bm      A
I like my toast done on one side.
   Em           A           Bm
And you can hear it in my accent when I talk:
A        Em           A       Bm    A
I'm an Englishman in New York.

       Em           A               Bm       A
2. You see me walking down Fifth Avenue,
   Em        A              Bm      A
a walking cane here at my side.
   Em          A              Bm
I take it everywhere I walk,
A        Em           A       Bm
I'm an Englishman in New York.
```

**Refrain:**
```
A  Em       A      Bm              A      Em          A        Bm
Woah, I'm an alien, I'm a legal alien, I'm an Englishman in New York.
A  Em       A      Bm              A      Em          A        Bm    A
Woah, I'm an alien, I'm a legal alien, I'm an Englishman in New York.
```

```
       Em           A           Bm          A
3. If "manners maketh man" as someone said,
   Em          A      Bm   A
he's the hero of the day.
   Em          A             Bm
It takes a man to suffer ignorance and smile.
A        Em          A               Bm
Be yourself, no matter what they say.
```

Refrain

**Bridge:**
```
D                              A
Modesty, propriety, can lead to notority
    Bm                         F#
but you could end up as the only one.
G                              A
Gentleness, sobriety are rare in this society
    F#/A#                         Bm   A
at night a candle's brighter than the sun.

       Em            A            Bm          A
4. It takes more than combat gear to make a man,
   Em           A              Bm     A
takes more than a license for a gun.
   Em         A           Bm
Confront your enemies, avoid them when you can,
A  Em          A              Bm    A
a gentleman will walk but never run.
```

Strophe 3

Refrain

M + T: Sting
© Copyright 1987 Steerpike Limited/Steerpike (Overseas)
Limited/EMI Music Publishing Limited.
All Rights Reserved. International Copyright Secured.

# UNA FESTA SUI PRATI

(ADRIANO CELENTANO)

E7
Una festa sui prati, una bella compania.
A
Panini, vino, un sacco di risate,
                                    E7
e luminosi sguardi di ragazze innamorate.

Ma che bella giornata, siamo tutti buoni amici.
A
Ma chi lo sa perche domani questo puo finire.
                                    E7
Vorrei sapere perche domani ci dobbiamo odiare.

E7
Incomincia la gara, la battaglia dell' denaro.
A
Non ce piu tempo ne per ridere ne per amare.
                              E7
Chi vuol' vincere deve saper lottare.

E7
Allora mi con colpo a te, e tu ridai, due colpi a me, ed io rido,
                                         A
tre colpi a te, finche ce forza per coprire fino a che,
      E7
un altra festa ce.

**Refrain:**
E7                                 A
La, la, la,  la, la, la, la, la.  La, la, la,  la, la, la, la, la.
E7                                 A
La, la, la,  la, la, la, la, la.  La, la, la,  la, la, la, la, la.

E7
Nuova festa sui prati, nuova bella compania.
A
Panini, vino, un sacco di risate,
                                    E7
e luminosi sguardi di ragazze innamorate.

No, non deve finire, questa bella passegiata.
A
Deve durare una intera vita,
                                  E7
se ce una gara e solo quella dell' amore.

E7
Allora do una mano a te, e tu la dai, due volte a me, ed io la do.
                                    A
Tre volte a te, finche ce forza per amare fino a che.
      E7
Un altra festa ce.

Refrain

M: Celentano
T: Beretta / Mogol / del Prete
© Clan Edizioni Musicali S.r.l. / Fama Edizioni Musicali S.r.l.
Für D/A: Sugar Musik-Verlags GmbH, Berlin

# SUMMER SON

(TEXAS)
[TRANSP. +1]

**Intro:** Em  Am  D  B7  Em

```
      C              D              C              D
1. I'm tired of singing the story, tired of telling it your way.
Bm                      Em
Yeah, I know what I saw, I know that I found the floor.
```

**Refrain:**
```
G                          C
Before you take my heart, reconsider,
G                          A7
before you take my heart, reconsider.
C                  D
I've opened the door, I've opened the door!
                 Em
Here comes the summer's son,
   Am              D           B7          Em
he burns my skin, I ache again, I'm over you.
```

```
      C         D              C              D
2. I thought I had a dream to hold, maybe that has gone.
Bm                              Em
Your hands reach out and touch me still, but this feels so wrong.
```

Refrain

```
                 Em
Here comes the winter's rain
   Am              D           B7          Em
to cleanse my skin, I wake again, I'm over you.
```

Refrain

```
                 Em
Here comes the winter's rain
   Am              D           B7          Em
to cleanse my skin, I wake again, I'm over you.
```

M + T: John McElhone, Sharleen Spiteri, Robert Hodgens and Edward Campbell
© Copyright 1999 Anxious Music Limited.
EMI 10 Music Limited/Universal/Anxious Music Limited.
All Rights Reserved. International Copyright Secured.

# THE BALLAD OF LUCY JORDAN

(MARIANNE FAITHFULL)
(DR. HOOK)
[TRANSP. -3]

```
      G                              C            G
1. The morning sun touched lightly on the eyes of Lucy Jordan
                            D7
in a white suburban bedroom in a white suburban town.
     G                             C               G
And she lay there neath the covers dreaming of a thousand lovers
         D7                                  G        G7
til the world turned to orange and the room went spinning round.
```

**Refrain:**
```
           C              G
At the age of 37 she realized she'd never

ride through Paris in a sports car
                  D7
with the warm wind in her hair.
       G                G7
So she let the phone keep ringing
       C              G
as she sat there softly singing
     D7
pretty nursery rhymes she'd memorized
    C            G
in her Daddy's easy chair.
```

```
      G                              C             G
2. Her husband he's off to work and the kids are off to school
                            D7
and there were oh so many ways for her to spend her days.
         G                            C              G
She could clean the house for hours or rearrange the flowers
     D7                                              G    G7
or run naked through the shady streets screaming all the way.
```
Refrain

```
      G                              C             G
3. The evening sun shines gently on the eyes of Lucy Jordan
                                                    D7
on the rooftop where she climbed when the laughter grew too loud.
      G                                   C                  G
And she bowed and curtsied to the man who reached and offered her his
hand
    D7                                              G    G7
and he led her down to the long white car that waited past the crowd.
```
Refrain

M + T: Shel Silverstein
© Evil Eye Music Inc.

# LUCILLE

(MICHAEL HOLM)

```
     C
1. Ich trank in der Bar so für mich einen Whisky,
                          G7
da spürt' ich, es schaut mich wer an.
   Dm7                G7
Es war eine Frau mit den herrlichsten Augen
      Dm7      G7       C
und ich bat sie zu mir heran.
     C
Sie erzählte und lachte und bald fing ich Feuer
                 C7         F
und merkte, sie macht es mir leicht.
  G7
Ich dachte, warum nicht,
                                                 C
ein Barabenteuer ist süß und gefährlich für alle zugleich.
```

2. Die Türe ging auf und ein Mann trat zu Ihr,
der war groß und so breit wie ein Bär.
Ich dachte, dass ich nun meine Zähne verlier,
doch der Blick seiner Augen war leer.
Er stand und ich sah: Seine Hände, die zittern
und die Not war bei ihm oft zu Gast.
Dann sagte er rauh, seine Stimme klang bitter:
Diese Worte, die ich nie vergaß:

**Refrain:**
```
C                        F
Musst du jetzt grade gehen, Lucille?
                                            C
Unsere Kinder sind krank und die Schulden so viel.
F                                                       C
Du hast geschworen, du bist die Frau, die das Leben mit mir teilen will.
     G7                  C
Musst du jetzt grade gehen, Lucille?
```

3. Er zog seinen Ring ab und warf ihn zu Boden,
dann ließ er uns beide allein.
Ich ging zur Theke, um Whisky zu holen
und fühlte mich schlecht und gemein.
Sie war eine Schönheit mit herrlichen Augen,
doch mit ihr gehn wollte ich nicht.
Denn was sie sagte, das konnt' ich nicht glauben
und es klang mir im Ohr, wie Ihr Mann zu Ihr spricht:

Refrain

```
F                                                       C
Du hast geschworen, du bist die Frau, die das Leben mit mir teilen will.
     G7                  C
Musst du jetzt grade gehen, Lucille?
```

M + T: Roger Bowling & Hal Bynum
© Copyright 1976 ATV Music Corporation, USA.
Sony/ATV Music Publishing (UK) Limited / Transamerika Musikverlag KG.
All Rights Reserved. International Copyright Secured.

# BROKEN WINGS

(MR. MISTER)
[TRANSP. -1]

**Intro:** Asus2 Gsus2 Dsus2
```
    Asus2
1. Baby, don't understand, why we can't just hold on
                     Gsus2 Dsus2
to each other's hands.
Asus2
This time might be the last I fear unless I make it all so clear.
            Gsus2    Dsus2
I need you so. Oooooh.
```

**Refrain:**
```
Dm
Take these broken wings
            C                              Bb
and learn to fly again, learn to live so free.
          Dm
When we hear the voices sing
            C                              Bb
the book of love will open up and let us in.

Dm                      Asus2
Take these broken wings.

      Asus2
2. Baby, I think tonight we can take what was wrong
                Gsus2 Dsus2
and make it right.
Asus2
Baby, it's all I know that you're half of the flesh and blood
              Gsus2         Dsus2
that makes me whole. I need you so.
```

Refrain

```
Dm
Take these broken wings.
              C                              Bb
You've got to learn to fly, learn to live a love so free.
          Dm
When we hear the voices sing
            C                              Bb
the book of love will open up for us and let us in.
Gm            Bb F Eb     Gm       Bb F Eb
Yeah, Yeah Let us in.      Yeah! Let us in.

      Asus2
3. Baby, it's all I know that you're half of the flesh and blood
                    Gsus2
that makes me whole. Yeah, Yeah, Yeah Yeah, Yeah.
Dsus2
Yeah, Yeah Yeah, Yeah. Oooooh.
```

Refrain

M + T: John Ross Lang, Steven Park George, Richard James Page
© 1985 WB Music Corp, Ali-Aja Music, Panola Park Music and Indolent Sloth Music,
Warner/Chappell North America Ltd, London. Reproduced by permission of Faber Music Ltd.
All Rights Reserved.

# IT'S ALL OVER NOW, BABY BLUE

(THEM)
(BOB DYLAN)

```
   G                                          C
1. You must leave now, take what you need, you think will last.
         G                                 C
But whatever you wish to keep, you better grab it fast.
Dm            F              C
Yonder stands your orphan with his gun,
Dm         F           C
crying like a fire in the sun.
E7                                    G
Look out, baby, the saints are coming through,
    Dm           F        C
and it's all over now, Baby Blue.

       G                                      C
2. The highway is for gamblers, better use your sense.
G                                  C
Take what you have gathered from coincidence.
     Dm         F               C
The empty-handed painter from your streets
     Dm          F        C
is drawing crazy patterns on your sheets.
E7                          G
This sky too, is folding under you
    Dm           F        C
and it's all over now, baby blue.

      G                                  C
3. All your seasick sailors, they are rowing home.
G                                 C
All your reindeer armies are all going home.
    Dm            F              C
The lover who just walked out your door
    Dm         F         C
has taken all his blankets from the floor.
E7                           G
The carpet, too, is moving under you
    Dm           F        C
and it's all over now, baby blue.

         G                                  C
4. Leave your stepping stones behind, something calls for you.
G                                C
Forget the dead you've left, they will not follow you.
     Dm        F             C
The vagabond who's rapping at your door
     Dm        F             C
is standing in the clothes that you once wore.
E7                               G
Strike another match, go start anew
    Dm           F        C
and it's all over now, baby blue.
```

M + T: Bob Dylan
© Copyright 1965 Warner Brothers Incorporated.
© Copyright Renewed 1993 Special Rider Music, USA.
All Rights Reserved. International Copyright Secured.

# FIRE WATER BURN

(BLOODHOUND GANG)

**Intro:** G  Em  G  Em
**Refrain:**
```
    G                     Em
The roof, the roof, the roof is on fire.
    G                     Em
The roof, the roof, the roof is on fire.
    G                     Em
The roof, the roof, the roof is on fire.
D                             C
We don't need no water, let the motherfucker burn.
C              G    Em   G    Em   G    Em   G    Em
Burn motherfucker, burn.
```

```
         G                              Em
1. Hello, my name is Jimmy Pop and I'm a dumb white guy.
            G                                    Em
I'm not old or new but middle school fifth grade like junior high.
                  G
I don't know mofo if y'all peeps be buggin givin
Em
props to my ho cause she's fly
          A
but I can take the heat cause I'm the
                                 C
other white meat known as kid funky fried.
```

```
2. Yeah, I'm hung like planet Pluto hard to see with the naked eye
but if I crashed into Uranus I would stick it where the sun don't shine
cause I'm kinda like Han Solo always stroking my own Wookie.
I'm the root of all that's evil, yeah, but you can call me cookie.
```

Refrain

```
3. Yo, Yo, this hardcore ghetto gangster image takes a lot of practice.
I'm not black like Barry White, no, I am white like Frank Black is.
So if man is five and the devil is six, then that must make me seven,
this honkie's gone to heaven.
```

```
4. But if I go to hell, well then I hope I burn well,
I'll spend my days with J.F.K, Marvin Gaye, Martha Raye,
and Lawrence Welk and Kurt Cobain, Kojak, Mark Twain,
and Jimi Hendrix's poltergeist
and Webster, yeah, Emmanuel Lewis cause he's the anti-christ.
```

Refrain

Everybody here we go

```
G                        Em
Come on party people put your hands in the air.
G                        Em
Come on party people wave em like you don't care.
G                        Em
Come on party people everybody say ho.
G
Come on party people
Em
everybody here we go.
```

M + T: Jerry Bloodrock, Celite Evans, Richard Lee Fowler, Jimmy Franks, Charles Pettifold, Gregory Calton Wigfall
© Songs of Polygram Int. Inc, Rudy Music Publishing, The Jimmy Franks Publishing, Stacey & Brothers Publishing, J.D: Music. Universal Songs of Polygram Ltd. / Universal/ MCA Music Ltd. / Frankly Music / Nanada Music BV.
All Rights Reserved. International Copyright Secured.

# AMAZING GRACE

```
      D              G         D                        A
1. Amazing grace, how sweet the sound that saved a wretch like me.
   D              G         D              A       D
I once was lost, but now am found, was blind but now I see.

         D                G         D                      A
2. 'Twas grace that taught my heart to fear and grace my fears relieved.
   D              G         D              A       D
How precious did that grace appear, the hour I first believed.

            D              G         D                A
3. Through many dangers, toils and snares, I have already come.
   D                G         D              A       D
'Tis grace has brought me safe thus far and grace will lead me home.

         D             G        D                A
4. How sweet the name of Jesus sounds in a believer's ear.
   D              G         D              A       D
It soothes his sorrows, heals his wounds and drives away his fear.

            D            G        D                     A
5. Must Jesus bear the cross alone, and all the world go free?
   D              G     D            A       D
No, there's a cross for everyone and there's a cross for me.
```

Traditionell
© 2005 by Edition DUX, Manching

# NOWHERE MAN

(THE BEATLES)

```
C                G
He's a real nowhere man,
F               C
sitting in his nowhere land,
F              Fm              C   Bb   F
making all his nowhere plans for nobody.

C                G
Doesn't have a point of view,
F              C
knows not where he's going to,
F         Fm             C
isn't he a bit like you and me?


          Em         F
Nowhere man, please listen,
             Em            F
you don't know what you're missing,
         Em       F             G7
nowhere man, the world is at your command.
```

He's as blind as he can be,
just sees what he wants to see,
nowhere man can you see me at all?

Doesn't have a point of view,
knows not where he's going to,
isn't he a bit like you and me?

Nowhere man, don't worry,
take your time, don't hurry,
leave it all 'till somebody else lends you a hand.

He's a real nowhere man,
sitting in his nowhere land,
```
F              Fm                C
making all his nowhere plans for nobody.
F              Fm                C
Making all his nowhere plans for nobody.
```

M + T: John Lennon & Paul McCartney
© Copyright 1965 Sony/ATV Music Publishing (UK) Limited.
All Rights Reserved. International Copyright Secured.

# HOMEWARD BOUND

(SIMON & GARFUNKEL)  
[TRANSP. +3]

**Intro:** G F C G

```
        G
1. I'm sittin in a railway station,
       Bm/F#                  Dm/F    E7
got a ticket for my destination.
Am
On a tour of one night stands
 F
my suitcase and guitar in hand
       G
and every stop is neatly planned
         D
for a poet and a one man band.
```

**Refrain:**
```
G          C              G            C
Homeward bound, I wish I was, homeward bound.
G                  Am
Home, where my thoughts escaping.
G                  Am
Home, where my music's playing.
G                  Am
Home, where my love lies waiting
 D         G
silently for me.
```

```
        G
2. Every day's an endless stream
       Bm/F#              Dm/F    E7
of cigarettes and magazines
      Am
and each town looks the same to me.
       F
The movies and the factories
         G
and every stranger's face I see
   D
reminds me that I long to be.     Refrain
```

```
        G
3. Tonight I'll sing my songs again,
       Bm/F#              Dm/F    E7
I'll play the game and pretend
         Am
but all my words come back to me.
       F
In shades of mediocrity
         G
like emptyness in harmony,
    D
I need someone to comfort me.     Refrain
```

```
Bm/F#      Dm/F        G  F  C  G
Silently for me ...
```

M + T: Paul Simon  
© 1965 by ELECT MUSIC Co., New York / Paul Simon Music (BMI). MELODIE DER WELT, J. Michel GmbH & Co. KG, Frankfurt am Main für Deutschland. All Rights Reserved. International Copyright Secured.

# DREAM ON

(AEROSMITH)

**Intro:** Fm   Fm7   Fm6   Bbm6/F   Fm   C7sus4/F   Fm

```
      Fm       Fm7          Fm6            Bbm6/F
1. Ev'ry time that I look in the mirror
Fm          Fm7           Fm6          Bbm6/F
all these lines on my face getting clearer.
Fm Fm7        Fm6 Bbm6/F
   The past is gone.
Fm         Fm7         Fm6         Bbm6/F
It went by like dusk to dawn.
```

**Bridge:**
```
Dm7b5          C    Dm7b5                 Bbm6
Isn't that the way ev'rybody's got their dues in life to pay?

C  Dbmaj7  D7  C7

Fm       Eb          Db                Eb
I know nobody knows where it comes and where it goes.
Fm          Eb            Db               Eb
I know it's ev'ryvody's sin; you got to lose to know how to win.

Fm   Fm7   Fm6   Bbm6/F   Fm   Fm9   Fm

      Fm        Fm7          Fm6            Bbm6/F
2. Half my life's in books' written pages
Fm          Fm7           Fm6          Bbm6/F
lived and learned from fools and from sages.
Fm            Fm7   Fm6 Bbm6/F
You know it's true.
Fm          Fm7         Fm6          Bbm6/F
All these things come back to you.
```

**Refrain:**
```
Fm           Eb
Sing with me, sing for the years.
Db                        Eb
Sing for the laughter and sing for the tears.
Fm                     Eb
Sing with me if it's just for today,
Dm7b5              Dbmaj7
maybe tomorrow the good Lord will take you away.
```

Solo
Refrain

```
Bb          C           Db          Eb                           Fm
Dream on, dream on, dream on, dream yourself a dream come true.
Bb          C           Db          Eb                           Fm
Dream on, dream on, dream on, and dream until your dream comes true.
Bb          C           D           Eb
Dream on, dream on, dream on, dream on,
F           G           Ab          Bb
Dream on, dream on, dream on, ah.
```

M + T: Steven Tyler
© Stage Three Music, a BMG company

Refrain

## WE SHALL OVERCOME

```
     C      F   C  Am C       F   C  Am
1. We shall overcome, we shall overcome,
   C      F   C   D    G    D G G7
   we shall overcome some day.
      C     F    C    F G   Am
   Oh deep in my heart I do believe
         C      F   C    G    C   F C G7
   that we shall overcome some day.
```

2. Black and white together, black and white together,
   black and white together some day.
   Oh deep in my heart I do believe
   that black and white together some day.

3. We'll walk hand in hand, we'll walk hand in hand,
   we'll walk hand in hand some day.
   Oh deep in my heart I do believe
   that we'll walk hand in hand some day.

4. We shall live in peace, we shall live in peace,
   we shall live in peace some day.
   Oh deep in my heart I do believe
   that we shall live in peace some day.

5. We shall all be free, we shall all be free,
   we shall all be free some day.
   Oh deep in my heart I do believe
   that we shall all be free some day.

6. We are not afraid, we are not afraid,
   we are not afraid today.
   Oh deep in my heart I do believe
   that we are not afraid today.

7. We shall overcome, we shall overcome,
   we shall overcome some day.
   Oh deep in my heart I do believe
   that we shall overcome some day.

M+T: Guy Carawane, Frank Hamilton, Zilphia Horton, Peter Seeger
© Ludlow Music Inc.

# BALLAD

(NEW MODEL ARMY)

**Intro:** C#m/G# C#m/F# C#m/E C#m/F# (2x)

```
            C#m/G#                         C#m/F#
1. When they look back at us and they write down their history.
C#m/E                     C#m/F#
What will they say about our generation?
            C#m/G#                       C#m/F#
We're the ones who knew everything, still we did nothing.
C#m/E                   C#m/F#
Harvested everything, planted nothing.
```

2. Well we live pretty well in the wake of the gold rush.
Floating in comfort on waves of our apathy.
Quietly knawing away at Her body,
until we mortgage the future, bury our children.

```
E                                  G#5
Storehouses full with the fruits we've been given,
   D                           C#m/G#
We send off the scragends to suckle the starving.
      E                             G#5
But still we can't feed this strange hunger inside.
D                     C#m/G#       B/F# Bsus4/F# B/F#
Greedy, resless and unsatisfied
```

3. I was never much one for the great big bang theory.
Going out in a blaze of suicidial glory.
Not foolish and brave, these leaders of ours.
Just stupid and petty, unworthy of power.

```
       E                          G#5
Just a little leak here and a small error there.
    D                   C#m/G#
Another square mile poisonend forever.
    E                        G#5
A series of sad and pathetic little fizzles.
     D                     C#m/G#         B/F# Bsus4/F# B/F#
And out go the lights, never to return.
```

4. The affair it is over, the passion is dead.
She stares at us now with ice in Her eyes.
But we turn away from these bitter reproaches,
And take up distractions to forget what we're doing.

5. Well I stand on these hills and I watch Her at night.
A thousand square miles, a million orange lights.
Wounded and scarred, She lies silent in pain.
Raped and betrayed in the cold acid rain.

```
       E                         G#5
And I wish and I wish and I wish and I wish
D                 C#m/G#
we could start over again.
       E                         G#5
Yes I wish and I wish and I wish and I wish
D C#m/G#              B/F#           Bsus4/F# B/F#
      we could win Her back once again.
```

M + T: Justin Edward Sullivan
© 1987 Attack-Attack Music and Intersong Music Limited.
Warner/Chappell Overseas Holdings Ltd, London.
Reproduced by permission of Faber Music Limited.
All Rights Reserved.

# RUBY, DON'T TAKE YOUR LOVE TO TOWN

(KENNY ROGERS)

```
              C                           F             G7    Dm
1. You've painted up your lips and rolled and curled your tinted hair.
C                           F            G7
Ruby are you contemplating going out somewhere?
    Dm                          G7                        Dm
The shadows on the wall tell me the sun is going down.
   C F   C/E Dm tacet              C
Oh Ruby,        don't take your love to town.

         Dm                     C
For it wasn't me that started that old crazy Asian war.
    Dm                       F         G7
But I was proud to go and do my patriotic chores.
    Dm                          G7                    Dm
And yes it's true, that I'm not the man I used to be.
   C F   C/E Dm tacet           C
Oh, Ruby,       I still need some company.

            C                         F              G7    Dm
2. It's hard to love a man whose legs are bent and paralized.
            C                         F             G7
And the wants and the needs of a woman your age, Ruby, I realize.
     Dm                          G7                      Dm
But it won't be long I heard them say until I'm not around.
   C F   C/E Dm tacet              C
Oh Ruby,        don't take your love to town.

            C                         F              G7    Dm
3. She's leaving now cause I just heard the slamming of a door.
         C                          F             G7
The way I know I've heard it slam one hundred times before.
        Dm                        G7                         Dm
And if I could move I'd get my gun and put her in the ground.
   C F   C/E Dm tacet              C
Oh Ruby,        don't take your love to town.
   C F   C/E Dm tacet
Oh Ruby,        for God's sake turn around.
```

M + T: Mel Tillis
© Copyright 1966 Universal Cedarwood Publishing.
Universal Music Publishing Limited. All Rights Reserved. International Copyright Secured.

## COME TOGETHER

(THE BEATLES)

```
Dm
Here come old flat top, he come grooving up slowly,
        Dm
he got joo joo eyeball, he one holy roller.
          A7
He got hair down to his knee,
G7
got to be a joker, he just do what he please.

Dm
He wear no shoe shine, he got toe jam football,
            Dm
he got monkey finger, he shoot coca cola.
          A7
He say, "I know you, you know me."
G7
One thing I can tell you is you got to be free.
        Bm     A      G     A        Dm
Come together, right now, over me.


Dm
He bag production, he got walrus gumboot,
Dm
he got Ono sideboard, he one spinal cracker.
          A7
He got feet down below his knee.
G7
Hold you in his armchair, you can feel his disease.
        Bm     A      G     A        Dm
Come together, right now, over me.


Dm
He roller coaster, he got early warning,
Dm
he got muddy water, he one Mojo filter.
          A7
He say, "One and one and one is three."
G7
Got to be good looking cause he's so hard to see.
        Bm     A      G     A        Dm
Come together, right now, over me.
```

M + T: John Lennon & Paul McCartney
© Copyright 1969 Sony/ATV Music Publishing (UK) Limited.
All Rights Reserved. International Copyright Secured.

# WHY WORRY

(DIRE STRAITS)

```
     E     B7                          E
1. Baby, I see this world has made you sad,
B7                 E
some people can be bad,
A             F#              B    C#m7 B
the things they do, the things they say.
     E     B7                          E
But baby, I'll wipe away those bitter tears,
B7                              E
I'll chase away those restless fears
A             F#            B    C#m7 B
that turn your blue skies into grey.


Refrain:
   E           A            B             E
Why worry? There should be laughter after pain.
A             B            E
There should be sunshine after rain,
A            B            E       A     B    E
these things have always been the same, so why worry now?


     E     B7                          E
2. Baby, when I get down I turn to you
B7                             E
and you make sense of what I do,
A          F#           B    C#m7 B
I know it isn't hard to say.
     E     B7                                E
But baby, just when this world seems mean and cold,
B7                              E
our love comes shining red and gold
A           F#            B    C#m7 B
and all the rest is by the way.


Refrain
```

M + T: Mark Knopfler
© Copyright 1985 Straitjacket Songs Limited.
Universal Music Publishing Limited. All rights in Germany
administered by Universal Music Publ. GmbH.
All Rights Reserved. International Copyright Secured.

# DIE KARAWANE ZIEHT WEITER

(HÖHNER)
[TRANSP. +1]

A
Dun mer ne, dun mer ne, dun mer ne Kloore!
Dun mer ne, dun mer ne, dun mer ne Kloore!

Han mer nit, han mer nit, han mer nit!
Han mer nit, han mer nit, han mer nit!

Oh jeh! Su ne Driss, su ne Driss, su ne Driss!
Oh jeh! Su ne Driss, su ne Driss, su ne Driss!

Jon mer in en andere Kaschämm! Schämm!
                          E
Jon mer in en andere Kaschämm!

**Refrain:**
     A                          D      A
Die Karawane zieht weiter, der Sultan hätt Doosch!
            E                  A
Der Sultan hätt Doosch! Der Sultan hätt Doosch!
                           D      A
Die Karawane zieht weiter, der Sultan hätt Doosch!
D     E            A
Der Sultan, der Sultan der hätt Doosch!

A
Dun mer ne, dun mer ne, dun mer ne Kloore!
Dun mer ne, dun mer ne, dun mer ne Kloore!

Han ävver, han ävver, han ävver nur Kabänes!
Han ävver, han ävver, han ävver nur Kabänes!

Wolle mer, wolle mer, wolle mer, wolle mer nit!
Wolle mer, wolle mer, wolle mer, wolle mer nit!

Jon mer in en andere Kaschämm! Schämm!
                          E
Jon mer in en andere Kaschämm!

Refrain

    D        A           D      A
Doch Nathan der Weise, der wusste Bescheid.
    D         A       B                   E
Der kannte ne Oase und die war nicht sehr weit!

Refrain

M + T: Jan-Peter Froehlich, Henning Krautmacher, Martina Neschen,
Monika Riedel, Hannes Schoener, Peter-Werner Jates, Franz-Martin Willizil
© Mit freundlicher Genehmigung von Vogelsang Musik.

## STAY

(SHAKESPEAR'S SISTER)

```
        G              D            C           D
If this world isn't worth a thing and you thinking on escape
        G              D            C           D
I'll go anywhere with you just wrap me up in chains.
             Em                 C              D
But if you'll try to go alone don't think I'll understand.
```

```
G    D7    Em7
Stay with me.
G    D7    Em7
Stay with me.
```

```
         G            D            C              D
In the silence of the room, in the darkness of your dream
             G             D         C         D
you must only think of me, there can be no in between.
             Em                C             D
When your pride is on the floor I'll make you beg for more.
```

```
G    D7    Em7
Stay with me.
G    D7    Em7
Stay with me.
```

```
                    Em
You better hope and pray
         C                    D
that you make it safe back to your own world.
                    Em
You better hope and pray
         C               D
that you wake one day in your own world.
                   Em
Cause when you sleep at night
         C                    D
they don't hear your cries in your own world.
         Em                     C
Only time will tell if you can break this bell
             D
back in your own world.

Em  C  D  Em  C  D
```

```
G    D7    Em7
Stay with me.
G    D7    Em7
Stay with me.
G    D7    Em7
Stay with me.
```

M + T: Siobhan Fahey, Marcella Detroit and David Stewart
© Reverb Music Limited/Universal Music Publishing MGB Limited/Chester Music Limited trading as Campbell Connelly & Co. Mit freundlicher Genehmigung von Bosworth Music GmbH.
All Rights Reserved. International Copyright Secured.

# TRUE COLORS

(CYNDI LAUPER)

**Intro:** Am G/B C F Am G/B C F

```
              Am   G/B    C
1. You with the sad eyes don't be discouraged.
       F         Am           G
Oh, I realize it's hard to take courage.
      C          Dm      C/E          F
In a world full of people you can lose sight of it all
         Am         G         F                C
and the darkness inside you can make you feel so small.
```

**Refrain:**
```
              F     C      Gsus4    G
And I'll see your true colors shining through.
            F       C       F        Gsus4 G
I'll see your true colors and that's why I love you.
     F        C        F      Am      F    C
So don't be afraid to let them show your true colors,
F    C         G              Am
true colors are beautiful like a rainbow.
```

```
              Am   G/B    C
2. Show me a smile then, don't be unhappy,
       F          Am            G
can't remember when I last saw you laughing.
      C              Dm             C/E         F
If this world makes you crazy and you've taken all you can bear
    Am        G        F             C
you call me up because you know I'll be there.
```

Refrain

M + T: Billy Steinberg & Tom Kelly
© Copyright 1986 Sony/ATV Tunes LLC, USA.
Sony/ATV Music Publishing.
All Rights Reserved. International Copyright Secured.

# COULD YOU BE LOVED

(BOB MARLEY)

**Intro:** Cm

```
Eb          Cm       Ab        Eb
Could you be loved and be loved?
Eb          Cm       Ab        Eb
Could you be loved and be loved?


Cm                         Fm
Don't let them fool you
Cm                         Fm         Cm
or even try to school you. Oh, no!

Cm
We've got a mind of our own.
          Ab        Cm/G                      Fm
So go to hell if what you're thinking is not right
Cm
Love would never leave us alone.
          Ab              Cm/G              Bb
In the darkness there must come out the light.

Could you be loved and be loved?
Could you be loved and be loved?


     Cm
The road of life is rocky
     Cm
and you may stumble too.
     Cm
So while you point your fingers
          Cm
someone else is judging you.

Cm
Could you be, could you be, could you be loved?
Cm
Could you be, could you be loved?
Cm
Could you be, could you be, could you be loved?
Cm
Could you be, could you be loved?

Don't let them change you, or even rearrange you. Oh, no!
We've got a life to live. They say only, only,
only the fittest of the fittest shall survive, stay alive.

Could you be loved and be loved?
Could you be loved and be loved?

You ain't gonna miss your water
until your well runs dry.
No matter how you treat him,
the man will never be satisfied.

Could you be, could you be, could you be loved?
Could you be, could you be loved? Say something...
```

M + T: Bob Marley
© Copyright 1980 Fifty-Six Hope Road Music Limited/Odnil Music Limited.
Blue Mountain Music Limited.
All Rights Reserved. International Copyright Secured.

# FIRST WE TAKE MANHATTAN

(LEONARD COHEN)
(JOE COCKER)

```
         Dm                              Am
1. They sentenced me to twenty years of boredom
         Dm                              Am
for trying to change the system from within.
         Dm                       Am
I'm coming now, I'm coming to reward them.
 G            Dm7 Esus4  E7       Am
First we take Manhattan, then we take Berlin.


2. I'm guided by a signal in the heavens.
I'm guided by this birthmark on my skin.
I'm guided by the beauty of our weapons.
First we take Manhattan, then we take Berlin.
```

**Refrain:**
```
     C                         G     F
I'd really like to live beside you, baby.
 G         C                      Am
I love your body and your spirit and your clothes.
         Dm                                    Am
But you see that line there moving through the station.
   G          F           Esus4    E7        Am
I told you, I told you, I told you I was one of those.


3. You loved me as a loser but now your worried that I just might win.
You know the way to stop me but you don't have the discipline.
How many nights I prayed for this: to let my work begin.
First we take Manhattan, then we take Berlin.


4. I don't like your fashion business, mister.
I don't like these drugs that keep you thin.
I don't like what happened to your sister.
First we take Manhattan, then we take Berlin.
```

Refrain

```
5. And I thank you for those items that you sent me.
The monkey and the plywood violin.
I practiced every night and now I'm ready.
First we take Manhattan, then we take Berlin.


6. Remember me, I used to live for music.
Remember me, I brought your groceries in.
It's Father's Day and everybody's wounded.
First we take Manhattan, then we take Berlin.
```

M + T: Leonard Cohen
© Copyright 1986 Sony/ATV Music Publishing (UK) Limited.
All Rights Reserved. International Copyright Secured.

## TAKE ON ME

(A-HA)

```
      Bm          E
1. Talking away,
A               D         A/C#
I don't know what I'm to say.
       Bm          E
I'll say it anyway,
     A          D         A/C#
today's another day to find you.
Bm         E
Shying away,
F#m                   E
I'll be coming for you love O.K.


Refrain:
A    C#m F#m D
Take on  me. Take on me.
A    C#m F#m D
Take me  on. Take on me.
A    C#m F#m D
I'll be gone
            A   C#m D E
in a day or two.


2. So needless to say
I'm odds and ends but that's me.
Stumbling away,
slowly learning that life is O.K.
Say after me
it's no better to be safe than sorry.

Refrain


3. The things that you say,
is it live or just to play
my worries away?
You're all the things I've got to remember.
You shying away,
I'll be coming for you anyway.

Refrain
```

M + T: Morten Harket, Mags Furuholmen & Pal Waaktaar
© Copyright 1984 ATV Music Limited.
Sony/ATV Music Publishing (UK) Limited.
All Rights Reserved. International Copyright Secured.

# MAMMA MIA

(ABBA)

```
   D         A/D       D                       G
1. I've been cheated by you since I don't know when.
D      A/D          D                   G
So I made up my mind, it must come to an end.
D
Look at me now, will I ever learn?
                                 G
I don't know but I suddenly lose control.
                          A
There's a fire within my soul.
G    D    A
Just one look and I can hear a bell ring,
G    D    A
one more look and I forget everything, whou ou.
```

**Refrain:**
```
D                       G C G             D
Mamma mia, here I go again. My my, how can I resist you?
D                        G C G                         D
Mamma mia, does it show again? My my, just how much I've missed you.
D         A/C#          Bm          F#m/A        G
Yes, I've been brokenhearted, blue since the day we parted.
C   G  Em       A
Why why did I ever let you go.
D        Bm           G C G  Em        A        D
Mamma mia, now I really know, my my, I could never let you go.
```

```
   D         A/D       D                          G
2. I've been angry and sad about the things that you do.
D      A/D          D                          G
I can't count all the times that I've told you we're through.
D
And when you go, when you slam the door,
                                        G
I think you know that you won't be away too long,
                          A
You know that I'm not that strong.
G    D    A
Just one look and I can hear a bell ring,
G    D    A
One more look and I forget everything, whou ou.
```

Refrain

M + T: Benny Andersson, Bjorn Ulvaeus & Stig Anderson
© Copyright 1975 Universal/Union Songs Musikforlag AB.
Universal Music Publishing Limited. All Rights Reserved.
International Copyright Secured.

# (I JUST) DIED IN YOUR ARMS TONIGHT

(CUTTING CREW)

**Refrain:**
```
Bm         Em              A
I, I just died in your arms tonight,
   F#m                Bm
it must've been something you said.
        Em             A
I just died in your arms tonight.
    Bm         Em             A
Oh, cause I just died in your arms tonight,
   F#m              Bm
it must've been some kind of kiss.
   Em        A
I should've walked away.
F#m               G
I should've walked away.
```

```
Bm
I keep looking for something I can't get.
Gmaj7
Broken hearts lie all around me and I
A                                F#sus4 F#
don't see an easy way to get out of this.
     Bm                              Gmaj7
Her diary sits by the bed side table. The curtains are closed the
Gmaj7            A
cat's in the cradle. Who would've thought that a boy like me could
F#sus4      F#
come to this?
```

Refrain

```
Is there any just cause for feeling like this?
On the surface I'm a name on a list.
I try to be discrete, then blow it again.
I've lost and found, it's my final mistake,
she's loving by proxy, no give and all take
cause I've been thrilled to fantasy one too many times.
```

Refrain

```
G
It was a long hot night,
Em
she made it easy. She made it feel right
G
but now it's over the moment has gone,
   F#                                       Bm
I followed my hands not my head. I know I was wrong.
```

|: Bm Em A F#m :| F#m

Refrain 2x

M + T: Nicholas Eede
© Copyright 1986 Sony/ATV Music Publishing.
All Rights Reserved. International Copyright Secured.

# SAG MAL WEINST DU

(ECHT)

**Intro:** C/E F C/G G

```
   C/E              F              C/E            F
1. Uns're Liebe ist am Boden, läuft langsam aus,
   C/E            F               Gsus4         G
   dreht noch 'ne Ehrenrunde bis sie still steht.
   Em           F            C/E        F
   Und du, ich geh' am Stock, will nie wieder schlafen,
   Em            F                    Gsus4            G
   solange du mich Nacht für Nacht in meinen Träumen besuchst.
```

**Refrain:**
```
                Am                    Bb
Jetzt lieg' ich neben dir, wir haben uns alles gesagt,
         F                   G
haben uns ausgesprochen, uns Luft gemacht.
    Am                      Bb
Ich fühl mich wie ausgekotzt, dir geht's nicht viel besser,
 C
da seh' ich es in deinen Augen glitzern.
      F                  Bb
Sag mal weinst du oder ist das der Regen,
 F                         Bb
der von deiner Nasenspitze tropft?
      F                       Bb
Sag mal weinst du etwa oder ist das der Regen,
 F                        C
der von deiner Oberlippe perlt?
          Am                Bb
Komm her, ich küss den Tropfen weg,
             Eb Bb  F          Eb Bb F
probier ihn, ob er salzig schmeckt.
```

```
   C/E        F            C/E                      F
2. Jetzt sitz' ich hier und schreibe nur noch blinde Liebeslieder,
   C/E               F
   von Herz und Schmerz und Schmalz
         Gsus4                G
   und sowas Tolles kommt nie wieder.
   Em          F           Em                 F
   Hätt' ich nie gedacht, noch vor ein paar Tagen
   Em             F                     Gsus4 G
   lagen wir uns Nacht für Nacht im Arm.
```

Refrain 2x

M: Joachim Schlüter, Jan Kelber, Stefan Endigkeit, Lars Plogschties, Dirk Zuther
T: Joachim Schlüter, Jan Kelber
© Movie Musikverlag & Co. / SMPG Publishing (Germany) GmbH.
Mit freundlicher Genehmigung von SMPG Publishing (Germany) GmbH.

# ON THE ROAD AGAIN

(WILLIE NELSON)

```
         E
1. On the road again,
                              G#7
just can't wait to get on the road again,
                         F#m
the life I love is making music with my friends
     A              B          E
and I can't wait to get on the road again.

         E
2. On the road again,
                     G#7
going places that I've never been,
                    F#m
seeing things that I may never see again,
A              B          E
I can't wait to get on the road again.
```

**Refrain:**
```
       A
On the road again
                                      E
like a band of gypsies we go down the highway.
          A
Doing the best for friends
                                E
insisting that the world keeps turning our way
    B
and our way is...
```

1. Strophe


Refrain

```
         E
3. On the road again,
                              G#7
just can't wait to get on the road again,
                         F#m
the life I love is making music with my friends
     A              B          E
and I feel good to get on the road again.
     A              B          E     A B E
And I feel good to get on the road again.
```

M + T: Willie Nelson
© Copyright 1980 by EMI Longitude Music.
Rechte für Deutschland, Österreich, Schweiz
EMI MUSIC Publishing Germany GmbH & Co. KG, Hamburg.
All Rights Reserved. International Copyright Secured.

# BELLA CIAO

**Dm**
1. Eines Morgens, in aller Frühe,
bella ciao bella ciao bella ciao ciao ciao,
      **Gm**                **Dm**            **A**             **Dm**
als ich aufstand, in aller Frühe, war der Feind schon in der Stadt.

**Dm**
2. Bevor ich draufgeh, ihr Partisanen,
bella ciao bella ciao bella ciao ciao ciao,
      **Gm**             **Dm**              **A**             **Dm**
geh ich mit euch in die Berge, mich bringt das Elend hier noch um.

**Dm**
3. Wenn ich sterbe als Partisane,
bella ciao bella ciao bella ciao ciao ciao,
      **Gm**            **Dm**          **A**          **Dm**
wenn ich sterbe als Partisane, bitte schaufelt mir ein Grab.

**Dm**
4. In den Bergen, steht eine Blume,
bella ciao bella ciao bella ciao ciao ciao,
      **Gm**             **Dm**           **A**           **Dm**
in den Schatten der kleinen Blume, bettet mich zur letzten Ruh.

**Dm**
5. Und die Leute, die sehn die Blume,
bella ciao bella ciao bella ciao ciao ciao,
      **Gm**            **Dm**          **A**          **Dm**
die sehn die Blume und werden sagen: Diese Blume ist so schön.

**Dm**
6. Es ist die Blume des Partisanen,
bella ciao bella ciao bella ciao ciao ciao,
      **Gm**            **Dm**         **A**          **Dm**
es ist die Blume des Partisanen, der für die Freiheit starb.
      **Gm**            **Dm**         **A**          **Dm**
Es ist die Blume des Partisanen, der für die Freiheit starb.

1. Una mattina mi son alzato,
o bella ciao bella ciao bella ciao ciao ciao,
una mattina, mi son alzato e ho trovato l'invasor.
2. O partigiano, porta mi via
o bella ciao bella ciao bella ciao ciao ciao,
O partigiano porta mi via che io mi sento di morir.
3. Se io muoio, da partigano
o bella ciao bella ciao bella ciao ciao ciao,
se io muoio, da partigiano, tu mi devi seppellir
4. Mi sepellirai là, sulla montagna,
o bella ciao bella ciao bella ciao ciao ciao,
mi sepellirai là, sulla montagna, sotto l'ombra d'un bel fior.
5. E tutti quelli che passeranno,
o bella ciao bella ciao bella ciao ciao ciao,
e tutti quelli che passeranno, diranno "o che bel fior"
6. Questo è il fiore del partigiano
o bella ciao bella ciao bella ciao ciao ciao,
questo è il fiore del partigiano, morto per la liberta.

Traditionell
© 2005 by Edition DUX, Manching

# NON, JE NE REGRETTE RIEN

(EDITH PIAF)

**Intro:** G D7/F# G

```
   G              D7/F#              G
1. Non, rien de rien, non, je ne regrette rien,
      C              C+         C6                    D
ni le bien qu'on m'a fait, ni le mal, tout ça m'est bien égal.
   G              D7/F#              G
Non, rien de rien, non, je ne regrette rien,
         C       Am         D7                G
c'est payé, balayé, oublié, je me fous du passé.
```

```
               G
Avec mes souvenirs j'ai allumé le feu,
D                                         G
mes chagrins, mes plaisirs je n'ai plus besoin d'eux.
                   G
Balayés mes amours avec leurs trémolos,
D            D7                G
balayés pour toujours je repars à zéro.
```

```
   G              D7/F#              G
2. Non, rien de rien, non, je ne regrette rien,
      C              C+         C6                    D
ni le bien qu'on m'a fait, ni le mal, tout ça m'est bien égal.
   G              D7/F#              G
Non, rien de rien, non, je ne regrette rien,
         C    C+       C6      C7     B7 D
car ma vie, car mes joies, aujourd'hui
         D7          G    Eb G
ça commence avec toi.
```

M: Charles Dumont
Original T: Michel Vaucaire
English T: by Hal David
© Copyright 1960 Editions Musicales Eddie Barclay, France.
Peermusic (UK) Limited.
All Rights Reserved. International Copyright Secured.

# 13 TAGE

(SCHWEIZER)  
[TRANSP. -2]

```
   C
1. Seit Tagen sitz' ich her am Telefon,
du bist in Griechenland und rufst nicht an.
Beim Skat verlier' ich einen Grand mit vier.
Bin in der U-Bahn blinder Passagier.
Ich schaue täglich Fernsehen, wie verrückt.
Solang bis Kulenkampff mich schlafen schickt.
Ich mach' mir Sorgen und ich bin nervös.
Bis endlich nachts dein Anruf mich erlöst.

Dm        G     C     Dm         G      C
U-uh, bald ist es soweit. U-uh, nur noch kurze Zeit.
Dm        G     C     G
U-uh, bald ist es soweit. Morgen kommst du, kommst du.
```

**Refrain:**
```
G          C        F           C         G
Dreizehn Tage und Nächte denk' ich nur noch an dich.
Am       F        C           G
So viele endlose Stunden für mich.
C           F          C          G
Dreizehn mal warten und ein Tag ist so lang.
Am       F         C  G
Dann bist du da wie ein Bumerang.
C         F            C          G
Tage und Nächte denk' ich nur noch an dich.
Am       F        C           G
So viele endlose Stunden für mich.
C           F          C          G
Dreizehn mal warten und ein Tag ist so lang.
Am       F         C  G
Dann bist du da wie ein Bumerang.
```

```
2. Der Wecker klingelt und ich sag' herein.
Nur ein paar Stunden und dein Zug fährt ein.
Der Münchner Himmel wie aus dem Prospekt.
Zum Frühstück erst einmal zwei Gläser Sekt.
Und auch die Katze merkt, dass was nicht stimmt,
wenn in der Milch ein Löffel Honig schwimmt.
Durch meine Bude fegt ein Wahnsinns Sound,
ich bin heut' einfach gut gelaunt.

U-uh, bald ist es soweit. U-uh, nur noch kurze Zeit.
U-uh, bald ist es soweit. Heute kommst du, kommst du.
Refrain

F          Em              G      C
Und noch am Bahnsteig fragst du wie es war,
F           Em           G      C
ich sag' ganz lässig, alles ganz normal!
F            Em           G        C
Du fragst mich leise hast du mich vermisst.
F         Em         G
Und ohne Antwort hab' ich dich geküsst.
```

Refrain

M + T: Klaus-Peter Schweizer-Ulm  
© Mambo Musik Verlags- und Produktion GmbH.  
Mit freundlicher Genehmigung von  
SMPG Publishing (Germany) GmbH.

# MÄRCHENPRINZ

(E. A. V.)

```
      A
Es ist Samstag Abend und die Dinge stehen schlecht,
  E                                A
ich bin auf der Suche nach dem weiblichen Geschlecht.
   A
Am Wochenende hat man in der Großstadt seine Not:
   E                     A
Zu viele Jäger sind der Hasen Tod.
    D                    C#m          D              E
Mir bleibt nur noch eine Chance: Hinein ins Auto und ab in die Provence.
```

Mit meinem Nobelhobel glüh ich auf der Autostrada,
einmal kurz auf's Gas und schon bin ich dada.
Ich betrete voll Elan den Tanzsalon
eingehüllt in eine Wolke Pitralon.
Weil es bei den Mädels tilt ist, wenn man riecht als wie ein Iltis.

**Refrain:**
```
                 A
Ich bin der Märchenprinz, Ma-ma-ma-Märchenprinz.
F                        A
Ma-ma-ma-ma-ma, ich bin der Märchenprinz.

Ich bin der Märchenprinz, Ma-ma-ma-Märchenprinz,
F                            A
in der Provinz bin ich der Märchenprinz.
G           Bm                D             E
Ma-ma-ma-ma-ma, uhu, aha, beim Vogeltanz bin ich die Nummer eins.
```

Da im Disco-Stadl regiert der Furchenadel
und der Landmann schwingt sein strammes Waderl.
Doch die girls von der Heide sind eine Augenweide
und ich frag eine Prinzessin: Na wie wärs denn mit uns beiden?
Das kost' mich fünf Tequilla. Ich bezahl' und fort ist die Ludmilla.

Dann geh' ich schnell zur Trixi und sag: Trink' ma noch na Whiskey,
doch leider hat der Norbert die Trixi grad in Arbeit.
Und auch bei der Babsi, bei der Zenzi und der Greta
hab ich keine Meter und es wird immer später.
Da is nur mehr die Dorli. Ich geh zur ihr und hauch ihr zart ins Ohrli:
Refrain

Da sagt die Pomeranze: Ja sigst net, dass I tanze?
Und gegen meinen Joschi hast du niemals eine Chance.
Drauf sag ich zum Joschi: Junge der Provinz,
in diesem Disko-Bunker bin ich der Märchenprinz!
Drauf haut mir doch der Joschi eine auf mein Großstadtgoschi.

Ich verlasse die Disko, denn der Joschi ist ein Mörder
So ein grober Lackl, also eing'sperrt 'ghört er.
Ich starte den Boliden, da hör ich den Befehl:
Her mit de Papiere und blas'n 's amol schnell!
Wo komm ma denn da hin?
Herr Inspektor, wer glaub'n sie, dass ich bin?
Refrain

M: Th.Spitzer / K.Eberhartiger / N.Holm / G.Breit / G. Schönberger
T: Thomas Spitzer
© Wintrup Musikverlag, Detmold / Blanko Musikverlag, München.

## DER TEUFEL UND DER JUNGE MANN

(PAOLA)

```
G              C             Em          F             C
La la la la la, la la la la la. La la la la la la la la.
F       G     C        Am       F              G    C
Hört euch die Geschichte an vom Teufel und dem jungen Mann.

        G              C                G            C
1. Es war einmal ein junger Mann, der trieb es leider ziemlich bunt.
   F         Em              F              G
Der Teufel kam, um ihn zu holen, dafür gab es manchen Grund.
     G             C              G              C
Der junge Mann hat wohl gewusst, dem Teufel macht das Wetten Spaß,
     F         Em               F   G   C
drum sagte er: Ich weiß ein Rätsel, was ist das:
```

**Refrain:**
```
G                 C                    Em
Man kann es nicht hör'n, man kann es nicht seh'n,
          F                    C
es tut oft weh und es ist doch schön,
     G            C      C7      F          Em            G
es ist kein Wein, doch es geht ins Blut, und es tut, es tut so gut.
         C                     Em
Es ist kein Gold, doch es macht reich,
      F                       C
ein Herz aus Eisen wird davon weich,
 C7      F        E7      Am      F       Bb          C
es ist kein Feuer, aber es brennt, sag mir, wie man das nennt!
```

2. Der Teufel fing zu raten an: Ich glaub' es könnt ein Ufo sein,
ein Nachtgespenst, ein Zaubervogel? Doch er hörte stets ein "nein".
Und schließlich sagte er voll Wut: Mir reicht jetzt diese Raterei,
wenn du mir nur die Lösung sagst, geb ich dich frei!

Refrain
```
G              C            Em              F             C    C7
Es ist schon alt und immer neu, es fängt dich ein und macht dich frei,
   F      E7                Am Ab  F      Bb           C
es ist etwas, was der Teufel nicht kennt, etwas, das man Liebe nennt!
```

Refrain

La la la la la, la la la la la. La la la la la la la la.
Es ist kein Wein, doch es geht ins Blut, und es tut, es tut so gut.
Es ist kein Gold, doch es macht reich,
ein Herz aus Eisen wird davon weich,
es ist kein Feuer, aber es brennt, das man Liebe nennt!

M: Roland Heck
T: Michael Kunze
© Birdland Music.
Mit freundlicher Genehmigung von Sony/ATV Music Publishing (Germany) GmbH.

# IT'S RAINING MEN

(THE WEATHER GIRLS)
(GERI HALLIWELL)
[TRANSP. +1]

Hi Hi! We're your Weather Girls, ah huh, and have we got news for you.
You better listen!
Get ready, all you lonely girls and leave those umbrellas at home.
Alright!

```
      Em
1. Humidity is rising. Barometer's getting low.
Em                                   B
According to all sources, the street's the place to go.
         Em                    Am
Cause tonight for the first time just about half-past ten,
        B
for the first time in history it's gonna start raining men.
```

**Refrain:**
```
              C         D            B       Em
It's Raining Men! Hallelujah! It's Raining Men! Amen!
        C             Am              B
I'm gonna go out to run and let myself get absolutely soaking wet!
              C         D            B       Em
It's Raining Men! Hallelujah! It's Raining Men! Every Specimen!
C      Em/B    Am         B
Tall, blonde, dark and lean, rough and tough and strong and mean.

    C          D        B          Em
2. God bless Mother Nature, she's a single woman too.
C          D        B              Em
She took off to heaven and she did what she had to do.
C          D        B          Em
She taught every angel to rearrange the sky.
         Am    G/B   C    A7/C#  B7/D#    Em    B7/F#  Em/G B7sus4 B7
So that each and every woman could find her perfect guy.
```

It's Raining Men! Hallelujah! It's Raining Men! Amen!
It's Raining Men! Hallelujah! It's Raining Men! Amen!

```
Em         D             C  B
I feel stormy weather moving in about to begin.
Em         D                         C
Hear the thunder. Don't you lose your head.
B
Rip off the roof and stay in bed.
```

2. Strophe
```
                        Em
It's Raining Men! Yeah!
```

1. Strophe

It's Raining Men! Hallelujah! It's Raining Men! Amen!
It's Raining Men! Hallelujah! It's Raining Men! Amen!
It's Raining Men! Hallelujah! It's Raining Men! Amen!

M + T: Paul A.W. Shaffer, Paul F. Jabara
© 1983 Postvalda Music, EMI Sosaha Music Inc and Olga Music. Warner/Chappell North America Ltd, London.
Reproduced by permission of Faber Music Limited
All Rights Reserved.

# KING OF THE ROAD

(ROGER MILLER)

```
   B      B/D#  E              F#           B
1. Trailer for sale or rent, rooms to let fifty cents.
              E                 F#
No phone, no pool, no pets, I ain't got no cigarettes.
         B    B/D#   E
Ah, but two hours of pushing broom
      F#              B
buys an eight by twelve four bit room.
            E                   F#         B
I'm a man of means, by no means king of the road.

   B      B/D#  E              F#          B
2. Third boxcar, midnight train, destination Bangor, Maine.
              E                 F#
Old worn out suits and shoes, I don't pay no union dues.
         B    B/D#   E
I smoke old stogies I have found,
F#              B
short but not too big around.
            E                   F#         B
I'm a man of means, by no means king of the road.

         C       C/E          F
3. I know every engineer on every train,
G                           C
all of the children and all of their names
                                F
and every handout in every town
      G
and every lock that ain't locked when no one's around,
I sing...

   C      C/E  F             G            C
1. Trailer for sale or rent, rooms to let fifty cents.
              F                 G
No phone, no pool, no pets, I ain't got no cigarettes.
         C    C/E    F
Ah, but two hours of pushing broom
      G              C
buys an eight by twelve four bit room.
            F                   G         C
I'm a man of means, by no means king of the road.

G          C     G           C
King of the road, king of the road.
```

M + T: Roger Miller
© 1963 Tree Publishing Co Inc.
Burlington Music Co Limited, London. Reproduced by permission of Faber Music Limited.
All Rights Reserved.

# HIGHWAY TO HELL

(AC/DC)

**Intro:** A D G   D G   D G   D A  (2x)

```
           A           D G         D G D      G      D        A
1. Living easy, loving free.   Season ticket on a one way ride.
   A           D G         D G D      G      D      A
Asking nothing, leave me be.   Taking everything in my stride.
   A             D G             D G D      G         D        A
Don't need reason, don't need rhyme.   Ain't nothing I would rather do.
   A         D G        D G D  G          D              E
Going down, party time.   My friends are gonna be there too.
```

**Refrain:**
```
             A           D   G D A          D   G D
I'm on the highway to hell.   Highway to hell.
             A           D   G D A          D   G D
I'm on the highway to hell.   Highway to hell.
```

```
   A            D G         D G D        G       D       A
2. No stop signs, speed limit.   Nobody's gonna slow me down.
   A        D G           D G D       G         D      A
Like a wheel  gonna spin it.   Nobody's gonna mess me around.
   A          D G         D G D      G           D       A
Hey Satan,  paid my dues.   I'm playing in a rocking band.
   A           D G         D G D       G             D         E
Ooh Mamma,  look at me.   I'm on the way to the promised land.
```

Refrain 2x

M + T: Malcom Young, Angus Young, Ronald Scott
© Copyright 1979 J. Albert & Son Pty. Limited.
All Rights Reserved. International Copyright Secured.

# STAND BY ME

(OASIS)

**Intro:** G B7 C D (2x)

```
    G                    B7              C
1. Made a meal and threw it up on Sunday I've
      G/B         D
gotta lot of things to learn.
   G                  B7
Said I would and I'll be leaving one day
    C          G/B       D
before my heart starts to burn.
```

**Bridge:**
```
C                        D
So what's the matter with you?
 G      D/F#       Em
Sing me something new. Don't you know
      A
the cold and wind and rain don't know,
      C                    D
they only seem to come and go away.
```

```
     G                         B7
2. Times are hard when things have got no meaning,
   C         G/B         D
I've found a key upon the floor.
   G                  B7
Maybe you and I will not believe in
    C            G/B      D
the things we find behind the door.
```

**Refrain:**
```
G         D          Am                      C  F  F#
Stand by me - nobody knows the way it's gonna be.
G         D          Am                      C  F  F#
Stand by me - nobody knows the way it's gonna be.
G         D          Am                      C  F  F#
Stand by me - nobody knows the way it's gonna be.
G         D          Am              C       D                  G
Stand by me - nobody knows - nobody knows the way it's gonna be.
```

```
    G                         B7
3. If you're leaving will you take me with you?
    C            G/B    D
I'm tired of talking on my phone.
G                    B7
There is one thing I can never give you,
    C            G/B    D
my heart can never be your home.
```

Bridge
Refrain 2x

M + T: Noel Gallagher
© Copyright 1997 Creation Songs Limited/Oasis Music (GB).
Sony/ATV Music Publishing.
All Rights Reserved. International Copyright Secured.

# AROUND THE WORLD

(ATC)

**Intro:** Am Em F G (2x)

```
          Am            Em   F              G
1. The kisses of the sun were sweet, I didn't blink,
     Am           Em   F        G
I let it in my eyes, like an exotic drink,
        Am            Em   F          G
the radio playing songs that I have never heard,
    Am                Em   F        G
I don't know what to say, oh, not another word just...
```

**Refrain:**
```
Am            Em   F        G
La la la la la, it goes around the world,
         Am            Em   F          G
just la la la la la, it's all around the world,
       Am            Em   F         G
just la la la la la, and everybody singing,
Am              Em   F         G
la la la la la, and now our bells are ringing.

Am            Em   F        G
La la la la la, la la la la la la la.
Am            Em   F        G
La la la la la, la la la la la la la.
Am            Em   F        G
La la la la la, la la la la la la la.
Am            Em   F        G
La la la la la, la la la la la la la.
```

```
         Am              Em   F          G
2. Inside an empty room my inspiration flows,
        Am                Em    F        G
can't wait to hear the tune, around my head it goes
       Am            Em   F       G
the magic melody you want to sing with me,
      Am            Em   F        G
just la la la la la, the music is the key.
```

```
         Am             Em   F             G
3. And now the night is gone, still it goes on and on,
      Am              Em   F        G
so deep inside of me, I want to set it free,
     Am             Em   F             G
I don't know what to do, just can't explain to you,
     Am             Em   F           G
I don't know what to say, oh, not another word just...
```

Refrain

M + T: Sergej Zhukow / Alexei Potechin / Alex Christensen / Peter Könemann
© 2000 Edition Alex C Music / 000Yrbis / Diana HC Edition. EMI Music Publishing Germany GmbH.
Mit freundlicher Genehmigung der EMI Music Publishing Germany GmbH.

## THESE BOOTS ARE MADE FOR WALKING

(BILLY RAY CYRUS)

```
   G
1. You keep saying, you got something for me,

something you call love, but confess.
   C
You've been a-messin' where you shouldn't have been a-messin'
            G
and now someone else is getting all your best.
```

**Refrain:**
```
        E                   C#m        E                      C#m
These boots are made for walking and that's just what they'll do
     E                           C#m                        G
and one of these days these boots are gonna walk all over you.
```

```
   G
2. You keep lying when you oughta be true then

and you keep loosing when you oughta not bet.
   C
You keep singing when you oughta been changing,
            G
now what's right is right, but you ain't been right yet.
```

Refrain

```
   G
3. You keep playing where you shouldn't be playing

and you keep thinking that you'll never get burnt, ha!
   C
I just found me a brandnew box of matches, yeah,
         G
and what you know you ain't have time to learn.
```

Refrain

M + T: Hazlewood, Lee
© Copyright 1965 & 1966 Criterion Music Corporation.
Universal Music Publishing Limited. All Rights Reserved. International Copyright Secured.

# PIANO MAN

(BILLY JOEL)

**Intro:** C F/C G/C F/C C
```
         C       Em/B      Am        C/G   F        C/E            D7    G
1. It's nine o'clock on a saturday. The regular crowd shuffles in.
                 C       Em/B     Am          C/G
There's an old man sitting next to me
         F       F/G        C   F/C  G/C  F/C
making love to his tonic and gin.
                 C         Em/B    Am       C/G     F          C/E          D7    G
He says son can you play me a memory,    I'm not really sure how it goes,
             C           Em/B      Am         C/G
but it's sad and it's sweet and I knew it complete
         F       F/G         C
when I wore a younger man's clothes.
```

**Refrain:**
```
Am       Am/G     D7/F#  F  Am    Am/G       D7/F#  G  G7/F C/E G7/D
Da da da da  de  de  da      da da da   de de da       da.
C         Em/B              Am       C/G    F        C/E      D7     G
Sing us a song, you're the piano man.    Sing us a song tonight.
             C           Em/B        Am        C/G        F
Well, we're all in the mood for a melody       and you've got
   F/G         C       F/C G/C F/G
us feeling alright.
```

2. Now John at the bar, he's a friend of mine, he gets me my drinks for free. And he's quick with a joke or to light up your smoke but there's some place that he'd rather be. He says Bill I believe this is killing me, as the smile ran away from his face. Well I'm sure that I could be a movie star if I could get out of this place.

3. Now Paul is a real estate novelist who never had time for a wife. And he's talking with Davy who's still in the navy, and probably will be for life. And the waitress is practicing politics as the businessmen slowly get stoned. Yes they're sharing a drink they call loneliness but its better than drinking alone.

4. It's a pretty good crowd for a saturday. And the manager gives me a smile. Cause he knows that its me they've been coming to see, to forget about life for a while. And the piano sounds like a carnival and the microphone smells like a beer. And they sit at the bar and put bread in my jar and say man what are you doing here?

M + T: Billy Joel
© Copyright 1973 Joelsongs.
Rondor Music International.
All Rights Reserved. International Copyright Secured.

# EIN BISSCHEN SPASS MUSS SEIN

(ROBERTO BLANCO)

**Refrain:**
```
A                    E
Ein bisschen Spaß muss sein,
                       A
dann ist die Welt voll Sonnenschein.
                    E
So gut wie wir uns heute verstehn,
            A
so soll es weitergehn.
                    E
Ein bisschen Spaß muss sein,
                          A
dann kommt das Glück von ganz allein.
                       E
Drum singen wir tagaus und tagein:
            E7       A
Ein bisschen Spaß muss sein.
```

```
           A          D
1. Heut nacht feiern wir,
       E          A
machen durch bis um vier.
         A             D
Fragen nicht nach Zeit und Geld,
       A         E7       A
weil es dir und auch mir so gefällt.
```

Refrain

```
              A            D
2. Draußen wird's langsam hell
         E                A
und die Zeit geht viel zu schnell.
            A           D
Noch ein Glas und einen Kuss,
          A         E7        A
ja, und dann ist noch lange nicht Schluss.
```

Refrain

M + T: Christian BRUHN, Günter LOOSE
© 1972 Edition Meridian Ralph Siegel KG, Germany.
Warner/Chappell Overseas Holdings Limited, London. Reproduced
by permission of Faber Music Limited.
All Rights Reserved.

# SAVE TONIGHT

(EAGLE EYE CHERRY)

**Intro:** Am F C G    Am F C G    Am F C G    Am F C G

```
           Am      F     C            G         Am     F      C
1. Come and close the curtains, cause all we need is candle light.
      Am  F        C           G          Am         F  C  G
You and me and a bottle of wine, and I'll hold you tonight. Ah.
    Am    F      C          G         Am     F        C                G
Well we know, I'm going away, and how I wish, I wish it weren't so.
           Am      F    C           G  Am            F           C
So take this wine and drink with me. Let's delay our misery.
```

**Refrain:**
```
G       Am      F   C                 G
Save tonight and fight the break of dawn.
           Am      F   C            G
Come tomorrow, tomorrow I'll be gone.
         Am      F   C                 G
Save tonight and fight the break of dawn.
           Am      F   C            G
Come tomorrow, tomorrow I'll be gone.
```

```
              Am     F     C    G      Am     F    C      G
2. There's a log on the fire and it burns like me for you.
           Am    F         C       G  Am          F C G
Tomorrow comes with one desire, to take me away.
           Am  F   C         G           Am     F     C         G
It ain't easy to say good-bye. Darling please, don't start to cry!
           Am                 F        C G  Am           F         C
Cause girl you know I got to go and Lord, I wish it wasn't so.
```

Refrain

```
           Am       F         C        G  Am          F      C         G
3. Tomorrow comes to take me away. I wish that I, that I could stay.
Am             F          C G  Am            F            C
Girl you know I got to go and Lord, I wish it wasn't so.
```

Refrain 2x

M + T: Eagle-Eye Cherry
© Published by Kobalt Music Publishing Ltd.

# ICH HAB MEIN HERZ IN HEIDELBERG VERLOREN
(FREDDY BRECK)

```
       G                   D7                  G
1. Es war an einem Abend, als ich kaum zwanzig Jahr',
             Em              A7             D
   da küsst' ich rote Lippen und gold'nes, blondes Haar.
   D7              G              E7           Am
   Die Nacht war blau und selig, der Neckar silberklar,
   Cm G          Cm G           D7            G    C G
   da wusste ich, da wusste ich, woran, woran ich war!
```

**Refrain:**
```
                  G              D7                    G
   Ich hab mein Herz in Heidelberg verloren, in einer lauen Sommernacht.
        E7                      Am
   Ich war verliebt bis über beide Ohren
           A7                D
   und wie ein Röslein hat ihr Mund gelacht!
              G                  D7
   Und als wir Abschied nahmen von den Toren,
           E7                         Am
   beim letzten Kuss, da hab' ich's klar erkannt,
               A7                       G
   dass ich mein Herz in Heidelberg verloren,
   C   G         C G  D7 G
   mein Herz, es schlägt am Neckarstrand!
```

```
          G                    D7                   G
2. Und wieder blüht wie damals am Neckarstand der Wein,
            Em            A7            D
   die Jahre sind vergangen und ich bin ganz allein.
   D7           G            E7         Am
   Und fragt ihr den Gesellen, warum er keine nahm,
   Cm   G       Cm    G             D7         G   C G
   dann sag' ich euch, dann sag' ich euch, ihr Freunde, wie es kam:
```

Refrain

```
          G                  D7                 G
3. Was ist aus dir geworden, seitdem ich dich verließ?
         Em          A7              D
   Altheidelberg, du feine, du deutsches Paradies!
   D7             G          E7                    Am
   Ich bin von dir gezogen, ließ Leichtsinn, Wein und Glück
   Cm  G        Cm    G            D7           G   C G
   und sehne mich, und sehne mich mein Leben lang zurück.
```

Refrain

M: Fred Raymond
T: Ernst Neubach / Beda
© Edition Wiener Boheme Verlag, Universal/MCA Music Publishing GmbH.

# UPTOWN GIRL

(BILLY JOEL)

```
D         Em7        F#m       G      A
Ohhh...
D
Uptown girl.
Em7                           F#m
She's been living in her uptown world,
G         A             D
I bet she never had a back street guy,
Em7                      F#m
I bet her mama never told her why.
G                A
I'm gonna try for an

Uptown girl.
She's been living in her white bread world
as long as anyone with hot blood can
and now she's looking for a downtown man.
That's what I am.

Bb              Gm             Cm                F
And when she knows what she wants from her time.
Bb              Gm            Cm            D
And when she wakes up and makes up her mind.
G              Em            Am          A
She'll see I'm not so tough just because I'm in love with an

Uptown girl.
You know I've seen her in her uptown world,
she's getting tired of her high class toys
and all her presents from her uptown boys.
She's got a choice.

Uptown girl.
You know I can't afford to buy her pearls
but maybe someday when my ship comes in
she'll understand what kind of guy I've been.
And then I'll win.

And when she's walking she's looking so fine.
And when she's talking she'll say that she's mine.
She'll say I'm not so tough just because I'm in love with an

Uptown girl.
She's been living in her white bread world
as long as anyone with hot blood can
and now she's looking for a downtown man.
That's what I am.

Uptown girl.
She's my uptown girl, you know I'm in love with an
uptown girl.
My uptown girl, you know I'm in love with an
uptown girl.
My uptown girl, you know I'm in love with an
uptown girl.
My uptown girl.
```

M + T: Billy Joel
© Copyright 1983 Joelsongs.
Rondor Music International.
All Rights Reserved. International Copyright Secured.

# GRACELAND

(PAUL SIMON)

**Intro:** E A C#m B E     E A C#m B E

```
E                                                      A
The Mississippi Delta was shining like a National guitar.
    C#m
I am following the river down the highway
                              B
through the cradle of the civil war.
```

**Refrain:**
```
A               E                              B
I'm going to Graceland, Graceland, Memphis, Tennessee.
             E          E D A
I'm going to Graceland.
E                               B                  E         E D A
Poorboys and Pilgrims with families and we are going to Graceland.

   E                           B
My traveling companion is nine years old.
         E              E D A
He is the child of my first marriage.
            E                    B            E       E D A
But I've reason to believe we both will be received in Graceland.

                     E                        A
She comes back to tell me she's gone as if I didn't know that,
                          C#m      B
as if I didn't know my own bed as if I'd never noticed
                                      E
the way she brushed her hair from her forehead.
              E                              A
And she said losing love is like a window in your heart.
                   C#m                             B
Everybody sees you're blown apart, everybody sees the wind blow.
```

Refrain

And my traveling companions are ghosts and empty sockets.
I'm looking at ghosts and empties
but I've reason to believe we all will be received In Graceland.

There is a girl in New York City who calls herself the human trampoline
and sometimes when I'm falling, flying
or tumbling in turmoil I say: Oh, so this is what she means.
She means we're bouncing into Graceland.
And I see losing love is like a window in your heart.
Everybody sees you're blown apart, everybody feels the wind blow.

In Graceland, in Graceland, I'm going to Graceland.
For reasons I cannot explain
there's some part of me wants to see Graceland.

And I may be obliged to defend every love, every ending
or maybe there's no obligations now.
Maybe I've a reason to believe we all will be received in Graceland.

In Graceland, in Graceland, in Graceland.
I'm going to Graceland.

M + T: Paul Simon
© Copyright 1986 Paul Simon (BMI).
All Rights Reserved. International Copyright Secured

## ITSY BITSY TEENIE WEENIE HONULULU-STRAND-BIKINI

(DIE TOTEN HOSEN)
(RAINER BERTRAM)
(BLUE DIAMONDS)

```
     G                        D
1. Am Strand von Rio, da ging sie spazieren
                         G
und was sie trug, hätte keinen gestört.
                  C
Nur eine einsame, pikfeine Lady
      G            D         G
fiel bald in Ohnmacht und war sehr empört.
```

**Refrain:**
```
8, 9, 10, na was gab's denn da zu seh'n?
G         D                        G
Es war der Itsy Bitsy Teenie Weenie Honolulu-Strand-Bikini.
D                             G
Er war schick und er war so modern.
        D                  G
Der Itsy Bitsy Teenie Weenie Honolulu-Strand-Bikini.
D                              G
Ja er gefiel ganz besonders den Herrn.

1, 2, 3, na was ist denn schon dabei?
```

**2.** Die Caballeros an Copa Cabana,
die rannten ihr immerzu hinterher.
Da lief sie weg und vor Schreck gleich ins Wasser,
dabei ertrank sie beinah' noch im Meer.

Refrain

**3.** Ja, in Venedig war grad Bienale,
ein Fotograf, der hielt sie für 'nen Star.
Doch in der Zeitung stand später zu lesen,
dass der Bikini nur Schuld daran war.

Refrain

```
G            D                           G
Und da zog sie den Bikini, den sie nirgends tragen kann
             D                    G
ganz alleine zu Hause in der Badewanne an.
```

M + T: Lee Pockriss & Paul J. Vance
© 1960 by Emily Music / Chrysalis Music Holdings GmbH.
Alle Rechte für Deutschland, Österreich und Schweiz bei Global Musikverlag, München.
Mit freundlicher Genehigung von Chrysalis Music Holdings GmbH.

# CECILIA

(SIMON AND GARFUNKEL)

**Refrain:**
```
    E            A           E
Cecilia, you're breaking my heart,
       A          E         B
you're shaking my confidence daily.
       A   E      A          E
Oh Cecilia, I'm down on my knees,
     A           E         B
I'm begging you please to come home.
          E
Come on home.
```

Refrain

```
E                   A      E
Making love in the afternoon with Cecilia
A    B      E
up in my bedroom.
                 A         E
I got up to wash my face,
                     A
when I come back to bed
           B         E
someone's taken my place ...
```

Refrain

```
E             A E A E B
Bo po bo bo ...

       A   E       A          E
Jubilation, she loves me again,
      A           E        B
I fall on the floor and I laughing.
          A E        A          E
Jubilation, she loves me again,
      A           E        B
I fall on the floor and I laughing.
       A  E   A E   A E B
Wo ho oooh ...
```

M + T: Paul Simon
© Copyright 1969 Paul Simon Music, USA.
All Rights Reserved. International Copyright Secured.

# WONDERFUL LIFE

(BLACK)

```
     Em          D/F#        G                      D/F#        Em
1. Here I go out to sea again, the sunshine fills my hair
              D/F#           G       D/F#
   and dreams hang in the air.
   Em          D/F#        G                      D/F#        Em
   Gulls in the sky and in my blue eye, you know it feels unfair.
              D/F#         G        D/F#
   There's magic everywhere.
```

**Refrain:**
```
Em          D/F#        G         Am         Em                  D/F#      G Am
Look at me standing here on my own again up straight in the sunshine.
              Em         G          Em         Am        D
No need to run and hide, it's a wonderful wonderful life.
              Em         G          Em         C         D
No need to laugh and cry, it's a wonderful wonderful life.

   Em                        D/F#        G
2. The sun's in your eyes, the heat is in your hair.
          D/F# Em        D/F#         G      D/F#
   They seem to hate you because you're there.
   Em                D/F# G                     D/F#      Em
   And I need a friend, oh I need a friend to make me happy.
              D/F#         G
   Not stand here on my own.
```

Refrain

```
Em                    D/F# G                     D/F#     Em
I need a friend, oh I need a friend to make me happy.
    D/F#    G     D/F#
Not so alone.
```

Refrain

M + T: Colin Vearncombe<br>
© Hornall Brothers Music Ltd.

# GOOD VIBRATIONS

(THE BEACH BOYS)
[TRANSP. -1]

```
    Em                          D
1. I, I love the colorful clothes she wears,
         C                           B
and the way the sunlight plays upon her hair.
  Em                        D
I, I hear the sound of a gentle word,
        C                             B      D
on the wind that lifts her perfume through the air.
```

**Refrain:**
```
G    C/G     G    C/G      G    C/G       G    C/G
I'm picking up good vibrations, she's giving me the excitations.
G    C/G     G    C/G      G    C/G       G    C/G
I'm picking up good vibrations, she's giving me the excitations.
A    D/A    A    D/A              A    D/A       A    D/A
Good, good, good, good vibrations, she's giving me the excitation.
B    E/B    B    E/B              B    E/B       B    E/B      B
Good, good, good, good vibrations, she's giving me the excitations.
```

```
    Em                          D
2. Close my eyes, she's somehow closer now,
C                            B
softly smile, I know she must be kind.
  Em                D
When I look in her eyes,
         C                      B    D
she goes with me to a blossom world.
```

Refrain

```
B
My, my, my, what elation,
  E
I don't know where but she sends me there.
                              B
My, my, my, what a sensation, my, my, my, what elation.

F#                      G#m               C#
Got to keep those lovely vibrations are happening with us.
F#                      G#m               C#
Got to keep those lovely vibrations are happening with us.
F#                      G#m               C#
Got to keep those lovely vibrations are happening with us.

F# G#m C#

B    E/B    B    E/B    B     E/B  B  E/B
Good, good, good, good vibrations.
A    D/A   A    D/A    A     D/A  A  D/A  A
Good, good, good, good vibrations.
```

M + T: Brian Wilson & Mike Love
© Sea of Tunes Publishing Co. Inc.
Subverlag: EMI Music Publishing Germany GmbH.

# WHY DOES IT ALWAYS RAIN ON ME?

(TRAVIS)

```
     E                      C#m
1. I can't sleep tonight. Everybody saying everything is alright.
E
Still I can't close my eyes.
C#m                                         A
I'm seeing a tunnel at the end of all these lights.
       B      A              B       A                           B
Sunny days, where have you gone? I get the strangest feeling you belong.
```

**Refrain:**
```
E                       B
Why does it always rain on me?
A                              B
Is it because I lied when I was seventeen?
E                       B
Why does it always rain on me?
A                                        B
Even when the sun is shining I can't avoid the lightning.
```

```
     E                    C#m
2. I can't stand myself, I'm being held up by an invisible man.
E
Still life on a shelf when
C#m                  A
I got my mind on something else.
       B      A              B       A                           B
Sunny days, where have you gone? I get the strangest feeling you belong.
```

Refrain

```
C#m               E/B
Oh, where did the blue skies go?
C#m           E/B       D         B
And why is it raining so? It's so cold.
```

```
     E                      C#m
3. I can't sleep tonight. Everybody saying everything is alright.
E
Still I can't close my eyes.
C#m                                         A
I'm seeing a tunnel at the end of all these lights.
       B      A              B       A                           B
Sunny days, where have you gone? I get the strangest feeling you belong.
```

Refrain

```
C#m               E/B
Oh, where did the blue skies go?
C#m           E/B       A         B
And why is it raining so? It's so cold.
```

Refrain

M + T: Fran Healy
© Copyright 1999 Sony/ATV Music Publishing (UK) Limited.
All Rights Reserved. International Copyright Secured.

# AGAIN

(LENNY KRAVITZ)

**Intro:** A F#m7 E D

```
     D                   E      F#
1. I've been searching for you,
   D             E      F#
I heard a cry within my soul,
     D                    E       F#
I never had a yearning quite like this before
                D              E        F#
now that you are walking right through my door.
```

**Refrain:**
```
A       F#m7               E
All of my life where have you been,
                      D          A
I wonder if I'll ever see you again.
              F#m7                    Em7
And if that day comes I know we could win,
                      D
I wonder if I'll ever see you again.
```

```
      D            E  F#
2. A sacred gift of heaven
D                    E  F#
for better, worse, wherever
          D                  E        F#
and I would never let somebody break you down
              D      E  F#
or take your crown, never.
```

**Refrain 2:**
```
A       F#m7               E
All of my life where have you been,
                      D          A
I wonder if I'll ever see you again.
              F#m7                    Em7
And if that day comes I know we could win,
                      D          Am
I wonder if I'll ever see you again.
```

**Bridge:**
```
          Am
I've searched through time I've always known
      Em
that you were there upon your throne.
   Am
A lonely queen without her king,
      Em
I've longed for you my love forever.
```

**Solo:** A F#m7 E D A F#m7 E D G A

Refrain 2x

M + T: Lenny Kravitz
© Copyright 2000 Miss Bessie Music, USA
EMI Virgin Music Limited, London, W8 5SW.
Reproduced by permission of International Music Publications
Limited (a trading name of Faber Music Ltd).
All Rights Reserved.

# TOTAL ECLIPSE OF THE HEART

(BONNIE TYLER)
[TRANSP. +1]

```
      Am                              G
1. Turn around, every now and then I get a little bit lonely and
you're never coming round.
      Am                              G
Turn around, every now and then I get a little bit tired of
listening to the sound of my tears.
C                                    Bb
Turn around, every now and then I get a little bit nervous that
the best of all the years have gone by.
C                                    Bb
Turn around, every now and then I get a little bit terrified and
then I see the look in your eyes.
Eb          Ab                                      Eb
Turn around, bright eyes. Every now and then I fall apart.
Eb          Ab                                      G
Turn around, bright eyes. Every now and then I fall apart.
2. Turn around, every now and then I get a little bit restless
and I dream of something wild.
Turn around, every now and then I get a little bit helpless
And I'm lying like a child in your arms.
Turn around, every now and then I get a little bit angry
And I know I've got to get out and cry.
Turn around, every now and then I get a little bit terrified and
Then I see the look in your eyes.
Turn around, bright eyes. Every now and then I fall apart.
Turn around, bright eyes. Every now and then I fall apart.
```

**Refrain:**
```
G      Em         C          D              G
And I need you now tonight. And I need you more than ever.
          Em         C        D          G
And if you only hold me tight we'll be holding on forever.
          Em            C              D
And we'll only be making it right cause we'll never be wrong.
   C/E              D/F#
Together we can take it to the end of the line,
     Em                                A
your love is like a shadow on me all of the time.
    G                   D/F#
I don't know what to do and I'm always in the dark,
     Em                           A
we're living in a powder keg and giving off sparks.
              G/B       D/A         G/B       C
I really need you tonight, forever's gonna start tonight,
    C/D        D        G
forever's gonna start tonight.
G                   Em             B                C
Once upon a time I was falling in love but now I'm only falling apart.
      Am7             D                G     Em C D
There's nothing I can do a total eclipse of the heart.
G                       Em                 B
Once upon a time there was light in my life but now there's only love
      C    Am7            D                G
in the dark. Nothing I can say a total eclipse of the heart.
```

Refrain
```
C D              G Em  C       D           G
A total eclipse of the heart. A total eclipse of the heart.
```
M + T: Jim Steinman
© Copyright 1983 by EMI Virgin Songs Inc./Lost Boys Music.
All Rights Reserved. International Copyright Secured

# DEINE SPUREN IM SAND

(HOWARD CARPENDALE)

```
         G                                      Am
1. Wir hatten Sonne und Sterne und die Dünen nur und das weite Meer.
                  D7                      G
Und mir war als ob die Zeit ganz fest in meinen Händen wär.
   G         G7                    C           Cm
Es gab nur uns beide für mich, ich wusste ich hatte dich.
     G/D                D7
Wie einfach und klar doch alles war.
```

**Refrain:**
```
G                C                       G
Deine Spuren im Sand, die ich gestern noch fand,
D             G         A                 D
hat die Flut mitgenommen, was gehört nun noch mir?
G                    C                  G
Deine Liebe, sie schwand, wie die Spuren im Sand,
D                    G    Am     D                G
was ist mir nur geblieben, nur die Sehnsucht nach dir.
          G                                             Am
2. Ich weiß nicht, wann du anfingst, ohne mich die Stadt entlang zu gehn
                               D7                  G
und wenn ich dich danach fragte, stumm an mir vorbeizusehn.
                  G7                        C             Cm
Bis man die ganze Wahrheit versteht, ist es nicht selten zu spät.
     G/D           D7
Da bin ich nun, was kann ich tun.
```

Refrain

M + T: Cliff Corbett / Neil Lancaster
deutscher T: Fred Jay
© 1975 Chrysalis Music Limited. Chrysalis Music Holdings GmbH.
All Rights Reserved. International Copyright Secured.

# BOYS DON'T CRY

(THE CURE)

```
A    Bm    C#m    D    (2x)

    A              Bm            C#m              D
1. I would say I'm sorry if I thought that it would change her mind
    A              Bm            C#m              D
but I know that this time I have said too much been too unkind.
C#m      Bm                C#m                    Bm
I try to laugh about it, cover it all up with lies,
C#m      Bm                C#m                    Bm
I try to laugh about it hiding the tears in my eyes
        A   Bm   C#m   D   A   Bm   C#m   D
'cause boys don't cry,     boys don't cry.

    A              Bm            C#m              D
2. I would break down at your feet and beg forgiveness plead with you
    A              Bm            C#m              D
but I know that it's too late and now there's nothing I can do.
C#m      Bm                C#m                    Bm
So I try to laugh about it, cover it all up with lies,
C#m      Bm                C#m                    Bm
I try to laugh about it hiding my tears in my eyes
        A   Bm   C#m   D   A   Bm   C#m   D
'cause boys don't cry,     boys don't cry.

    A              Bm            C#m              D
3. I would tell you that I loved you if I thought that you would stay
    A              Bm            C#m              D
but I know that there's no use in you've already gone away,
E          F#m    E              F#m
mis-judged your limit pushed you too far,
E          F#m
took you for granted,
D                    E
felt that you needed me more, more, more.
    A              Bm            C#m              D
Now I would do most anything to get you back by my side
    A         Bm            C#m                   D
but I just keep on laughing hiding the tears in my eyes
        A   Bm   C#m   D   A   Bm   C#m   D
'cause boys don't cry,     boys don't cry.

A   Bm   C#m   D   D   C#m   Bm   A
```

M + T: Michael Dempsey / Robert Smith / Laurence Tolhurst
© Copyright 1979 Fiction Songs Limited.
All Rights Reserved. International Copyright Secured.

# DU HATTEST KEINE TRÄNEN MEHR
(PETER MAFFAY)

**Intro:** A B D E D E A
```
         B         D              E
1. Ich glaube nicht, dass ich nur einem Menschen fehlen würde,
   D              E
denn dem ich fehlen möchte, der macht sich nichts aus mir.
   A        B      D              E
Ich glaube nicht, dass ich etwas versäumen würde,
   D              E                 A
denn was ich kennen lernte, daraus machte ich mir nichts.

   E                      Em
Ich glaube nicht, dass ich was zu erwarten habe,
   D                   G      E
worauf ich warten wollte, ist Zärtlichkeit von ihr!
   A        B      D              E
Ich glaube nicht, ja ich glaube nicht, dass ich noch länger leben möchte
   D
wenn ich jetzt sterben würde,
   E                      A
könnte ich die Welt mir träumen wie sie nicht war.
```

**Refrain:**
```
   A        E        D    E                     A
Du hattest keine Tränen mehr, gestern als wir uns trafen,
   Bm             D        E
du zittertest, dein Blick war leer.
   A        E        D        E              F#m
Ich hörte zu und wärmte dich und zog dich von der Straße
   D       E       A
und nahm dich mit zu mir.

   A              B        D                    E
2. Auch ich glaubte nicht, dass du dem Menschen fehlen würdest,
   D       E
dem du so fehlen möchtest, der passte nicht zu dir.
   A        B      D              E
Ich glaube schon, dass du etwas versäumen würdest,
   D              E                     A
denn was du kennen lerntest, das war der Anfang nur.

   E                      Em
Ich weiß genau, dass du was zu erwarten hättest,
   D            G                E
worauf du warten solltest, ist Zärtlichkeit von mir.
   A        B      D              E
Ich wünsch mir sehr, ja, ich wünsch mir sehr,
   E
dass du noch länger leben möchtest,
   D                   E                       A
wenn wir zusammenhalten, ertragen wir die Welt so, wie sie ist.
```

Refrain 2x

M: Peter Maffay
T: Volker Lechtenbrink
© 1980 Autarc Edition GmbH / Ed. Re-Ro / Neue Welt Musikverlag GmbH & Co.
KG. Musik-Edition Discoton GmbH (Universal Music Publishing Group),
Warner/Chappell Overseas Holdings Ltd, London. Reproduced by permission of
Faber Music Limited. All Rights Reserved.

# THE CARPET CRAWLERS

(GENESIS)

```
E          F#m7/E            E           F#m7/E
There is lambswool under my naked feet.
     F#m7                    C#
The wool is soft and warm, gives off some kind of heat.
  C#m
A salamander scurries into flame to be destroyed.
     D                  A                       E
Imaginary creatures are trapped in birth on celluloid.
     F#m7                        C#
The fleas cling to the golden fleece, hoping they'll find peace.
        C#m
Each thought and gesture are caught in celluloid.
              D                        A         D
There's no hiding in my memory. There's no room to void.


      D                    Em                       D
1. The crawlers cover this floor in the red ochre corridor.
                         Em                              D
For my second sight of people, they've more lifeblood than before.
          Em                      D
They're moving in time to a heavy wooden door,
                        Em
where the needle's eye is winking, closing on the poor.
```

**Refrain:**
```
     F#m
The carpet crawlers heed their callers:
A                      G    A                          G
We've got to get in to get out. We've got to get in to get out.
D                 C         Em D
We've got to get in to get out.
```

2. There's only one direction in the faces that I see;
it's upward to the ceiling where the chambers said to be.
Like the forest fight for sunlight that takes root in every tree.
They are pulled up by the magnet believing they are free.

Refrain

3. Mild mannered supermen are held in kryptonite and the wise
and foolish virgins giggle with their bodies glowing bright.
Through a door a harvest feast is lit by candlelight;
it's the bottom of a staircase that spirals out of sight.

Refrain

4. The porcelain mannequin with shattered skin fears attack.
The eager pack lift up their pitchers, the carry all they lack.
The liquid has congealed, which has seeped out through the crack
and the tickler takes his stickleback.

Refrain

M + T: Phil Collins, Peter Gabriel, Tony Banks & Stephen Hackett
© Copyright 1974 Genesis Music Limited.
Hit & Run Music (Publishing) Limited.
All Rights Reserved. International Copyright Secured.

# HELLO AGAIN

(HOWARD CARPENDALE)  
[TRANSP. -1]

```
C                          Am
Hello again, du ich möchte dich heut noch sehen,
                 Dm                              G
ich will dir gegenüberstehen, viel zu lang war die Zeit.
G C Dm  G               C        Am  G C Dm  G    C Am G
Uhhuhuhuhu, ich sag nur hello again,    uhhuhuhuhu.

       C                   Am                               G
1. Ein Jahr lang war ich ohne dich, ich brauchte diese Zeit für mich.
   C                                Am
   Kann sein, dass ich ein anderer bin, als der, der damals von dir ging.
   G
   Ich geh die Straße lang wie immer, da ist noch Licht in deinem Zimmer.
   C                       F
   Ich weiß, du wirst mich nicht viel fragen,
   C                      G
   wie damals werd ich einfach sagen:
```

**Refrain:**
```
     C                      Am
Hello again, ich sag einfach hello again,
             F           Dm                G
du ich möchte dich heut noch sehen, dort, wo alles begann.
          C                    Am
Oh, hello again, dort am Fluss, wo die Bäume stehen,
         F             Dm                G
will ich dir in die Augen sehen, ob ich dableiben kann.
G C Dm  G               C        Am  G C Dm  G    C Am G
Uhhuhuhuhu, ich sag nur hello again,    uhhuhuhuhu.

       C                        Am                            G
2. Noch ein paar Stufen bis zur Tür, ich spür ein wenig Angst in mir.
   C                              Am
   Wie kann ich nur so sicher sein, vielleicht lebst du nicht mehr allein.
   G
   Ich würde gern für immer bleiben, das kann ich nicht allein entscheiden.
   C                          F
   Vielleicht wird uns noch viel verbinden,
   C                       G
   Vielleicht musst du erst zu mir finden.
```

Refrain

M + T: Howard Carpendale / Joachim Horn-Bernges / Irma Holder  
© 1984 Hanseatic Musikverlag GmbH & Co KG,  
Warner/Chappell Overseas Holdings Limited, London.  
Reproduced by permission of Faber Music Limited.  
All Rights Reserved.

# WHO BY FIRE

(LEONARD COHEN)

```
         Am   G   Am           G   Am
1. And who by fire, who by water,
C    G       C            G        C
who in the sunshine, who in the night time,
Am   G   Am              G   Am
who by high ordeal, who by common trial,
C           G         C
who in your merry, merry month of may,
C       G      C
who by very slow decay,
     Am            Fmaj7   E
and who shall I say is calling?

         Am   G    Am              G   Am
2. And who in her lonely slip, who by barbiturate,
C    G      C               G   C
who in these realms of love, who by something blunt,
     Am   G   Am            G   Am
and who by avalanche, who by powder,
C   G         C         G       C
who for his greed, who for his hunger,
     Am            Fmaj7   E
and who shall I say is calling?

         Am   G   Am              G   Am
3. And who by brave assent, who by accident,
C    G    C             G         C
who in solitude, who in this mirror,
Am       G          Am           G     Am
who by his lady's command, who by his own hand,
C    G  C                G    C
who in mortal chains, who in power,
     Am            Fmaj7   E
and who shall I say is calling?
```

M + T: Leonard Cohen
© Copyright 1974 Sony/ATV Songs LLC, USA.
Chrysalis Songs Limited.
All Rights Reserved. International Copyright Secured.

# CODO

(DÖF)

**Intro:** Em G6 Bm D

```
      Em                        G6
1. Hässlich, ich bin so hässlich,
         Bm                       D
so grässlich hässlich, ich bin der Hass.
   Em                  G6              Bm              D
Hassen, ganz hässlich hassen, ich kann's nicht lassen, ich bin der Hass.
Em G6 Bm D
Uuuuuuuuuuh.
G                                                   D
Codo, der dritte, aus der Sternenmitte, bin ich der dritte von links.
Em G6 Bm D
Uuuuuuuuuuh.
```

**Refrain:**
```
             G                        D
Und ich düse, düse, düse, düse im Sauseschritt
              C                      G
und bring die Liebe mit von meinem Himmelsritt.
                                           D
Denn die Liebe, Liebe, Liebe, Liebe, die macht viel Spaß,
C                          G
viel mehr Spaß, als irgendwas.
```

```
      Em              G6                Bm              D
2. Ätzend, ich bin so ätzend, alles zersetzend, ich bin der Hass.
   Em                 G6              Bm              D
Mächtig, undendlich mächtig, und niederträchtig, so ist mein Hass.
Em G6 Bm D
Uuuuuuuuuuh.
C                                                           G D7
Codo aus der Ferne der leuchtenden Sterne, ich düse so gerne durchs All.
```

Refrain 2x


M: Annette Humpe, Josef Prokopetz, Manfred Tauchen
T: Annette Humpe, Josef Prokopetz, Manfred Tauchen & Georg Januszewski
© 1997 Lafite Musik Wien, Bingen Edition Inga Humpe, Austria and Ambulanz
Musikverlag Annette Humpe administered by Kobalt Music Publishing Ltd.
Warner/Chappell Overseas Holdings Ltd, London. Reproduced by permission of
Faber Music Ltd. All Rights Reserved.

# (LET ME BE YOUR) TEDDY BEAR

(ELVIS PRESLEY)

**Intro:** G6 F#6 F6 F#6 G6

C
Baby let me be your lovin' Teddy Bear.
F
Put a chain around my neck
                    C
and lead me anywhere.
            G7           C
Oh, let me be your teddy bear.

**Bridge:**
    F             G7
I don't wanna be a tiger
        F           G7
cause tigers play too rough.
    F           G7
I don't wanna be a lion
        F           G7
cause lions ain't the kind
            C
you love enough.

**Refrain:**
                C
Just wanna be your teddy bear.
F
Put a chain around my neck
                    C
and lead me anywhere.
            G7           C
Oh, let me be your teddy bear.


C
Baby let me be around you every night.
F
Run your fingers through my hair
                    C
and cuddle me real tight.
            G7           C
Oh, let me be your teddy bear.

Bridge

Refrain
            G7           C        C
Oh, let me be your teddy bear. I just wanna be your teddy bear.

M + T: Kal Mann & Bernie Lowe
© Copyright 1957 Gladys Music Incorporated, USA.
Carlin Music Corporation.
All Rights Reserved. International Copyright Secured.

# FUN FUN FUN

(THE BEACH BOYS)
[TRANSP. +1]

```
      D
1. Well, she got her daddy's car
                                 G
and she cruised through the hamburger stand, now.
          D                                            A
Seems she forgot all about the library, like she told her old man, now.
         D                                          G
And with the radio blasting goes cruising just as fast as she can, now.
```

**Refrain:**
```
            D         F#m       G          A      D
And she'll have fun, fun, fun, 'til her daddy takes the T-bird away.
D       G          D/F#            Em      D
Fun, fun, fun, 'til her daddy takes the T-bird away.
```

```
             D
2. Well, the girls can't stand her
                                    G
cause she walks, looks, and drives like an ace, now.
(You walk like an ace, now, you walk like an ace)
               D                                    A
She makes the Indy 500 look like the Roman chariot race, now.
(You look like an ace, now, you look like an ace)
           D
A lot of guys try to catch her
                                   G
but she leads 'em on a wild goose chase, now.
(You drive like an ace, now, you drive like)
```

Refrain

```
             D                                             G
3. Well, you knew all along that your dad was getting wise to you, now.
(You shouldn't-a lied, now, you shouldn't-a lied)
          D
And since he took your set of keys,
                            A
you been thinkin' that your fun is all through now.
(You shouldn't-a lied, now, you shouldn't-a lied)
        D                                                       G
But you can come along with me 'cause we got a lot of things to do now.
(You shouldn't-a lied, now, you shouldn't-a lied)
```

```
              D        F#m
And you'll have fun, fun, fun,
      G                A
now that daddy takes the T-bird away.
D        G         D/F#             Em       D
Fun, fun, fun, now that daddy takes the T-bird away.
D        F#            G              A
fun, fun, fun, now that daddy takes the T-bird away.
D        G         D/F#             Em       D
Fun, fun, fun, now that daddy takes the T-bird away.
```

M + T: Brian Wilson, Mike Love
© Sea-Of-Tunes Publishing Company / Robert Mellin Musikverlag KG.
Mit freundlicher Genehmigung der Bosworth Music GmbH, Berlin.

# ALL MY LOVING

(THE BEATLES)
[TRANSP. +2]

```
          Em           A7         D            Bm
1. Close your eyes and I'll kiss you, tomorrow I'll miss you,
   G         Em          C    A7
remember I'll always be true.
          Em           A7         D            Bm
And then while I'm away I'll write home everyday
          G            A           D
and I'll send all my loving to you.

           Em           A7         D             Bm
2. I'll pretend that I'm kissing, the lips I am missing
    G            Em              C     A7
and hope that my dreams will come true.
          Em           A7         D            Bm
And then while I'm away I'll write home everyday
          G            A           D
and I'll send all my loving to you.
```

**Refrain:**
```
      Bm      F#7           D
All my loving I will send to you.
          Bm     F#7          D
All my loving, darling I'll be true.
```

```
          Em           A7         D            Bm
1. Close your eyes and I'll kiss you, tomorrow I'll miss you,
   G         Em          C    A7
remember I'll always be true.
          Em           A7         D            Bm
And then while I'm away I'll write home everyday
          G            A           D
and I'll send all my loving to you.
```

Refrain

M + T: John Lennon & Paul McCartney
© Copyright 1963 Sony/ATV Music Publishing.
All Rights Reserved. International Copyright Secured.

# THE NIGHT CHICAGO DIED

(PAPER LACE)

```
        Dm         G7                                  C
1. In the heat of a summer night, in the land of the dollar bill,
             Dm        G7                       C
when the town of Chicago died and they talk about it still.
              Dm         G7                    C
When a man named Al Capone tried to make this town his own.
                   Dm          G7                 C
And he called his gang to war with the forces of the law.
```

**Refrain:**
```
              C                                     Dm
I heard my Mama cry. I heard her pray the night Chicago died.
G7
Brother what a night it really was, brother what a fight it really was.
C
Glory be.
                                                    Dm
I heard my Mama cry. I heard her pray the night Chicago died.
G7
Brother what a night the people saw, brother what a fight the people saw
C
Yes indeed.
```

```
                          Dm    G7
2. And the sound of the battle rang through the streets of the old east
C                            Dm    G7                    C
side. Till the last of the hoodlum gang had surrendered up or died.
                     Dm          G7                C
There was shouting in the street and the sound of running feet.
                Dm              G7                C
And I asked someone who said "About a hundred cops are dead."
```

Refrain

```
                         Dm    G7                       C
3. Then there was no sound at all but the clock upon the wall.
                     Dm        G7              C
Then the door burst open wide and my Daddy stepped inside.
                    Dm         G7                C
And he kissed my Mama's face and he brushed her tears away.
```

Refrain

```
C                                                   Dm
The night Chicago died. Na, na, na... The night Chicago died.
G7
Brother what a fight the people saw, brother what a fight the people saw
C
Yes indeed.
C                                                   Dm
The night Chicago died. Na, na, na... The night Chicago died.
G7
Brother what a night it really was, brother what a fight it really was.
C
Glory be.
```

M + T: Mitch Murray & Peter Callander
© Copyright 1974 Universal/Dick James Music Limited.
All Rights Reserved. International Copyright Secured.

# MARIA

(BLONDIE)

```
          G                D    Em              C
1. She moves like she don't care, smooth as silk, cool as air,
   G      D               C
   ooh, it makes you wanna cry.
        G                D            Em                  C
   She doesn't know your name, and your heart beats like a subway train,
   G      D               C
   ooh, it makes you wanna die.
                    D          Em C      D               Em
   Ooh, don't you wanna take her, wanna make her all your own?
```

**Refrain:**
```
    G    D/F#       Em     C  G           D              C
   Maria, you've got to see her, go insane and out of your mind!
     G    D/F#    Em C  G          D           C
   Regina, Ave Maria, a million and one candle lights!


          G                D        Em                    C
2. I've seen this thing before in my best friend and the boy next door,
   G       D          C
   fool for love and full of fire.
         G            D          Em              C
   Won't come in from the rain, she's oceans running down the drain,
   G       D      C
   blue as ice and desire.
             D       Em C           D             Em
   Don't you wanna make her? Ooh, don't you wanna take her home?
```

Refrain

```
   C          D            Em C           D              Em
   Ooh, don't you wanna break her? Ooh, don't you wanna take her home?

           G              D       Em            C
3. She walks like she don't care, you wanna take her ev'rywhere,
   G      D               C
   ooh, it makes you wanna cry.
               G            D    Em            C
   She's like a millionaire, walking on imported air,
   G      D               C
   ooh, it makes you wanna die.
```

Refrain

```
                    D          Em C      D               Em
   Ooh, don't you wanna take her, wanna make her all your own?
```

M + T: James Destri
© Copyright 1999 Dick Johnson Songs/Famous Music LLC, USA. Sony/ATV Harmony (UK) Limited.
All Rights Reserved. International Copyright Secured.

# SUMMER OF '69

(BRYAN ADAMS)

```
         D                     A
1. I got my first real six string. Bought it at the "Five and Dime".
D                              A
Played it till my fingers bled. Was the summer of '69.
D                           A
Me and some boys from school. Had a band, we tried real hard.
D                              A
Jimmy quit and Jody got married, should have known we never get far.

Bm       A          D                        G
And if I look back now, the summer seemed to last forever.
Bm       A            D                   G
And if I had a choice, yeah, I always wanna be there.
Bm           A              Dsus2
Those were the best days of my life.
D Dsus4 D Dsus2 D Asus2 A Asus4 A Asus2 A
     D                            A
2. Ain't no use in complaining when you got a job to do.
D
Spent my evenings down at the Drive-In.
A
And that's where I met you.

Bm            A              D                    G
Standing on your mother's porch you told me that you'll wait forever.
Bm          A            D             G
And when you held my hand I knew that it was now or never.
Bm           A              Dsus2
Those were the best days of my life.
D Dsus4 D Dsus2 D Asus2 A Asus4 A Asus2 A
                        Dsus2 D Dsus4 D Dsus2 D Asus2 A Asus4 A Asus2 A
Back in the summer of '69.
Oh yeah.

F         Bb                     C
Man we were killing time, we were young and restless,
   Bb              F       Bb            C
we needed to unwind. I guess nothing can last forever, forever. No yeah.
Dsus2 D Dsus4 D Dsus2 D Asus2 A Asus4 A Asus2 A
     D
3. Now the times they are changing.
A
Look at everything that's come and gone.
D
Sometimes when I play that old sixstring,
A
I think about you, wonder what went wrong.
Bm           A              D                 G
Standing on your mothers porch you told me that it lasts forever.
Bm            A            D             G
And the way you held my hand I knew that it was now or never.
Bm           A              Dsus2
Those were the best days of my life.
D Dsus4 D Dsus2 D Asus2 A Asus4 A Asus2 A
```

M + T: Bryan Adams & Jim Vallance
© Copyright 1984 Almo Music Corporation, USA/Adams Communications
Incorporated/Testatyme Music, USA/Irving Music Corporation, USA
Rondor Music International Inc. All Rights Reserved. International Copyright Secured.

# BELIEVER

(MARLA GLEN)

**Intro:** Am G Am G Am G Am G

```
   F           G            E         Am    G
1. Like a believer we are out to find.
   F           G            E              Am    G
Like a believer we are living on our minds.
   F           G            E           Am    G
Like a believer we don't waste any time.
   F           G            E        Am    G
Like a believer we stand our ground.
```

**Refrain:**
```
F              C
I just can't understand this,
E                                Am                       G
why it's so hard to take each other by the hand and,
F              C         E  Am G
and say that I love you.
F                          G
Like a believer we can't let this go,
E                  Am                G
no more war, no more war, no more war,
F              C         E  Am G
just say that I love you.
Am                      Em G Am                    Em G
This world is in trouble.     We got to find a way
Am              Em G Am                    Em G
to come together     and make a better way.
Am                       Em G Am Em G
I can't understand this,      no.
```

```
   F           G                  E                 Am       G
2. Troubled the world there's no time for children and their hearts.
   F              G                  E              Am  G
Just look at their eyes. Can't you see you're tearing them apart?
   F           G            E          Am  G
So I ask you believe us, don't waste any time.
   F           G            E         Am  G
Let's stay together and save our world.
```

Refrain

```
Am                      Em G Am                    Em G
This world is in trouble.     We got to find a way.
Am                  Em G Am Em G  Am Em G Am Em G
I can't understand this,    no.
Am                          Em G Am Em G
I just can't understand this,    no.
Am                          Em G Am Em G
I just can't understand this,    no.
Am
This world is in trouble.
```

M + T: Marla Glen
© Michael Menges Musikverlag

**338**

# VIDEO KILLED THE RADIO STAR

(THE BUGGLES)
[TRANSP. -1]

```
    D            G6              Asus4         A
1. I heard you on my wireless back in Fifty Two,
    D         G6        Asus4       A
lying awake intent at tuning in on you.
    D          G6            Asus4            A
If I was young it didn't stop you coming through.
    D      G6
Oh-a, oh.

    D              G6              Asus4        A
2. They took the credit for your second symphony.
    D            G6           Asus4    A
Rewritten by machine on new technology
    D            G6            Asus4      A
and now I understand the supernova scene.
    D     G6 Asus4    A
Oh-a, oh. I met your children
    D    G6   Asus4       A
Oh-a, oh. What did you tell them?
```

**Refrain:**
```
D                       G
Video killed the radio star.
D                       G
Video killed the radio star.
D      A/F#     G            D       A/F#        G
In my mind and in my car we can't rewind, we've gone too far.
A          Bm7 A        Bm7
Oh-a-a-a oh. Oh-a-a-a oh

    D             G6              Asus4        A
3. And now we meet in an abandoned studio.
    D            G6              Asus4         A
We hear the playback and it seems so long ago.
    D             G6           Asus4     A
And you remember the jingles used to go.
    D    G6  Asus4        A
Oh-a, oh. You were the first one.
    D    G6  Asus4       A
Oh-a, oh. You were the last one.
```

Refrain

```
D      A/F#     G            D       A/F#        G
In my mind and in my car we can't rewind, we've gone to far.
D         A/F#      G               D           A/F#        G
Pictures came and broke your heart, so put all the blame on VCR.
      D  G6 Asus4 A        D G6 Asus4 A
You are           the radio star.
```

M + T: Bruce Woolley, Geoff Downes, Trevor Charles Horn
© 1979 Carlin Music Corp administered by Artemis Muziekuitgeverij B.V. / Island Music Ltd.
Warner/Chappell Artemis Music Ltd, London / Universal Music Publishing Limited. Reproduced by permission of Faber Music Limited. All Rights Reserved.

# IS THIS LOVE

(BOB MARLEY)

```
F#m   F#m   D   A
F#m   F#m   D   A

C#m         F#m         D              A
I wanna love you and treat you right.
C#m         F#m             D              A
I wanna love you every day and every night.
        C#m   F#m           D                   A
We'll be together with a roof right over our heads.
        C#m         F#m         D              A
We'll share the shelter of my single bed.
        C#m         F#m         D                A
We'll share the same room, jah provide the bread.
```

**Refrain**:
```
            C#m
Is this love, is this love, is this love,
                           Bm
is this love that I'm feeling?
            C#m
Is this love, is this love, is this love,
                           Bm
is this love that I'm feeling?

Bm  C#m  D      E

Dmaj7                                   Bm  C#m  D    E
I wanna know, wanna know, wanna know now.
C#m
I've got to know, got to know, got to know now.
C#m                 Bm
I... I'm willing and able,
    F#m                    E     D C#m Bm
so I throw my cards on your table.


        F#m
I wanna love you.
        D           A           C#m         F#m
I wanna love and treat, love and treat you right.
        A               D           A
I wanna love you every day and every night.
        C#m   F#m           D                   A
We'll be together with a roof right over our heads.
        C#m         F#m         D              A
We'll share the shelter of my single bed.
        C#m         F#m         D                A
We'll share the same room, jah provide the bread.

A       C#m         F#m         D              A
We'll share the shelter of my single bed.
```

M + T: Bob Marley
© Copyright 1978 Fifty-Six Hope Road Music Limited/Odnil Music Limited.
Blue Mountain Music Limited.
All Rights Reserved. International Copyright Secured.

# WALK OF LIFE

(DIRE STRAITS)

**Intro:** E B A C#m B G#m A C#m B

E
1. Here comes Johnny singing oldies, goldies.

Be-Bop-A-Lula, baby what I say.

Here comes Johnny singing, I gotta woman,

down in the tunnels, trying to make it pay.
A
He got the action, he got the motion.
E
Yeah, the boy can play.
A
Dedication, devotion,
E
turning all the night time into the day.

                    E                         B
He do the song about the sweet lovin' woman.
                    E          A
He do the song about the knife.
               E   B              A    B                   E
He do the walk, he do the walk of life, he do the walk of life.

Intro

2. Here comes Johnny and he'll tell you the story,
hand me down my walkin' shoes.
Here come Johnny with the power and the glory,
backbeat the talkin' blues.
He got the action, he got the motion.
Yeah, the boy can play.
Dedication, devotion,
turning all the night time into the day.

He do the song about the sweet lovin' woman.
He do the song about the knife.
He do the walk, he do the walk of life, he do the walk of life.

1. Strophe

     E                             B
And after all the violence and double talk
            E                           A
there's just a song in all the trouble and the strife.
            E   B             A     B                E
He do the walk, you do the walk of life, you do the walk of life.

M + T: Mark Knopfler
© Copyright 1985 Straitjacket Songs Limited.
Universal Music Publishing Limited. All Rights Reserved.
International Copyright Secured.

# HEY, HEY WICKIE

(ERIC FRANTZEN CHOR)

**Refrain:**
E
Hey, hey, Wickie, hey, Wickie, hey, zieh fest das Segel an.
A                                          E
Hey, hey, Wickie, die Wikinger sind hart am Winde dran.
B           A         E
Nananana, nanananana, nana, Wickie.


E
Hey, hey, Wickie, hey, Wickie, hey, so heißt der kleine Held.
A                                         E
Er denkt kurz nach, dann hat er ihn: den Trick, der ihm gefällt.
B         A         E
   Nananana, nanananana, nana, Wickie.


F                                  E
Die Angst vorm Wolf macht ihn nicht froh und im Taifun ist's ebenso.
F                        B
Doch Wölfe hin, Taifune her, die Lösung fällt ihm gar nicht schwer.


**Refrain:**
E
Hey, hey, Wickie, hey, Wickie, hey, zieh fest das Segel an.
A                                          E
Hey, hey, Wickie, die Wikinger sind hart am Winde dran.
B           A         E
Nananana, nanananana, nana, Wickie.

M + T: Christian Bruhn, Andrea Wagner
© Copyright by Filmkunst-Musikverlag Edition FKM-Junior, München.
All Rights Reserved. International Copyright Secured.

# IT'S MY LIFE

(BON JOVI)

**Intro:** Cm Ab/C Cm (2x)

```
    Cm                                      Cm Ab/C Cm
1. This ain't a song for the broken-hearted,
    Cm                                 Cm Ab/C Cm
no silent prayer for the faith-departed.
Cm                      Ab/C
I ain't gonna be just a face in the crowd,
             F/C
you're gonna hear my voice when I shout it out loud!
```

**Refrain:**
```
         Cm         Ab           Eb            Bb/D
It's my life, it's now or never, I ain't gonna live forever.
Cm            Ab            Bb
I just want to live while I'm alive.
      B° Cm                          Ab
It's my life, my heart is like an open highway,
Eb            Bb/D
like Frankie said, I did it my way.
Cm           Ab              Bb
I just wanna live while I'm alive.

      B° Cm     Ab G Cm Ab G
It's my life!
```

```
     Cm                                      Cm Ab/C Cm
2. This is for the ones who stood their ground,
     Cm                              Cm Ab/C Cm
for Tommy and Gina who never backed down.
   Cm                      Ab/C
Tomorrow's getting harder make no mistake,
F/C
luck ain't even lucky, got to make your own breaks.
```

Refrain

```
     B° Ab    Bb Ab/C F
It's my life!
```

```
Cm
Better stand tall when they're calling you out,

don't bend, don't break, baby, don't back down!
```

Refrain 2x

```
     B° Cm
It's my life!
```

M + T: Jon Bon Jovi / Richie Sambora
© Copyright 2000 Aggressive Music, USA/Bon Jovi Publishing, USA/GV-MXM.
Kobalt Music Publishing Limited/Sony/ATV Music Publishing.
All Rights Reserved. International Copyright Secured.

# SEHNSUCHT

(PURPLE SCHULZ)

**Intro:** Am F/A C Dm7  Am F C Dm7

```
Am            F/A         C             Dm7
Regen fällt, kalter Wind, Himmel grau, Frau schlägt Kind.
Am            F/A         C             Dm7
Keine Nerven und so allein. Das Paradies kann das nicht sein.
Am            F/A         C             Dm7
Männer kommen müd nach Haus. Die kalte Seele fliegt hinaus.
Am            F/A
Kind muss weinen, Kind muss schrein.
C             Dm7
Schrein macht müde, Kind schläft ein.
```

**Refrain:**
```
        Am      Em/A G          F
Ich hab Heimweh.        Fernweh?
     Am     Em/A G              F
Sehnsucht?   Ich weiß nicht, was es ist.

Am         F/A         C             Dm7
Keine Sterne in der Nacht. Kleines Kind ist aufgewacht.
Am             F/A          C             Dm7
Kind fragt, wo die Sterne sind. Ach, was weiß denn ich, mein Kind.
Am           F/A           C           Dm7
Ist der große Schwefelmond eigentlich von wem bewohnt?
Am             F/A         C           Dm7
Warum ist der Himmel leer? Ist da oben keiner mehr?

        Am      Em/A G F Am Em/A G F
Ich hab Heimweh.
```

Refrain
```
            Am                          F/A C Dm7 Am F/A C Dm7
Ich will nur fort. Ganz weit fort. Ich will raus!

Am            F/A         C             Dm7
Warum hast du mich geborn? Bevor ich da war, war ich schon verlorn.
Am            F/A         C             Dm7
Land der Henker, Niemandsland. Das Paradies ist abgebrannt.
```

```
Am Em/A G F       Am    Em/A G F
        Ich hab Heimweh.
                Am
Ich will nur weg. Ganz weit weg.
                Am                      F/A C Dm7 Am F/A C Dm
Ich will nur fort. Ganz weit fort. Ich will raus!
```

M: Hans-Günther Schmitz
T: Purple Schulz
© Copyright 1983 by Papagayo Musikverlage Hans Gerig OHG,
Bergisch Gladbach & Miau Musikverlag GmbH, Berlin.

# GIRL, YOU'LL BE A WOMAN SOON

(NEIL DIAMOND)

```
Gm      C         F      Gm
Girl, you'll be a woman, soon.

   Gm
I love you so much, can't count all the ways,
      Gm
I've died for you girl and all they can say is
F
"He's not your kind."
      Gm
They never get tired of putting me down
     Gm
and I'll never know when I come around
F                                    Eb
what I'm gonna find. Don't let them make up your mind.


Don't you know:
Gm      C         F     Gm
Girl, you'll be a woman soon.
Gm        C            F
Please, come take my hand.

Gm      C         F     Gm
Girl, you'll be a woman soon.
Gm        C            F
Soon, you'll need a man.

          Gm
I've been misunderstood for all of my life
                Gm
but what they're saying girl it cuts like a knife.
 F
"The boy's no good."
     Gm
Well I've finally found what I'm a looking for
        Gm
but if they get their chance they'll end it for sure.
F                          Eb
Surely would. Baby I've done all I could.


Now it's up to you:
Gm      C         F     Gm
Girl, you'll be a woman soon.
Gm        C            F
Please, come take my hand.
Gm      C         F     Gm
Girl, you'll be a woman soon.
Gm        C            F
Soon, you'll need a man.
```

M + T: Neil Diamond
© Copyright 1967 Tallyrand Music Incorporated, USA.
Universal/MCA Music Limited. All Rights Reserved. International Copyright Secured.

# SUMMER MOVED ON

(A-HA)
[TRANSP. -2]

```
     Dm         Am7         G7            F              Em
1. Summer moved on and the way it goes you can't tag along.
   Dm         Am7         G7            F         Em
   Honey moved out and the way it went leaves no doubt.
   Am         Fmaj7      Em            Dm         G
   Moments will pass in the morning light, I found out.
   Am          Fmaj7      Em             G         Dm
   Seasons can't last and there's just one thing left to ask.
```

**Refrain:**
```
Am      G               Fmaj7     E7sus4      E7
Stay! Don't just walk away and leave me another
Am      G               Fmaj7     E7sus4 E7      Fmaj7
day! A day just like today with nobody else around.
```

```
     Dm         Am7    G7           F              Em
2. Friendships move on until the day you can't get along.
   Dm         Am7         G7            F         Em
   Handshakes unfold and the way it goes, no one knows.
   Am         Fmaj7      Em            Dm         G
   Moments will pass in the morning light, I found out.
   Am          Fmaj7      Em             G         Dm
   Seasons can't last, so there's just one thing left to ask.
```

Refrain

Dm Am G F Em

```
Am          Fmaj7          Em             G         Dm
Seasons can't last and there's just one thing left to ask.
```

Refrain

Am G F Em Am G F

```
Em              Am
Summer moved on.
```

M + T: Pal Waaktaar, Magne Furuholmen, Morton Harket
© 2000 Chart Promotions Limited,
Warner/Chappell Music Limited, London.
Reproduced by permission of Faber Music Limited.
All Rights Reserved.

# HELLO (TURN YOUR RADIO ON)

(SHAKESPEAR'S SISTER)

**Intro:** C D F C

```
          C                          D
1. Woke up this morning and the streets were full of cars,
   F                              C
   all bright and shiny like they'd just arrived from mars,
   C                           D
   and as I stumbled through last nights drunken debris,
   F                           C
   the paperboy screamed out the headlines in the street,
   Gm                        F
   another war, and now the pound is looking weak,
   Eb                        Dm
   and tell me, have you read about the latest freak?
   Gm                         F
   We're bingo numbers and our names are obsolete,
   Eb                      D
   why do I feel bitter, when I should feel so sweet?
```

**Refrain:**
```
       G          Em          Bm7    D
   Hello, hello, turn your radio on,
            G              Em            Bm7       D
   is there anybody out there, help me sing this song?
             Am              G/B
   La la la life is a strange thing,
   C                   D                     G    D/F#
   just when you think you've learned how to use it it's gone.


          C                         D
2. Woke up this morning and my head was in a daze,
   F                           C
   a brave new world has dawned upon the human race,
   C                      D
   where words are meaning less and everything's so real,
   F                                C
   gonna have to reach my friends to find out how I feel.
   Gm                           F
   And if I taste the honey - is it really sweet?
   Eb                       Dm
   And do I eat it with my hands or with my feet?
   Gm                     F
   Does anybody really listen when I speak?
   Eb                   D
   Or will I have to say it all again next week?
```

Refrain
M + T: Marcella Levy, Siobhan Fahey, David Stewart & Jean Gouit
© Copyright 1992 Eligible Music Limited / Grow Your Own Music/Make Zee Music/Punclose Limited.
BMG Music Publishing Limited (25%)/Wintrup Musikverllag, Detmoldfrom(37.5%)/EMI MusicPublishing Limited (37.5%)/ Reverb Music Ltd./Für D/A/CH Musikverlag Progressive GmbH.
All Rights Reserved. International Copyright Secured.

# NEW YEAR'S DAY

(U2)
[TRANSP. -1]

**Intro:** Am C Em

Yeah...
Am        C          Em
All is quiet on New Year's Day.
Am             C          Em
A world in white gets underway.
Am           C                    Em
I want to be with you, be with you night and day.
Am           C          Em
Nothing changes on New Year's Day.
Am C   Em
   On New Year's Day.


**Refrain:**
G                   Am
I will be with you again.
G                   Fmaj7
I will be with you again.


Under a blood red sky
a crowd has gathered in black and white.
Arms entwined, the chosen few.
The newspapers says, says.
Say it's true it's true...
And we can break through
though torn in two.
We can be one.


Refrain

Oh...
Maybe the time is right
Oh... maybe tonight...

Refrain

And so we're told this is the golden age.
And gold is the reason for the wars we wage.
Though I want to be with you,
be with you night and day.
Nothing changes.
On New Year's Day.
On New Year's Day.

M + T: Larry Mullen, Adam Clayton, Dave Evans & Paul David Hewson
© Copyright 1982 Blue Mountain Music Limited/Mother Music/Taiyo Music
Incorporated/PolyGram International Music Publishing Limited.
All Rights Reserved. International Copyright Secured.

# ALONG COMES MARY

(BLOODHOUND GANG)

**Intro:** G 6x  C 2x  D 6x  C 2x  D# 6x  D 2x  C 6x  D 2x

```
      G                                        D
1. Every times I think that I'm the only one who's lonely,
        D#         C
someone calls on me.
 G                                        D
And every now and then I spend my time at rhyme and verse and curse
       D#         C
those faults in me.
```

**Refrain:**
```
          G                Bb             G                  B
And then along comes Mary. Mary Mary. Then along comes Mary. Mary Mary.

              G              D           D#
And does she want to give me kicks and be my steady chick
     C              G            Bb
and give me pick of memories.
              G              D              D#
Or maybe rather gather tales from all the fails
      C              G          Bb
and tribulations no one ever sees.
 D       D#              D   C
When we met I was sure out to lunch.
            D  G              D       D#                G
Now my empty cup tastes as sweet as the punch. Sweet as the punch.
```

Intro
```
2. When vague desire is the fire in the eyes of chicks whose sickness is
the games they play.
And when the masquerade is played and neighbor folks make jokes as who
is most to blame today.

And then along comes Mary. Mary Mary. Then along comes Mary. Mary Mary.

And does she want to set them free and let them see reality
from where she got her name.
And will they struggle much when told that such a tender touch of hers
Will make them not the same.
When we met I was sure out to lunch.
Now my empty cup tastes as sweet as the punch. Sweet as the punch.

3. And when the morning of warnings passed the gassed and flacid kids
are flung across the stars.
The psychodramas and the traumas gone, the songs are left unsung
and hung upon the scars.

And then along comes Mary. Mary Mary. Then along comes Mary. Mary Mary.

And does she want to see the strains the dead remains of all the pains
She left the night before.
Or will their waking eyes reflect the lies
and make them realize their urgent cry
for sight no more.
When we met I was sure out to lunch.
Now my empty cup tastes as sweet as the punch. Sweet as the punch.
```

M + T: Tandyn Almer
© Copyright 1964 Rondor Music (London) Limited.
All rights in Germany administered by Rondor Musikverlag
GmbH. All Rights Reserved. International Copyright Secured.

# I'M STILL STANDING

(ELTON JOHN)
[TRANSP. +1]

**Intro:** Am Dm/A E/A F/A G/A

```
    A                        D/A
1. You could never know what it's like,
      E/A                   A
your blood like winter freezes just like ice.
          Bm7/A               D/A         E
And there's a cold lonely light that shines from you,
      F#m              D                  A
you'll wind up like the wreck you hide behind that mask you use.

    A                        D/A
2. And did you think this fool could never win?
      E/A                   A
Well look at me, I'm coming back again,
         Bm7/A          D/A      E
I got a taste of love in a simple way
     F#m                        D              A      Bm7/A  A
and if you need to know while I'm still standing you just fade a----way.
```

**Refrain:**
```
             Am7                                 Em7/A
Don't you know I'm still standing better than I ever did,
                Dm7                    Fmaj7      G
looking like a true survivor, feeling like a little kid.
Am7                    Em7/A
I'm still standing after all this time,
              Dm7                         E7
picking up the pieces of my life without you on my mind.
        Am       Dm7       E7
I'm still standing...yeah yeah yeah!
        Am       Dm7       E7     F G
I'm still standing...yeah yeah yeah!
```

```
    A                     D/A
3. Once I never could hope to win,
      E/A                    A
you starting down the road leaving me again.
     Bm7/A                D/A    E
The threats you made were meant to cut me down
          F#m             D              A      Bm7/A  A
and if our love was just a circus you'd be a clown by    now.
```

Refrain

<sub>M + T: Elton John & Bernie Taupin
© Copyright 1983 HST Management Limited/Rouge Booze Incorporated.
Universal Music Publishing Limited.
All Rights Reserved. International Copyright Secured.</sub>

# DIE AFFEN RASEN DURCH DEN WALD

   A  
1. Die Affen rasen durch den Wald, der eine macht den andern kalt.

**Refrain:**  
        E        A  
Die ganze Affenbande brüllt:  
    A  
Wo ist die Kokosnuss? Wo ist die Kokosnuss?  
      E        A  
Wer hat die Kokosnuss geklaut?  
    A  
Wo ist die Kokosnuss? Wo ist die Kokosnuss?  
      E        A  
Wer hat die Kokosnuss geklaut?

2. Die Affenmama sitzt am Fluss und angelt nach der Kokosnuss.

Refrain

3. Der Affenonkel, welch ein Graus, reißt ganze Urwaldbäume aus.

Refrain

4. Der Affenmilchmann, welch ein Schlick, er lauert auf die Kokosmilch.

Refrain

5. Der Elefant im Urwald spricht: Hier in dem Dickicht ist sie nicht.

Refrain

6. Die Affenbraut denkt selbst beim Kuss nur immer an die Kokosnuss.

Refrain

7. Das Affenbaby voll Genuss hält in der Hand die Kokosnuss.  
Die ganze Affenbande brüllt:  
Hier ist die Kokosnuss! Hier ist die Kokosnuss!  
Es hat die Kokosnuss geklaut.  
Hier ist die Kokosnuss! Hier ist die Kokosnuss!  
Es hat die Kokosnuss geklaut.

8. Und die Moral von der Geschicht', klau keine Kokosnüsse nicht.  
Weil sonst die ganze Bande brüllt:  
Wo ist die Kokosnuss? Wo ist die Kokosnuss?  
Wer hat die Kokosnuss geklaut?  
Wo ist die Kokosnuss? Wo ist die Kokosnuss?  
Wer hat die Kokosnuss geklaut?

Traditionell  
© 2005 by Edition DUX, Manching

# SPICKS AND SPECKS

(BEE GEES)

**Intro:** G

```
      G           D         Em          B
1. Where is the sun that shone on my head?
C         G           D           G
The sun in my life it is dead, it is dead.
G           D             Em          B
Where is the light that would play in my streets?
C              G              D           G
And where are the friends I could meet, I could meet.

      G         D       Em        B
2. Where are the girls I left all behind?
C             G             D           G
The spicks and the specks of the girls on my mind.
G          D        Em         B
Where is the sun that shone on my head?
C         G           D           G
The sun in my life it is dead, it is dead.

       Ab         Eb        Fm         C
3. Where are the girls I left all behind?
Db             Ab            Eb          Ab
The spicks and the specks of the girls on my mind.
A          E         F#m         C#
Where are the girls I left all behind?
D             A             E           A
The spicks and the specks of the girls on my mind.

A          E        F#m         C#
Where is the girl I loved all along?
D          A           E         A
The girl that I loved she's gone, she's gone.

      A         E        F#m         C#
4. All of my life I call yesterday.
D              A            E            A
The spicks and the specks of my life, 've gone away.
A       E       F#m       C#
All of my life I call yesterday.
D              A            E            A
The spicks and the specks of my life, 've gone away.
D       A       D        A
Spicks and Specks! Spicks and Specks!
```

M + T: Barry Gibb
© 1967 Crompton Songs, Warner/Chappell Music Ltd, London.
Reproduced by permission of Faber Music Limited.
All Rights Reserved.

# DICH ZU LIEBEN

(ROLAND KAISER)
[TRANSP. +1]

```
    Am                              E
1. Weil du mich liebst, ist der Tag wieder Leben für mich.
Am                                 E
Weil du mich brauchst, ist die Nacht wieder Liebe für mich.
C                                G
Was du mir gibst, hab ich niemals zu träumen gewagt.
Am                         E      E7
Du hast in mir ein erloschenes Feuer entfacht.
```

**Refrain:**
```
       A                      Bm
Dich zu lieben, dich berühren, mein Verlangen, dich zu spüren,
   E7
deine Wärme, deine Nähe
       A      F#m        Bm       E
weckt die Sehnsucht in mir auf ein Leben mit dir.
A
Du bist die Frau, die jedes Lächeln,
          Bm
jede Zärtlichkeit an mich verschenkt.
E7                                 F#m     C#m Esus4 E
Du bist die Frau, die alles gibt, was man Liebe nennt.
```

```
    Am                                 E
2. Du liegst bei mir und ich atme den Duft deiner Haut.
Am                                 E
Und jeder Schlag deines Herzens ist mir so vertraut.
C                                 G
Du lässt mich sagen, was ich jeder Frau sonst verschwieg.
Am                             E    E7
Du gibst dem Himmel die wärmende Sonne zurück.
```

Refrain 2x

M: Joachim Heider
T: Roland Kaiser / Norbert Hammerschmidt
© 1981 by Edition Intro Meisel GmbH.

# VIVA FOREVER

(SPICE GIRLS)

**Intro:** Dm Am Bb F

```
   Dm                         Am
1. Do you still remember how we used to be?
Bb
Feeling together, believe in whatever,
      F
my love has said to me.
Dm                        Am
Both of us were dreamers, young love in the sun,
Bb
felt like my saviour, my spirit I gave ya,
      F
we'd only just begun.
```

**Refrain:**
```
Dm        Am     Bb         F
Hasta manana, always be mine.
         Dm                Am
Viva forever, I'll be waiting,
     Bb             F
everlasting, like the sun.
         Dm               Am
Live forever, for the moment,
     Bb              F
ever searching, for the one.


   Dm                       Am
2. Yes, I still remember every whispered word,
     Bb
the touch of your skin giving life from within
        F
like a love song that I'd heard.
Dm                       Am
Slipping through our fingers like the sands of time,
Bb
promises made, every memory saved,
       F
has reflections in my mind.
```

Refrain

```
     Dm                   Am
3. But we're all alone now, was it just a dream?
Bb
Feelings unfold, they will never be sold
       F
and the secret's safe with me.
```

Refrain

M + T: Victoria Adams, Emma Bunton, Melanie Brown, Melanie Chisholm, Geri Halliwell, Richard Stannard & Matthew Rowbottom
© Copyright 1997 EMI Music Publishing (WP) Limited/Universal Music Publishing Limited. All rights in Germany administered by Universal Music Publ. GmbH. All Rights Reserved. International Copyright Secured.

# ALWAYS LOOK ON THE BRIGHT SIDE OF LIFE
(MONTY PYTHON)

```
         Am              Cm           G              Em
1. Some things in life are bad, they can really make you mad.
     Am7       D7             G
Other things just make you swear and curse.
             Am            Cm          G              E7
When you're chewing on life's gristle don't grumble, give a whistle
    Am7                           D7
and this'll help things turn out for the best.

     G       Em        Am      D7      G     Em Am D7
And always look on the bright side of life.
    G       Em       Am      D7      G     Em Am D7
Always look on the light side of life.

         Am            D           G              Em
2. If life seems jolly rotten there's something you've forgotten
     Am             D            G
and that's to laugh and smile and dance and sing.
             Am        D    G             E7
When you're feeling in the dumps don't be silly chumps,
    A7                          D7
just purse your lips and whistle that's the thing.

     G       Em        Am      D7      G     Em Am D7
And always look on the bright side of life.
          G       Em       Am      D7      G     Em Am D7
Come on always look on the bright side of life.

       Am             D        G              Em
3. For life is quite absurd and death's the final word,
         Am         D           G
you must always face the curtain with a bow.
       Am          D          G         E7
Forget about your sin, give the audience a grin,
    A7                          D7
enjoy it, it's your last chance anyhow.

    G       Em        Am      D7      G     Em Am D7
So always look on the bright side of death.
   G       Em       Am      D7      G     Em Am D7
just before you draw your terminal breath.

       Am           D       G           Em
4. Life's a piece of shit when you look at it.
 Am               D                  G
Life's a laugh and death's a joke, it's true.
          Am          D        G              E7
You'll see it's all a show, keep'em laughing as you go,
    A7                       D7
just remember that the last laugh is on you.

     G       Em        Am      D7      G     Em Am D7
And always look on the bright side of life.
    G       Em       Am      D7      G     Em Am D7 G
Always look on the right side of life.
```

M + T: Eric Idle
© Copyright 1990 Python Monty Pictures Limited.
Universal Music Publishing Limited. All Rights Reserved.
International Copyright Secured.

# RED, RED WINE

(UB40)
[TRANSP. +1]

```
          C F G F         C F G
Red, red wine  goes to my head,
F            C         F G F                G F
makes me forget that I   still need her so.
G          C F G F          C F G F          C         F G
Red, red wine, it's up to you. All I can do I've done.
F            G F G             C    F G
Memories won't go, memories won't go.

F       G         C       F                       C
Life is fine every time, thoughts of you leave my head.
       G          C           F                  G
I was wrong, now I find just one thing makes me forget.

              C F G F              C F G F          C  F G
Refrain: Red, red wine, stay close to me.  Don't let me be alone.
       F        G  F G    C      F G    C F G
It's tearing apart my blue heart.
```

I have sworn every time thoughts of you would leave my head.
I was wrong, now I've found just one thing makes me forget. Refrain

```
C                         F
Red red wine, you make me feel so fine,
       G                 F
You keep me rockin' all of the time.
```
Red red wine, you make me feel so grand,
I feel a million dollar when you're just in my hand.
Red red wine, you make me feel so sad,
Any time I see you go, it make me feel bad.
Red red wine, you make me feel so fine,
Monkey back and ease up on the sweet deadline.

Red red wine, you give me holy pahzing.
Holy pahzing, you make me do my own thing.
Red red wine, you give me not awful love.
Your kind of loving like a blessing from above.
Red red wine, I loved you right from the start,
Right from the start, and with all of my heart.
Red red wine in an eighties style.
Red red wine in a modern beat style. Yeah.

Give me a little time, let me clear out my mind.
Give me a little time, let me clear out my mind.
Give me red wine, the kind make me feel fine.
You make me feel fine all of the time.
Red red wine, you make me feel so fine.
Monkey back and ease up on the sweet deadline.
The line broke, the money get choked,
Bunbah, ganjapani, little rubber boat.
Red red wine, I'm gonna hold on to you,
Hold on to you cause I know you love truth.
Red red wine, I'm gonna love you till I die,
Love you till I die, and that's no lie.
Red red wine, can't get your off my mind.
Wherever you may be, I'll surely find,
I'll surely find. Make no fuss, just leave us.

M + T: Neil Diamond
© Copyright 1966 Tallyrand Music Incorporated, USA
Universal/MCA Music Limited.
All Rights Reserved. International Copyright Secured.

# LASS UNS SCHMUTZIG LIEBE MACHEN

(DIE SCHRÖDERS)

**Intro:** G Am C D  G Am C G

G         Am  
Samstag nacht, halb zwei, alle sind bedient, nur ich bin noch dabei.  
  C  
Den ganzen Abend war ich tapfer, hab gebaggert und geschaut.  
D  
Neben dir, du süße Braut.  
  G  
Wir reden über Filme, was dein Ex-Freund grad' studiert.  
  Am  
Ich schlaf schon fast im Stehen ein und tu doch interessiert.  
  C  
Du sagst, du stehst auf Liebesfilme und auf Pferdesport.  
  D  
Ich denke: Jockey wär ich auch ganz gerne, doch, wenn's geht, sofort.

**Refrain:**  
G        Am  
Lass uns schmutzig Liebe machen, alle diese wilden Sachen,  
C         D  
die man nur aus Filmen kennt, die man nie beim Namen nennt.  
G        Am  
Lass uns schmutzig Liebe treiben, Körper aneinander reiben.  
C       D  
Lass's uns wie die Tiere tun, hier und jetzt und nun.

    G  
Come on Baby.  
G    Am    C    D  
La, la la la la, la la la la, la la la la lala.  
G    Am    C    G  
La, la la la la, la la la la, la la la la.

G         Am  
Hör gut zu, was ich dir sage: Zu mir oder dir, das ist hier die Frage.  
  C  
In der Hose ist der Teufel los, und du kapierst es nicht.  
 D  
Ich schaue in deine Bluse, Kleines, du in mein Gesicht.

Refrain 2x

    G  
Come on Baby.  
G    Am    C    D  
La, la la la la, la la la la, la la la la lala.  
G    Am    C    G  
La, la la la la, la la la la, la la la la.  
G    Am    C    D  
La, la la la la, la la la la, la la la la lala.  
G    Am    C    G  
La, la la la la, la la la la, la la la la.

M: Marc Stresemann / Hagen Goedicke / Daniel Kreuter  
T: Jens Burger  
© 1996 by EMI Music Publishing Germany / SMV Schacht Musikverlage GmbH & Co. KG.  
Mit freundlicher Genehmigung der EMI Music Publishing GmbH.

# LESSONS IN LOVE

(LEVEL 42)

```
   G        B              Em              C                G
1. I'm not proud, I was wrong and the truth is hard to take.
       B              Em              C              G
I felt sure we had enough but our love went overboard.
   G          B        Em            C                   G
Lifeboat lies lost at sea, I've been trying to reach your shore.
            B                   Em
Waves of doubt keep drowning me.

Em       Cmaj7            Am7         B          Em
All the dreams that we were building we never fulfilled them.
         Cmaj7            Am7         B      E   D
Could be better, should be better for lessons in love.

2. For restless eyes egos burn and the mold is hard to break.
Now we've waded in too deep and love is overboard.
Heavy hearts token words, all the hopes I ever had
fade like footprints in the sand.

Em       Cmaj7          Am7        B       Em
All the homes that we were building we never lived in.
         Cmaj7            Am7     B       Em
Could be better, should be better lessons in love.
         Cmaj7         Am7       B            Em
If we lose the time before us the future will ignore us.
         Cmaj7         Am7           B          E    D
We should use it, we could use it, yeah, lessons in love.
C            E D A
Lost without love.

C          G         F           C    D
Lessons in love, when will you ever learn?
              G           F             C    D
Lessons in love, when there's nowhere left to turn.
              G       F             C    D
Lessons in love, don't let your spirit burn.
              G       F           C    D
Lessons in love, I'll wait 'till you return.


All the dreams that we were building we never lived them.
We could lose it, we should use it, lessons in love, lessons in love.
All the homes that we were building we never lived in.
Could be better, could be better, should be better lessons in love.
If we lose the time before us the future will ignore us.
We should use it, we could use it, good god lessons in love.
```

M + T: Mark King, Roland Gould & Waliou Badarou
© 1984 Ruby Ruby Ltd / ISHE / BMG Rights Management (UK) Limited. Peermusic (UK) Limited.
All Rights Reserved. International Copyright Secured.

# NARCOTIC

(LIQUIDO)

**Intro:** C Dm F C C G   C Dm F C C G

```
       C                  Dm                      F
1. So you face it with a smile, there is no need to cry
                                C
for a trifle's more than this.
                     Dm                         F
Will you still recall my name and the month it all began,
                             C
will you release me with a kiss?
C                   Dm                         F
Have I tried to draw the veil, if I have, how could I fail?
                     C
Did I fear the consequence?
C               Dm           Ab Bb C
Dazed by careless words, cosy in my mi.....nd.
```

**Refrain:**
```
C        Dm         F        C          G
I don't mind, I think so, I will let you go.
C        Dm         F        C          G
I don't mind, I think so, I will let you go.
```

```
        C              Dm                        F
2. Now you shaped that liquid wax, fit it out with crater cracks,
                          C
sweet devotion, my delight.
                        Dm                           F
Oh, you're such a pretty one, and the naked thrills of flesh and skin
                         C
would tease me through the night.
                      Dm                       F
Now I hate to leave you bare, if you need me I'll be there,
                       C
don't you ever let me down.
                   Dm           Ab Bb C
Dazed by careless words, cosy in my mi.....nd.
```

Refrain

```
       C              Dm                    F           C
3. And I touched your face, narcotic mind from lazed Mary-Jane.
                    Dm                         F
And I called your name, like an addicted to cocaine,
                         C
calls for the stuff he'd rather blame.
                   Dm                       F          C
And I touched your face narcotic mind from lazed Mary-Jane.
                   Dm         F
And I called your name - my cocaine.
```

Refrain

M + T: Wolfgang Schödl
© Arabella Musikverlag GmbH / EMI Music Publishing Germany GmbH. Arabella Musikverlag GmbH. Mit freundlicher Genehmigung der EMI Music Publishing Germany GmbH.

# SON OF A PREACHER MAN

(DUSTY SPRINGFIELD)

```
       E
1. Billy Ray was a preacher's son
            A                  E
and when his daddy would visit he'd come along.
When they'd gather 'round and started talking
B7
that's when Billy would take me walking,
a-through the back yard we'd go walking,
then he'd look into my eyes. Lord knows to my surprise.
```

**Refrain:**
```
     E                              A              E
The only one who could ever reach me was the son of a preacher man.
     E                              A              E
The only boy who could ever teach me was the son of a preacher man.
          B     A        E
Yes he was, he was, mmm, yes he was.
```

```
2. Being good isn't always easy,
no matter how hard I'd try.
When he started sweet-talkin' to me
he'd come and tell me everything is all right
he'd kiss and tell me everything is all right!
Can I get away again tonight?
```

Refrain

```
        D
Yes, he was. How well I remember
A
the look was in his eyes. Stealin' kisses from me on the sly,
B7
takin' time to make time. Tellin' me that he's all mine.
E7
Learnin' from each other's knowin', look at us here how much we've grown
```

**Refrain (höher):**
```
          A                              D              A
And the only one who could ever reach me was the son of a preacher man.
     A                              D              A
The only boy who could ever teach me was the son of a preacher man.
          E     D7
Yes he was, he was, ooh, yes he was.

     A                              D              A
The only one who could ever reach me was the son of a preacher man.
                  (He was the sweet-talking son of a preacher man)
The only boy who could ever teach me was the son of a preacher man.
                  (A kiss-stealin' son of a preacher man)
The only one who could ever move me was the son of a preacher man.
The only one who could ever groove me was the son of a preacher man.
```

M + T: John Hurley & Ronnie Wilkins
© Copyright 1968 Tree Publishing Company Incorporated, USA.
Sony/ATV Music Publishing (UK) Limited.
All Rights Reserved. International Copyright Secured.

# LOVE ME TENDER

(ELVIS PRESLEY)

```
   D              E7
1. Love me tender, love me sweet,
A7           D
never let me go.
                E7
You have made my life complete
A7           D
and I love you so.
```

**Refrain:**
```
D       F#7     Bm      D7
Love me tender, love me true,
G       Gm          D
all my dreams fulfill
        B7      E7
for my darling, I love you,
A7           D
and I always will.
```

```
   D              E7
2. Love me tender, love me long,
A7           D
take me to your heart.
                E7
For it's there that I belong
A7           D
and will never part.
```

Refrain

```
   D              E7
3. Love me tender, love me dear,
A7           D
tell me you are mine.
                E7
I'll be yours through all the years
A7           D
till the end of time.
```

Refrain

M + T: Elvis Presley & Vera Matson
© Copyright 1956 Elvis Presley Music.
All Rights Reserved. International Copyright Secured.

# DO WAH DIDDY DIDDY

(MANFRED MANN)

```
E                      A               E
There she was, just-a walking down the street.
          E                   A            E
Singing do wah diddy, diddy dum, diddy do.
E                     A              E
Snapping her fingers and shuffling her feet.
          E                   A            E
Singing do wah diddy, diddy dum, diddy do.
```

She looked good (she looked good).
She looked fine (she looked fine).
She looked good, she looked fine
and I nearly lost my mind.

Before I knew it she was walkin' next to me.
Singing do wah diddy, diddy dum, diddy do.
Holding my hand just as natural as can be.
Singing do wah diddy, diddy dum, diddy do.
We walked on (walked on). To my door (to my door).
We walked on to my door. Then we kissed a little more.

```
E           C#m
Whoa-oa, I knew we was falling in love.
A                     B7
Yes, I did and so I told her all the things I'd been dreaming of.
```

Now we're together nearly every single day.
Singing do wah diddy, diddy dum, diddy do.
We're so happy and that's how we're gonna stay.
Singing do wah diddy, diddy dum, diddy do.

Well, I'm hers (I'm hers) She's mine (she's mine).
I'm hers, she's mine. Wedding bells are gonna chime.

```
B7
Whoa... oh, yeah.
E             A              E
Do wah diddy, diddy dum diddy do. Well, sing it to me!
E             A              E
Do wah diddy, diddy dum diddy do. Oh, oh yeah!
E             A              E
Do wah diddy, diddy dum diddy do.
```

M + T: Jeff Barry & Ellie Greenwich
© Songs of Polygram International Inc / Trio Music Co.
Inc.Universal Music Publishing Limited / BMG Rights
Management (UK) Limited.
All Rights Reserved. International Copyright Secured.

# TEENAGE DIRTBAG

(WHEATUS)

**Intro:** E B E A (2x)
```
   E           B        E           A
1. Her name is Noel, I have a dream about her.
E           B         E            A
She rings my bell, I got gym class in half an hour.
E            B         E         A
Oh, how she rocks in Ked's and tube socks
      C#m         A         B
but she doesn't know who I am
    C#m         A        B
and she doesn't give a damn about me.
```

**Refrain:**
```
         E           A       B          C#m
Cause I'm just a teenage dirtbag, baby.
        E           A       B          C#m
Yeah, I'm just a teenage dirtbag, baby.
E       A    B        C#m             E
Listen to Iron Maiden, baby, with me.
A     B  C#m
Ooooh.
```

Intro

```
2. Her boyfriend's a dick and he brings a gun to school
and he'd simply kick my ass if he knew the truth.
He lives on my block and he drives and I rock
but he doesn't know who I am.
And he doesn't give a damn about me.
```

Refrain

```
E A      E A      E A   C#m         A         B
 Oh yeah. Dirtbag. No, she doesn't know what she's missing.
E A      E A      E A   C#m         A         B  E
 Oh yeah. Dirtbag. No, she doesn't know what she's missing.
```

```
3. Man, I feel like mold, it's prom night and I am lonely.
Low and behold she's walking over to me,
this must be fake, my lip starts to shake.
How does she know who I am?
And why does she give a damn about it?
```

```
            E         A      B        C#m
I've got two tickets to Iron Maiden, baby.
E             A       B           C#m
Come with me Friday, don't say maybe.
E          A     B         C#m         E    A B C#m A B
I'm just a teenage dirtbag, baby, like you.
```

```
E A      E A      E A   C#m         A         B
 Oh yeah. Dirtbag. No, she doesn't know what she's missing.
E A      E A      E A   C#m         A         B  E
 Oh yeah. Dirtbag. No, she doesn't know what she's missing.
```

M + T: Brendan Browne
© EMI Blackwood Music Inc. / Montauk Mantis Productions Inc.
Mit freundlicher Genehmigung der EMI Music Publishing Germany GmbH.

# HELTER SKELTER

(THE BEATLES)

```
E7                                                A
When I get to the bottom I go back to the top of the slide
                                 C
where I stop and I turn and I go for a ride
                                G
till I get to the bottom and I see you again.
            E7
Yeah, yeah, yeah!


Do you, don't you want me to love you?
I'm coming down fast but I'm miles above you.
                         G
Tell me, tell me, come on, tell me the answer.
    A                                   E7
You may be a lover but you ain't no dancer.

A               E7              A              E7
Helter skelter, helter skelter, helter skelter. Yeah!

Will you, won't you want me to make you?
I'm coming down fast but don't let me break you.
Tell me, tell me, tell me the answer.
You may be a lover but you ain't no dancer.

Look out, helter skelter, helter skelter, helter skelter.
Look out cause here she comes.

When I get to the bottom I go back to the top of the slide
and I stop and I turn and I go for a ride
and I get to the bottom and I see you again.

Well, do you, don't you want me to make you?
I'm coming down fast but don't let me break you.
Tell me tell me tell me the answer.
You may be a lover but you ain't no dancer.

Look out, helter skelter, helter skelter, helter skelter.
Look out, helter skelter.
She's coming down fast.
Yes, she is
Yes, she is.
```

M + T: John Lennon & Paul McCartney
© Copyright 1968 Sony/ATV Music Publishing (UK) Limited.
All Rights Reserved. International Copyright Secured.

# BIG IN JAPAN

(ALPHAVILLE)
[TRANSP. -2]

**Intro:** Em C D   Em C D B

```
     Em                     C
1. Winter's cityside, crystal bits of snowflakes
   D                             B
all around my head and in the wind,
   Em                    C
I had no illusions that I'd ever find
    D                          B
a glimpse of summer's heatwaves in your eyes.
```

**Bridge:**
```
Em      C              D             Bm        C
You did what you did to me, now it's history I see,
         Am                   B
here's my comeback on the road again.
Em        C               D
Things will happen while they can,
       Bm                 C
I will wait here for my man tonight,
      Am            B
it's easy when you're big in Japan.
```

**Refrain:**
```
                      Em       C
Aah, when you're big in Japan tonight.
         D      Bm           C
Big in Japan, be tight. Big in Japan.
         Am             B
Ooh the eastern sea's so blue.
                  Em     C
Big in Japan alright.
         D                Bm
Pay! Then I'll sleep by your side,
              C
things are easy when you're
Am       B
big in Japan.
                      Em    C D Bm C Am B    Em C D Bm C Am B
Oh, when you're big in Japan.
```

```
     Em                C
2. Neon on my naked skin,
                 D                          B
passing silhouettes of strange illuminated mannequins.
   Em             C
Shall I stay here at the zoo
                        D                          B
or should I go and change my point of view for other ugly scenes?
```

Bridge
Refrain 2x

M: Gold, Marian / Lloyd, Bernhard / Mertens, Frank
T: Gold, Marian
© 1984 Rolf Budde Musikverlag GmbH, Berlin.

# OLD TIME ROCK AND ROLL

(BOB SEGER)

**Intro:** E B (2x)

                                E
1. Just take those old records off the shelf,
                     A
I'll sit and listen to them by my self.
                B
Todays music ain't got the same soul,
                    E
I like that old time rock and roll.

                       E
2. Don't try to take me to a disco,
                 A
you'll never even get me out on the floor.
                  B
In ten minutes I'll be late for the door,
                    E
I like that old time rock and roll.

**Refrain:**
B                  E
Still like that old time rock and roll,
                   A
that kind of music just soothes the soul.
                      B
I reminisce about the days of old
              E
with that old time rock and roll.

   B                       E
3. Won't go to hear them play a tango,
                   A
I'd rather hear some blues or funky old soul.
                    B
There's only one sure way to get me to go
              E
start playing old time rock and roll.

                      E
4. Call me a relic, call me what you will,
                A
say I'm oldfashioned say I'm over the hill.
                B
Today's music ain't got the same soul,
                  E
I like that old time rock and roll.

Refrain 2x

M + T: George Jackson / Tom Jones III
© Copyright 1983 Muscle Shoals Sound Publishing,
USA/Peermusic III Limited
Peermusic (UK) Limited
All Rights Reserved. International Copyright Secured.

## IT'S A HEARTACHE

(BONNIE TYLER)

```
        C                        Em
It's a heartache, nothing but a heartache.
              F                          C      G
Hits you when it's too late. Hits you when you're down.
        C                       Em
It's a fool's game. Nothing but a fool's game.
              F                      C      G
Standing in the cold rain, feeling like a clown.

        C                        Em
It's a heartache, nothing but a heartache.
                F                        C      G
Love him till your arms break, then he lets you down.

        F                G
It ain't right with love to share.
         Em           Am        G
When you find he doesn't care, for you.
        F                G
It ain't wise to need someone,
          Em           Am     G
as much as I depended on, on you.

        C                        Em
It's a heartache, nothing but a heartache.
              F                          C      G
Hits you when it's too late. Hits you when you're down.
        C                       Em
It's a fool's game. Nothing but a fool's game.
              F                      C      G
Standing in the cold rain, feeling like a clown.

        F                G
It ain't right with love to share.
         Em           Am        G
When you find he doesn't care, for you.
        F                G
It ain't wise to need someone,
          Em           Am     G
as much as I depended on, on you.

        C                        Em
It's a heartache, nothing but a heartache.
              F                          C      G
Hits you when it's too late. Hits you when you're down.
        C                       Em
It's a fool's game. Nothing but a fool's game.
              F                      C      G
Standing in the cold rain, feeling like a clown.
```

M + T: Ronnie Scott / Steve Wolfe
© 1977 Lojo Music Limited / Universal Music Careers. Universal Music Publishing MGB Limited.
Rechte für D/A/CH: Rolf Budde Musikverlag GmbH. International Copyright Secured.
All Rights Reserved.

# ÜBERDOSIS GFÜHL

(STS)

**Intro:** Gm D+/F# Bb/F Em7b5 Eb Dm7 F Bb

```
   Bb            D7           Eb           F             Bb
1. Manchesmal, da spür i so a Ziehen in der Brust und dann is Zeit,
                     D7                Eb
   aus heiter'm Himmel packt's mi, und dann waß i,
           F            Gm              D+/F#
   jetzt is wieder amal soweit. Da gibt's gar nix,
          Bb/F      Em7b5          Eb      F      Bb
   da brauch i net überlegen, heut muass i mir's wieder geben.

   Bb             D7           Eb          F           Bb
2. Da führt ka Weg vorbei, alles andere is vollkommen egal,
                   D7                Eb             F        Gm
   das is ma eh net neu, plötzlich bin i dann total sentimental,
       D+/F#      Bb/F            Em7b5
   und dann waß i, was i brauch und was i will,
           Eb  F   Bb
   i brauch mei Überdosis G'fühl.
   Gb                       Bb
   Dann muss i a paar alte Hadern hör'n
   Gb                         Bb
   und muss zu de paar alten Hadern plärr'n.
   Gb                        Bb
   Rinnen muss das Schmalz und i sag, Gott erhalt's,
   F          Bb/F         F7
   schenk mir no a Viertel ein und denk, was sein muss, des muss sein.

   Bb              D7            Eb            F
3. Mit "Long and Winding Road," da fang i an und bald bin i bei
         Bb             D7                 Eb
   "Let it Be", die Rührung und der Wein steigen mir in's Hirn,
                  F            Gm
   jetzt is ka Zeit mehr zu verlier'n.
    D+/F#    Bb/F           Em7b5          Eb     F      Bb
    "Angie"  und "If You Leave Me Now", gleich bin i endgültig dran.
   Gb                         Bb
   So geht's bis viertel Viere in der Fruah,
   Gb                         Bb
   bald geht die Sunn auf, i hab no net g'nua.
   Gb                        Bb
   Die Straßn menschenleer mei Kopf verraucht und schwer,
   F          Bb/F            F7
   soviel Bilder, soviel G'schichten, soviel Schmerz und soviel Herz!

   Bb             D7                        Eb
4. Jetzt is es um mi g'scheh'n, jetzt heb i ab,
                F              Bb             D7
   jetzt halt mi wirklich nix mehr auf, so is es halt im Leben,
           Eb             F              Gm
   manchmal nimmt das Schicksal gnadenlos sein' Lauf.
       D+/F#      Bb/F         Em7b5          Eb  F     Bb
   Und i lass mi eini ohne Maß und Ziel, gib mir mei Überdosis G'fühl.
   Gm   D+/F#      Bb/F         Em7b5          Eb  F     Bb
   Und i lass mi eini ohne Maß und Ziel, gib mir mei Überdosis G'fühl.
```

M + T: Gert Steinbäcker
© Copyright by Edition SCHEIBMAIER
All Rights Reserved. International Copyright Secured.

# FREUDE SCHÖNER GÖTTERFUNKEN

```
   C              G          C            G
1. Freude, schöner Götterfunken, Tochter aus Elysium.
   C          G            Am    G   C   G    C
   Wir betreten feuertrunken, Himmlische, dein Heiligtum!
   G   C       G       C          C E/G# Am   D G
   Deine Zauber binden wieder, was die Mode streng geteilt.
   C              G        Am      G  C  G      C
   Alle Menschen werden Brüder, wo dein sanfter Flügel weilt.
   G    C          G   C       G    C   E/G# Am D  G
   Seid umschlungen, Millionen! Diesen Kuss der ganzen Welt!
      C            G       Am       G   C  G     C
   |: Brüder, überm Sternenzelt muss ein lieber Vater wohnen. :|
```

**2.** Wem der große Wurf gelungen, eines Freundes Freund zu sein,
Wer ein holdes Weib errungen, mische seinen Jubel ein!
Ja, wer auch nur eine Seele sein nennt auf dem Erdenrund!
Und wer's nie gekonnt, der stehle weinend sich aus diesem Bund!
Was den großen Ring bewohnet, huldige der Sympathie.
|: Zu den Sternen leitet sie, wo der Unbekannte thronet. :|

**3.** Freude trinken alle Wesen an den Brüsten der Natur,
Alle Guten, alle Bösen folgen ihrer Rosenspur.
Küsse gab sie uns und Reben, einen Freund, geprüft im Tod,
Wollust ward dem Wurm gegeben, und der Cherub steht vor Gott.
Ihr stürzt nieder, Millionen? ahnest du den Schöpfer, Welt?
|: Such ihn überm Sternenzelt! Über Sternen muß er wohnen. :|

**4.** Freude heißt die starke Feder, in der ewigen Natur,
Freude, Freude treibt die Räder in der großen Weltenuhr.
Blumen lockt sie aus den Keimen, Sonnen aus dem Firmament,
Sphären rollt sie in den Räumen die des Sehers Rohr nicht kennt.
Froh wie seine Sonnen fliegen durch des Himmels prächtigen Plan,
|: Wandelt Brüder, eure Bahn, freudig wie ein Held zum Siegen! :|

**5.** Aus der Wahrheit Feuerspiegel lächelt sie den Forscher an.
Zu der Tugend steilem Hügel leitet sie des Dulders Bahn.
Auf des Glaubens Sonnenberge sieht man ihre Fahnen wehn,
Durch den Riß gesprengter Särge sie im Chor der Engel stehn.
Duldet mutig, Millionen! Duldet fur die beßre Welt!
|: Droben überm Sternenzelt wird ein großer Gott belohnen. :|

**6.** Festen Mut in schweren Leiden, Hilfe, wo die Unschuld weint,
Ewigkeit geschwornen Eiden, Wahrheit gegen Freund und Feind,
Männerstolz vor Königsthronen - Brüder, gält' es Gut und Blut:
Dem Verdienste seine Kronen, Untergang der Lügenbrut!
Schließt den heilgen Zirkel dichter! Schwört bei diesem goldnem Wein,
|: Dem Gelübde treu zu sein, schwört es bei dem Sternenrichter! :|

M: Ludwig van Beethoven
T: Friedrich Schiller
© 2005 by Edition DUX, Manching

# JAWOHL, MEINE HERR'N

(HEINZ RÜHMANN, HANS ALBERS)

```
   Eb         Fm7   Bb7   Fm7      Bb7   Eb
1. Wer hinter'm Ofen sitzt und die Zeit wenig nützt,
Bb7         Eb     F7                Bb7    Fm7 Bb7
schont zwar seine Kraft, aber wird auch nichts erreichen.
Eb        Fm7   Bb7    Fm7      Bb7 Eb
Wer aber nicht lang fragt und geht los unverzagt,
F7               Bb          F7           Bb7 Fm7  Bb7
für den gibt's kein Fragezeichen und dergleichen bis er's schafft.
```

**Refrain:**
```
G+ Ab                Eb° Eb       Ebmaj7
Jawohl, meine Herr'n, so hab'n wir es gern,
Eb  A°  Bb7              Fm7    Bb7 Eb
nur mit Mut kommt man gut durch die Welt.
G+ Ab                Eb° Eb         C7      Fm7       Bb7   Eb   Ab
Jawohl, meine Herr'n, dann hat man dich gern und tut, was dir gefällt.
Eb        G7              C7
Doch hat die Welt dich einmal schwach geseh'n,
F7            Fm7  Abm Bb7
ist es auch um dich gescheh'n.
G+ Ab                Eb° Eb            C7
Jawohl, meine Herr'n, darauf könn'n sie schwör'n,
  Fm7    Bb7    Eb     Bb7
jawohl, jawohl, jawohl!
```

2. Wenn heiß die Sonne brennt runter vom Firmament, wünscht sich jeder Mann, so zu gehen, wie einst Herr Adam. Schlips, Kragen, Anzug, Hut, weg damit bei der Glut. Und man sitzt bei Schulz und Co im Badehöschen im Büro. Jawohl, meine Herr'n, so hab'n wir es gern, denn die Glut tut nicht gut und macht matt. Jawohl, meine Herr'n, so hab'n wir es gern, drum her ein Feigenblatt. Doch vorteilhafter wär's für manchen Mann, er behielt den Anzug an. Jawohl, meine Herr'n, darauf könn'n sie schwörn, jawohl, jawohl, jawohl!

3. Schlägt dich ein Weib in Bann, schmachte sie nicht lang an, steh nicht sehnsuchtsvoll nachts vor'm Haustor deiner Schönen. Schick ihr 'nen Rosenstrauß, lad sie ein, fahrt mal raus. Wenn's dann dunkelt, sei verwegen, denn dagegen hat sie nichts. Jawohl, meine Herr'n; so hab'n sie es gern, ihr wird warm, wenn im Arm sie dich hält. Jawohl, meine Herr'n, so hab'n sie es gern, weil das den Frau'n gefällt. Denn bist du schüchtern, macht sie sich nichts draus und geht mit nem andern aus. Jawohl, meine Herr'n, darauf könn'n sie schwör'n, jawohl, jawohl, jawohl!

4. Wenn du ein Eh'mann bist und auch gern andre küsst, und kommst spät nach Haus, macht dein Frauchen meist'ne Scene. Viel netter wäre sie, fragte sie in der Früh: Wer hat dich denn perfümiert und hast du dich auch amüsiert? Jawohl, meine Herr'n, so hätt'n wir es gern, dass sie nie mehr ein Wort dürber spricht. Jawohl, meine Herr'n, so hätt'n wir es gern, doch solche Frau gibt's nicht. Sie schreit dich an, dass jede Scheibe klirrt und dir grün vor Augen wird. Jawohl, meine Herr'n, darauf könn'n sie schwör'n, jawohl, jawohl, jawohl!

M: Hans Sommer
T: Richard Busch
© Dreiklang- Dreimasken Bühnen- Musikverlag GmbH

# BALLROOM BLITZ

(SWEET)

Are you ready, Steve? Uh huh. Andy? Yeah. Mick? Okay.
Alright fellas, let's go!
**Intro:** E
```
A                                                    E
Ah it's been getting so hard living with the things you do to me, uh huh
   A
Why things are getting so strange?
                                         E
I'd like to tell you everything I see, mmm.


             E
Oh, I see a man at the back as a matter of fact,
his eyes are as red as the sun.
And the girl in the corner that no one ignored,
she thinks she's the passionate one.

                    F#m                        A
```
**1.** Oh yeah, it was like lightning, everybody was frightening
```
                    C                          E
cause the music was soothing and they all started grooving.
Yeah. Yeah. Yeah. Yeah. Yeah.
```

**Refrain:**
```
      F#m                      A
And the man at the back said "everyone attack"
      B                  E
and they turned into a ballroom blitz.
      F#m                        A
And the girl in the corner said "boy I wanna warn you,"
      B               E         D D#   E
it'll turn into a ballroom blitz, ballroom blitz.
D  D#   E      D  D#   E     D  D#   E
Ballroom blitz, ballroom blitz, ballroom blitz.
```

Ah, ah, ah, reaching out for something, touching nothing's all I ever do
Oh, I softly call you over
and you appear there's nothing left of you, uh huh.

And the man at the back ready to crack
as he raises his hands to the sky.
And the girl in the corner is everyone's morning,
she could kill you with the wink of her eye.

**2.** Oh yeah, it was electric, suprisingly hectic
and the band started leaving, cause they all stopped breathing.
Yeah. Yeah. Yeah. Yeah. Yeah.

Refrain
1. Strophe
Refrain

It's, it's a ballroom blitz. It's, it's a ballroom blitz.
It's, it's a ballroom blitz. It's, it's a ballroom blitz.

M + T: Nicky Chinn / Mike Chapman
© Copyright 1973 Chinnichap Publishing Incorporated, USA.
Universal Music Publishing MGB Limited.
All Rights Reserved. International Copyright Secured.

# GO DOWN MOSES

```
            Dm      A7      Dm      Gm7    A              Dm
1. When Israel was in Egypt's Land; let my people go.
   Dm          A7          Dm      Gm7    A              Dm
Opressed so hard they could not stand; let my people go.
```

**Refrain:**
```
Dm        Gm        Dm   A7        Dm
Go down, Moses, way down in Egypt's Land.
Bb        Dm        A7              Dm
Tell old Pharoah, let my people go.
```

2. Thus said the Lord, bold Moses said; let my people go.
If not, I'll smite your first-born dead; let my people go.

Refrain

3. No more shall they in bondage toil; let my people go.
Let them come out with Egypt's spoil; let my people go.

Refrain

4. The Lord told Moses what to do; let my people go.
To lead the Hebrew children through; let my people go.

Refrain

5. O come along Moses, you'll not get lost; let my people go.
Stretch out your rod and come across; let my people go.

Refrain

6. As Israel stood by the waterside; let my people go.
At God's command it did divide; let my people go.

Refrain

7. When they reached the other shore; let my people go.
They sang a song of triumph o'er; let my people go.

Refrain

Traditionell
© 2005 by Edition DUX, Manching

# WEISSE ROSEN AUS ATHEN

(NANA MOUSKOURI)

**Refrain:**
```
E                  B7                A    E/G# F#m E
Weiße Rosen aus Athen sagen dir: "Komm recht bald wieder,"
E                B7                    E
sagen dir: "Auf Wiedersehn," weiße Rosen aus Athen.
```

```
   E
1. Der Tag erwacht, die Sonne, sie kommt wieder
            B7                         E
   und wieder kommt nun auch der Abschied für uns zwei.

   Nun fährt dein Schiff hinaus mit Wind und Wogen,
            B7                       E
   doch es sind Grüße aus der Heimat mit dabei.
```

Refrain

```
E                 B7                 A    E/G# F#m E
Weiße Rosen blüh'n an Bord in der weiten, weiten Ferne,
E                        B7             E
blüh'n für dich allein so schön, weiße Rosen aus Athen.
```

```
   E
2. Im fernen Land, wo keiner auf dich wartet,
               B7                       E
   da seh'n die Sterne in der Nacht ganz anders aus.

   Dort ist die Welt so fremd und du bist einsam,
           B7                          E
   darum begleiten dich heut' Blumen von Zuhaus.
```

Refrain
```
E    B7   E       B7    E      B7    E
Auf Wiedersehn. Auf Wiedersehn. Auf Wiedersehn.
```

M + T: MANOS HADJIDAKIS / HANS BRADKE
© 1957 by Edition Ed Kassner Musikverlag.

# ER HAT EIN KNALLROTES GUMMIBOOT

(WENCKE MYRHE)

**Refrain:**
```
      G          D7
Er hat ein knallrotes Gummiboot,
                       G
mit diesem Gummiboot fahrn wir hinaus.
            D7
Er hat ein knallrotes Gummiboot
                       G    Em Am D G
und erst im Abendrot kommen wir nach Haus.
```

```
   G
1. Johnny der fühlt sich wie Christoph Columbus
D7
und hat sogar einen Bart.

Vor den Gefahren der christlichen Seefahrt
G
warnt er mich vor jeder Fahrt:
    C             G          D            G
"Das Küssen an Bord ist verboten, ich sage dir auch warum.
A           D                 A           D
Das Boot ist eine Konstruktion, die kippt beim Küssen um!"
```
Refrain

```
    C              G           D              G
Wir haben kein Segel und keinen Motor und keine Kombüse, o nein!
    C             G              A          D
Wir schaukeln mit Liebe und sehr viel Humor ins große Glück hinein.
```

Refrain

```
   G
2. Johnny ist mutig und stolz wie Lord Nelson,
D7
auch noch bei Windstärke drei.
                                        G
Brausen die Stürme und plätschert der Regen, ruft er verwegen: Ahoi!
    C              G           D                G
Und sollte die Luft uns entweichen, ja das nimmt er gerne in Kauf.
A              D         A            D
Die Fahrradpumpe ist im Boot, und er, er pumpt es auf!
```

Refrain 2x

M: Schmidt, Bobby
T: Bradtke, Hans
© Edition Primus Rolf Budde KG / Hanseatic Musikverlag GmbH & Co. KG.
With courtesy of Budde Music, Berlin.

# STRANGERS IN THE NIGHT

(FRANK SINATRA)
[TRANSP. -2]

```
     G
1. Strangers in the night, exchanging glances,

wond'ring in the night, what were the chances,
                         Bm      A#°      Am7
we'd be sharing love, before the night was through.

Something in your eyes was so inviting,

something in your smile was so exciting,
D                                        G
something in my heart told me I must have you.

Dm/B
Strangers in the night, two lonely people,
       E7
we were strangers in the night, up to the moment
        Am                    Cm/A
when we said our first "Hello", little did we know,
G/D          Em7            Am7              D7
love was just a glance away, a warm embracing dance away.

        G
2. And ever since that night we've been together,

lovers at first sight, in love forever,
Am7             D7                G
it turned out so right, for strangers in the night.

Solo: Dm/B E7 Am Cm/A

G/D          Em7            Am7              D7
Love was just a glance away, a warm embracing dance away.

     A
And ever since that night we've been together,

lovers at first sight, in love forever,
  Bm7            E7                A
it turned out so right, for strangers in the night.
```

M: Bert Kaempfert
T: Charles Singleton & Eddie Snyder
© Copyright 1966 Screen Gems-EMI Music Limited/Songs Of Universal Inc.
Universal/MCA Music Limited.
All Rights Reserved. International Copyright Secured.

# A HARD RAIN'S GONNA FALL

(BOB DYLAN)

```
      E                    Esus4    E  Esus4 E
1. Oh, where have you been, my blue-eyed son?
      E                              B7
Oh, where have you been, my darling young one?
      A              B7             E
I've stumbled on the side of twelve misty mountains,
      A              B7           E
I've walked and I've crawled on six crooked highways,
      A             B7           E
I've stepped in the middle of seven sad forests,
      A              B7          E
I've been out in front of a dozen dead oceans,
      A                 B7              E
I've been ten thousand miles in the mouth of a graveyard.
```

**Refrain:**
```
              E           B7         E            A
And it's a hard, and it's a hard, it's a hard, and it's a hard,
         E       B7      E   Esus4 E
and it's a hard rain's a-gonna fall.


      E                    Esus4    E  Esus4 E
2. Oh what did you see, my blue-eyed son?
      E                              B7
And what did you see, my darling young one?
           A           B7             E
I saw a new born baby with wild wolves all around it,
           A              B7          E
I saw a highway of diamonds with nobody on it,
           A              B7          E
I saw a black branch with blood that kept dripping,
           A              B7          E
I saw a room full of men with their hammers a-bleeding,
           A              B7          E
I saw a white ladder all covered with water,
           A              B7          E
I saw ten thousand talkers whose tongues were all broken,
           A              B7          E
I saw guns and sharp swords in the hands of young children.
```

Refrain

```
      E                    Esus4    E  Esus4 E
3. And what did you hear, my blue-eyed son?
      E                              B7
And what did you hear, my darling young one?
           A              B7             E
I heard the sound of a thunder that roared out a warning,
           A              B7             E
I heard the roar of a wave that could drown the whole world,
           A              B7          E
I heard one hundred drummers whose hands were a-blazing,
           A              B7          E
I heard ten thousand whispering and nobody listening,


           A                       B7            E
I heard one person starve, I heard many people laughing,
```

```
            A                B7              E
I heard the song of a poet who died in the gutter,
            A              B7          E
I heard the sound of a clown who cried in the alley.
```

Refrain

```
       E                     Esus4     E    Esus4 E
4. Oh who did you meet, my blue-eyed son?
       E                                B7
And who did you meet, my darling young one?
     A                B7          E
I met a young child beside a dead pony,
     A              B7              E
I met a white man who walked a black dog,
     A                  B7            E
I met a young woman whose body was burning,
     A               B7          E
I met a young girl, she gave me a rainbow,
     A              B7              E
I met one man who was wounded in love,
     A                  B7             E
I met another man who was wounded in hatred.
```

Refrain

```
       E                     Esus4     E    Esus4 E
5. And what'll you do now, my blue-eyed son?
       E                           B7
And what'll you do now, my darling young one?
         A                   B7             E
I'm a going back out before the rain starts a-falling,
            A              B7             E
I'll walk to the depth of the deepest dark forest
            A                   B7            E
where the people are many and their hands are all empty,
            A                  B7              E
where the pellets of poison are flooding their waters,
            A               B7            E
where the home in the valley meets the damp dirty prison
                    A             B7         E
and the executioner's face is always well hidden,
              A              B7             E
where hunger is ugly, where the souls are forgotten,
            A              B7            E
where black is the colour, where none is the number.
           A                  B7           E
And I'll tell it and speak it and think it and breathe it
            A                  B7             E
and reflect from the mountain so all souls can see it.
              A              B7             E
Then I'll stand on the ocean until I start sinking
            A              B7              E
but I'll know my song well before I start singing:
```

Refrain

M + T: Bob Dylan
© Copyright 1963 Warner Brothers Incorporated.
© Copyright Renewed 1991 Special Rider Music, USA.
All Rights Reserved. International Copyright Secured.

## I'D LOVE YOU TO WANT ME

(LOBO)
[TRANSP. +1]

```
   A                                            Bm
1. When I saw you standing there I about fell off my chair.
                   D      E                         A
When you moved your mouth to speak I felt the blood go to my feet.

   A                                             Bm
2. Now it took time for me to know what you tried so not to show.
                   D        E                       A
Something in my soul just cried, I see the want in your blue eyes.
```

**Refrain:**
```
A                   Bm
Baby, I'd love you to want me.
          D                     A
The way that I want you, the way that it should be.
A                   Bm
Baby, you'd love me to want you.
          D           E         A
The way that I want to if you'd only let it be.
```

```
   A                                                    Bm
3. You told yourself years ago you'd never let your feelings show.
                    D     E                       A
The obligation that you made for the title that they gave.
```

Refrain

```
   A                                             Bm
4. Now it took time for me to know what you tried so not to show.
                   D        E                      A
Something in my soul just cried I see the want in your blue eyes.
```

Refrain 2x

M + T: Kent Lavoie
© Copyright 1972 Famous Music Publishing Limited.
All Rights Reserved. International Copyright Secured.

# YOU'RE THE DEVIL IN DISGUISE

(ELVIS PRESLEY)

**Intro:** Bb C F C

**Refrain:**
```
       F
You look like an angel, walk like an angel,
Bb                        C7
talk like an angel but I got wise.
                    F                      Dm
You're the devil in disguise, oh yes, you are,
           F       Dm
devil in disguise.
```

```
      F                         Dm
1. You fooled me with your kisses, you cheated and you schemed.
   F              Dm             Bb      C7        F
   Heaven knows how you lied to me, you're not the way you seemed.
```

Refrain

```
      F                          Dm
2. I thought that I was in heaven but I was sure surprised.
   F            Dm            Bb      C7      F
   Heaven help me I didn't see the devil in your eyes.
```

Refrain

```
                     F                   Dm
You're the devil in disguise, oh yes, you are.
                 F          Dm
Devil in disguise, oh yes, you are.
                 F          Dm
Devil in disguise, oh yes, you are.
                 F          Dm
Devil in disguise, oh yes, you are.
```

M + T: Bill Giant, Bernie Baum & Florence Kaye
© Copyright 1963 Elvis Presley Music, USA.
Carlin Music Corporation.
All Rights Reserved. International Copyright Secured.

# WHENEVER, WHEREVER

(SHAKIRA)

**Intro:** C#m C#m F#m B    C#m C#m F#m B
```
       C#m                                     G#7
1. Lucky you were born that far away so, so we could both make fun of
distance.
A                             E                              B
Lucky that I love a foreign land for the lucky fact of your existence.
C#m                                   G#7
Baby, I would climb the Andes solely to count the freckles on your body.
A                                 E                           B
Never could imagine there were only ten million ways to love somebody.
```

**Refrain:**
```
F#m                   C#m                A             B
Lero lo le lo le. Lero lo le lo le. Can't you see? I'm at your feet.
C#m      A          E              B
Whenever, wherever we'll learn to be together
C#m               A           F#m                    B
I'll be there and you'll be near and that's the deal, my dear.
C#m           A          E            B
Thereover, hereunder you'll never have to wonder,
C#m             A          F#m                  B
we can always play by ear but that's the deal, my dear.

C#m C#m F#m B    C#m C#m F#m B  C#m


      C#m                                       G#7
2. Lucky that my lips not only mumble, they spill kisses like a fountain
A
Lucky that my breasts are small and humble,
E                          B
so you don't confuse them with mountains.
C#m                                    G#7
Lucky I have strong legs like my mother to run for cover when I need it
A                                 E                         B
and these two eyes are for no other, the day you leave we'll cry a
river.
```

Refrain
C#m C#m F#m B    C#m C#m F#m B

```
F#m                   C#m                A              B
Lero lo le lo le. Lero lo le lo le. Sink or fly, say it again.
F#m                   C#m
Lero lo le lo le lo le. Tell me one more time
A             B                  C#m
that you'll live lost in my eyes.

C#m      A          E              B
Whenever, wherever we'll learn to be together
C#m               A           F#m                    B
I'll be there and you'll be near and that's the deal, my dear.
C#m           A          E            B
Thereover, hereunder you'll never have to wonder,
C#m             A          F#m                  B
we can always play by ear but that's the deal, my dear.
```

M: Shakira & Tim Mitchell T: Shakira & Gloria Estefan
© 2002 Foreign Imported Production & Publishing, Aniwi Music Llc./ Universal Music Publishing GmbH, Aniwi Music Llc.
All rights in Germany administered by Universal/MCA Music Publ. GmbH)/Sony/ATV Music Publishing
All Rights Reserved. International Copyright Secured

# BEDS ARE BURNING

(MIDNIGHT OIL)

**Intro:** E G A

E
Out where the river broke.

The bloodwood and the desert oak.

Holden wrecks and boiling diesels.

Steam in forty five degrees.

E
The time has come.
   D/E
To say fair's fair.
   A/E
To pay the rent.
   E
To pay our share.

E
The time has come.
  D/E
A fact's a fact.
   A/E
It belongs to them.
      F#        E G A
Let's give it back.

**Refrain:**
Em                      C                G
How can we dance when our earth is turning.
Em                      C                D
How do we sleep while our beds are burning.
Em                      C                G
How can we dance when our earth is turning.
Em                      C                D
How do we sleep while our beds are burning.

**Refrain 2:**
    Em              C
The time has come to say fair's fair.
   G              D              E
to pay the rent, now to pay our share.
E
Four wheels scare the cockatoos.
From Kintore East to Yuendemu.
The western desert lives and breathes.
In forty five degrees.

Refrain
Refrain 2
Refrain

            M + T: Peter Garrett, Robert Hirst & James Moginie
            © Copyright 1988 Sprint Music.
            Sony/ATV Music Publishing(UK) Limited.
            All Rights Reserved. International Copyright Secured.

# THIS IS WHERE I CAME IN

(BEE GEES)

```
    Em              Am          C                   Em
1. I've seen the story I've read it over once or twice.
Em              Am          C              Em
I said that you say a little bit of bad advice.
Em           Am         C                      Em
I've been in trouble happened to me all of my life.
Em            Am          C                           Em
I've lied and you lie and who would get the sharpest knife.
                      Em                Am
You know I couldn't be somebody like that.
                                        Em
I'm not the kind of man to throw his hat into the ring
                 Am                     C                 Em
and go down without following through the day turns into night.
         Am                   C             Em
Go down following through the day turns into night.

Em A   Em A    Em A    C
Oohhh, oohhh, oohhh, this is just where I came in.
G    D/F# Em                Am
Hope rides on, but I'll go anywhere, yes, I'll go anywhere with you.
G    D/F# Em                Am
Time has gone, but I'll go anywhere, yes, I'll go anywhere with you.
```

**Refrain:**
```
Em           C            G             Am
This is the danger zone. This is where I came in.
Em           C              G           Am
They know not what they do. Forgive them all their sins.
Em          C              G          Am
They cannot take away what you have given me.
Em A   Em A    Em A    C
Oohhh, oohhh, oohhh, this is just where I came in.
```

2. Fade into color, color into black and white.
Under the bedclothes everything will be alright.
I know that you know nothing ever stays the same.
Said so, I said so the love will never speak its name.
Never gonna find somebody like you: Beauty with a brain and a body too.
I could never make a move on a woman that leads me on.
She's got a little bit of something for everyone.
It's a little too late and the wolf is on the run.

Hope rides on, but I'll go anywhere, yes, I'll go anywhere with you.
Time has gone, but I'll go anywhere, yes, I'll go anywhere with you.

I always told myself I would regret this day,
that I would fall apart and watch you walk away,
that you would cry out loud and I would stand aside.

Oohhh, oohhh, oohhh, this is just where I came in.
Oohhh, oohhh, oohhh, this is just where I came in.
I can't lie, but I'll go anywhere, yes, I'll go anywhere with you.
Time has gone, but I'll go anywhere, yes, I'll go anywhere with you.

Refrain   M + T: Maurice Gibb * / Robin Gibb * / Barry Alan Gibb
© Crompton Songs / Universal Music Publishing International MGB Limited. Warner/Chappell Music Limited, London / Universal Music Publishing MGB Limited. Reproduced by permission of Faber Music Limited. All Rights Reserved. International Copyright Secured.

## I GUESS THAT'S WHY THEY CALL IT THE BLUES
(ELTON JOHN)

**Intro:** C G/B F   C G/B F
```
     G
1. Don't wish it away.
       Em7          F        C      F C F C F
Don't look at it like it's forever
     C           G
between you and me.
              Bm7        F                    C      F C F C F
I could honestly say that things can only get better
     C       G      B7               Em
and while I'm away bust out the demons inside.
Dm         C                          G
And it won't be long before you and me run
                 Am      F       G    G7
to the place in our hearts where we hide.
```

**Refrain:**
```
        C                    G/B           F
And I guess that's why they call it the blues.
           C              G               F
Time on my hands could be time spent with you.
C              G              Am
Laughing like children, living like lovers,
C/E       F                D/F#
rolling like thunder under the covers
       F                  G          C     Em7 F
and I guess that's why they call it the blues.


     G
2. Just stare into space.
Em7           F        C      F C F C F
Picture my face in your hands.
C              G
Live for each second
          Bm7       F                       C    F C F C F
without hesitation, never forget I'm your man.
C          G      B7                   Em
Wait on me girl, cry in the night if it helps
Dm          C                     G
but more than ever I simply love you.
          Am      F       G    G7
More than I love life itself.
```

Refrain

```
     G
3. Solo: G Em7 F C F C F C F   C G Bm7 F C F C F C F

C          G      B7                   Em   G/D
Wait on me girl, cry in the night if it helps
            C                     G
but more than ever I simply love you.
          Am      F       G    G7
More than I love life itself.
```

Refrain

M + T: Elton John; Davey Johnstone & Bernie Taupin
© Copyright 1983 Big Pig Music Limited/Rouge Booze Incorporated/HST Publishing Limited. Universal Music Publishing Limited.
All Rights Reserved. International Copyright Secured.

# OHNE DICH (SCHLAF ICH HEUT NACHT NICHT EIN)

(MÜNCHENER FREIHEIT)
[TRANSP. +1]

**Intro:** D Bm G  D

```
     D
1. Ich will mich nicht verändern, um dir zu imponieren,
Bm
nicht den ganzen Abend Probleme diskutieren,
     G                               D
aber eines geb ich zu: Das was ich will bist du.
     D
Ich will nicht's garantieren, was ich nicht halten kann,
       Bm
will mit dir was erleben, besser gleich als irgendwann.
       G                               D
Und ich gebe offen zu, das was ich will bist du.
```

**Refrain:**
```
     D               Bm                F#m
Ohne dich schlaf ich heut nacht nicht ein.
                                G
Ohne dich fahr ich heut nacht nicht heim.
          Bm/F#           Em
Ohne dich komm ich heut nicht zur Ruh.
         A         D
Das was ich will bist du.
              Bm                F#m
Ohne dich schlafe ich heut nacht nicht ein.
                                G
Ohne dich fahr ich heut nacht nicht heim.
          Bm/F#           Em
Ohne dich komme ich heut nicht zur Ruh.
         A         D
Das was ich will bist du.
```

```
        D
2. Ich will nicht alles sagen, nicht soviel erklären,
Bm
nicht mit soviel Worten den Augenblick zerstören,
     G                               D
aber eines geb ich zu: Das was ich will bist du.
     D
Ich will auch nichts erzählen, was dich eh nicht interessiert,
       Bm
will mit dir was erleben, was uns beide fasziniert
       G                               D
und ich gebe offen zu, das was ich will bist du.
```

Refrain 2x

M: Stefan Zauner, Aron Strobel
T: Stefan Zauner, Aron Strobel, Michael Kunze
© Mambo Musik Verlags- und Prod. GmbH / Edition Metro-Pool.
Mit freundlicher Genehmigung von SMPG Publishing (Germany) GmbH.

# COSE DELLA VITA – CAN'T STOP THINKING OF YOU
(EROS RAMAZZOTTI & TINA TURNER)

Intro: F#m D F#m D F#m D F#m D

```
F#m     D          A        E  F#m D           A       E
Sono umane situazioni   quei momenti fra di noi
F#m     D          A        E  F#m D           A       E
I distacchi e i ritorni   da capirci niente poi
Bm   A       E      Bm      A         E  F#m D A E           F#m D A E
Giá come vedi? Sto pensando a te.       Si. Da un po'
F#m              D          A         E  F#m      D              A        E
They're just human contradictions   feeling happy, feeling sad.
F#m         D            A        E  F#m       D              A        E
These emotional transitions,   all the memories we've had.
Bm    A             E         Bm           A            E
Yes, you know it's true, I just can't stop thinking of you!
  A                       C#m7                          Bm
No I just can't pretend all the time that we spent could die,
     F#m
wanna feel it again all the love we felt then.
   A                  C#m7           Bm
Confinanti di cuore solo che ognuno sta
    F#m             C#m         Bm
Dietro gli steccati degli orgogli suoi
         F#m D A E             F#m D A E
Sto pensando a te.    Sto pensando a noi.

G#m    E       B    F# G#m    E           B F#
Sono cose della vita   vanno prese un pó cosí
G#m          E             B    F# G#m               E             B F#
Some for worse and some for better but through it all we've come so far.
C#m  B    F#    C#m         B        F#
Giá come vedi? Io sto ancora in piedi.
     G#m                             E
Perché sono umani questi sogni miei
B                        F#
con le mani io li prenderei, si perché
G#m                              E   B                        F#
What is life without a dream to hold? Take my hand and never let me go.
Am    F           C    G Am        F           C     G
It's part of life together  but what future does it hold?
Am    F          C     G Am        F           C  G
Sono cose della vita  ma la vita poi dov'é
Dm   C              G    Dm             C            G
Yes, you know it's true, I just can't stop thinking of you!
    C                   Em7               Dm
Questa notte che passa piano accanto a me
         Am
cerco di affrontarla, afferrarla
        C                  Em7                    Dm
If our hearts miss a beat or get lost like a ship at sea
        Am              Em            Dm
I want to remember, I can never forget.
                  Am F C G          Am F C G
Can't stop thinking of you   Sto pensando a noi
                  Am
Can't stop thinking of you.
```

M + T: Pierangelo Cassano / Eros Ramazzotti / Adelio Cogliati
© Unalira Ed. Musicali (administered by Warner Chappell Music Italiana) /
Emi Music Publishing (Sony Atv).

# WHAT'S LOVE GOT TO DO WITH IT

(TINA TURNER)
[TRANSP. -1]

```
       Am                                            G/A
1. You must understand that the touch of your hand makes my pulse react.
         Am                              G/A
That it's only that thrill of boy meeting girl: Opposites attract.
     Fmaj7 G         Fmaj7 G
It's physical, only logical.
          Fmaj7                  G
You must try to ignore that it means more than that.
```

**Refrain:**
```
      C         G          Fmaj7       G
Oh oh, what's love got to do, got to do with it?
C       G         Fmaj7            G
What's love but a second hand emotion?
C       G            Fmaj7        G
What's love got to do, got to do with it?
C           G            Fmaj7         G
Who needs a heart when a heart can be broken?
```

```
2. It may seem to you that I'm acting confused when you're close to me.
If I tend to look dazed I've read it someplace I've got cause to be.
There's a name for it, there's a phrase that fits.
But whatever the reason, you do it for me.
```

Refrain

```
C/D              D            C/D              D
I've been taking on a new direction but I have to say.
Bb                 C/Bb
I've been thinking about my own protection,
    Am7              D
it scares me to feel this way.
```

Refrain (ein Ton höher)

```
Oh oh, what's love got to do, got to do with it?
What's love but a sweet old fashioned notion?
What's love got to do, got to do with it?
Who needs a heart when a heart can be broken?
```

Refrain

M + T: Terry Britten and Graham Lyle
© 1984 Goodsingle Limited. Rechte für Deutschland, Österreich, Schweiz und Osteuropa: TJ MUSICSERVICE GMBH, W B Music Corp, Warner/ Chappell North America Ltd, London.
Reproduced by permission of Faber Music Limited. All Rights Reserved.

# BROWN GIRL IN THE RING

(BONEY M.)

```
G
Brown girl in the ring, sha la la la la,
         D7
there's a brown girl in the ring, sha la la la la la.
G
Brown girl in the ring, sha la la la la,
                       D7           G
she looks like a sugar in the plum, plum, plum.

G
Show me a motion, sha la la la la,
         D7
come on, show me a motion, sha la la la la,
G
show me a motion, sha la la la la,
                  D7          G
she looks like a sugar in a plum, plum, plum.

G            D7                       G
Old head water run dry, nowhere to wash my clothes.
G            D7                           G
Old head water run dry, got nowhere to wash my clothes.
     G            D7                              G
I remember one saturday night, we had fried fish and Johnny cakes.
     G            D7                              G
I remember one saturday night, we had fried fish and Johnny cakes,
      D7 G          D7
dang-adang, dang-a-dang.
```

M + T: DP / Franz Reuther
© Far Musikverlag GmbH.
Mit freundlicher Genehmigung von Far Musikverlag GmbH & Co. KG.

# SUZANNE

(LEONARD COHEN)

```
     E
1. Suzanne takes you down to her place near the river.
         F#m
You can hear the boats go by, you can spend the night beside her.
         E
And you know that she's half crazy but that's why you want to be there.
     G#m                                  A
And she feeds you tea and oranges that come all the way from China.
              E                              F#m
And just when you mean to tell her that you have no love to give her
         E                              F#m
then she gets you on her wavelength and she lets the river answer
              E
that you've always been her lover.

             G#m                        A
And you want to travel with her and you want to travel blind
        E
and you know that she will trust you
         F#m                                    E
for you've touched her perfect body with your mind.
```

2. And Jesus was a sailor when he walked upon the water
and he spent a long time watching from his lonely wooden tower
and when he knew for certain only drowning men could see him.
He said "All men will be sailors then until the sea shall free them."
But he himself was broken long before the sky would open.
Forsaken, almost human he sank beneath your wisdom like a stone.

And you want to travel with him and you want to travel blind
and you think maybe you'll trust him
for he's touched your perfect body with his mind.

3. Now Suzanne takes your hand and she leads you to the river.
She is wearing rags and feathers from Salvation Army counters.
And the sun pours down like honey on our lady of the harbour.
And she shows you where to look among the garbage and the flowers.
There are heroes in the seaweed there are children in the morning.
They are leaning out for love and they will lean that way forever
while Suzanne holds the mirror.

And you want to travel with her and you want to travel blind
and you know that you can trust her
for she's touched your perfect body with her mind.

M + T: Leonard Cohen
© Copyright 1966 Stranger Music Inc. Sony/ATV Music Publishing (UK) Limited.
All Rights Reserved. International Copyright Secured.

# SCHOOL'S OUT

(ALICE COOPER)

**Intro:** Em A Em G Em A G (6x)

```
              Em   A Em G Em A G
1. Well, we got no choice,
       Em     A Em G Em A G
all the girls and boys
         Em  A Em G Em A G
makin' all that noise
              Em    A Em G Em A G
cause they found new toys.

         C
Oh, we can't salute ya, can't find a flag.
D   Eb
If that don't suit ya, that's a drag.
```

**Refrain:**
```
Gm          Bb   C    F Gm
School's out for summer.
Gm          Bb   C    F Gm
School's out forever.
Gm              Bb     C   F  Gm  A F
School's been blown to pieces.
C
No more pencils, no more books.
D
No more teacher's dirty looks.
```

Intro 4x

2. Well, we got no class
and we got no principles
and we got no innocence.
We can't even think of a word that rhymes.

Refrain

```
C
Out for summer, out till fall.
D
We might not come back at all.

Gm          Bb   C   F Gm
School's out forever.
Gm          Bb   C    F Gm
School's out for summer.
Gm          Bb   C    F Gm
School's out with fever.
Gm          F        C
School's out completely.
```

M + T: Alice Cooper, Michael Bruce, Dennis Dunaway, Neal Smith & Glen Buxton
© Copyright 1972 Bizarre Music Incorporated & Ezra Music Corporation/Bizarre Music Incorporated, USA.
Carlin Music Corporation.
All Rights Reserved. International Copyright Secured.

# MÄDCHEN

(LUCILECTRIC)

**Intro:** E A B E E A B E

```
        E                        A
1. Was 'n das für'n wundervoller Hintern,
       B                E
der da nebenan am Tresen steht?
          E                     A
Und der Typ, der da am Hintern noch mit dran ist,
       B              E
hat sich grade zu mir umgedreht.
     A            B            A              B
Und ich lach ihm zu, oh prima, den nehm ich nach Hause mit.
        A              B
Und dann lehn ich mich zurück und lass dem Mann den ersten Schritt.
                         E         A       B         E
Mir geht's so gut, weil ich 'n Mädchen bin, weil ich 'n Mädchen bin.
```

**Refrain:**
```
              E                          A
Komm doch mal rüber, Mann, und setz dich zu mir hin,
       B                      E
Weil ich 'n Mädchen bin, weil ich 'n Mädchen bin.
         E                          A
Keine Widerrede, Mann, weil ich ja sowieso gewinn,
       B         E
weil ich 'n Mädchen bin.
```

Intro

2. Und der Hintern kauft mir viele schöne Sachen
und dann lädt er mich zum Essen ein.
Klar lass ich mich auch ganz ohne Kohle küssen,
doch wenn er meint, das muss so sein, sag ich nicht nein.

Ich bin so froh, dass ich ein Mädchen bin, dass ich ein Mädchen bin.
Refrain 2x

3. Und nach'm Essen gehn wir Kaffee bei ihm trinken
und der Schweiß, der steht ihm im Gesicht.
Ob der Größte, der's am längsten kann von allen,
heute nacht auch wirklich hält, was er verspricht?

Ich bin so froh, dass ich ein Mädchen bin, dass ich ein Mädchen bin.
Refrain 2x

Mir geht's so gut, weil ich 'n Mädchen bin, weil ich 'n Mädchen bin.

Refrain

Intro

Refrain 2x

M: Ralf Goldkind
T: Lucie van Org
© SMPG Publishing (Germany) GmbH.
Mit freundlicher Genehmigung von SMPG Publishing (Germany) GmbH.

# DAVE DUDLEY

(TRUCK STOP)

**Intro:** A D E A D E A

```
       A                               Bm
1. Es ist schon bald nach Mitternacht, mein Tag ist längst vorbei.
         D                 E                  A
   Mir fallen gleich die Augen zu, verdammte Fahrerei.
      A                            Bm
   Der NDR bringt Tanzmusik, ich krieg nichts andres rein.
        D                      E
   Das geht so durch bis sechs Uhr früh,
                          A
   ich glaub', ich schlaf' gleich ein.
```

**Refrain:**
```
       D              A              E                A
   Ich möcht so gern Dave Dudley hörn', Hank Snow und Charlie Pride,
        D            A              E       A
   'nen richtig schönen Countrysong, doch AFN ist weit.
       D              A              E                A
   Ich möcht so gern Dave Dudley hörn', Hank Snow und Charlie Pride,
        D            A              E       A
   'nen richtig schönen Countrysong, doch AFN ist weit.
```

```
      A                                    Bm
2. Schneesturm auf der Autobahn und vor mir keine Spur.
        D               E                              A
   Ich seh die blauen Schilder kaum und ahn die Fahrbahn nur.
        A                              Bm
   Drum nehm ich mir mein Funkgerät, Kanal 410.
        D             E                              A
   An alle, hier spricht Gunther G., ich hab da ein Problem.
```

Refrain

```
          A                                 Bm
3. Ich halt am nächsten Rasthof an und leg 'ne Pause ein.
        D                     E                                A
   Ich schlaf am Tisch, ein Kellner kommt und fragt: Was soll's denn sein?
        A                                     Bm
   Ich schau ihn an und weiß genau, der Mann wird's nicht verstehn.
        D                E                             A
   Ich möchte weder Milchkaffee, noch will ich schwarzen Tee.
```

```
        D            A                E                A
   Ich möchte nur Dave Dudley hörn', Hank Snow und Charlie Pride,
        D            A              E       A
   'nen richtig schönen Countrysong, doch AFN ist weit.
        D            A                E                A
   Ich möchte nur Dave Dudley hörn', Hank Snow und Charlie Pride,
        D            A              E       A
   'nen richtig schönen Countrysong, doch AFN ist weit.
```

M + T: Bach, Rainer / Grabowsky, Holger
© Edition Joe Menke / Universal Music Publishing GmbH.

# NEVER BE THE SAME AGAIN

(MELANIE C)

**Intro:** Gm Eb Bb F#+   (8x)

Come on. Ooh, yeah. Never be the same again.

```
Gm          Eb           Bb                F#+
I call you up whenever things go wrong.
Gm          Eb                Bb                   F#+
You're always there, you are my shoulder to cry on.
Gm          Eb           Bb              F#+
I can't believe it took me quite so long
Gm                       Eb
to take the forbidden step.
          Bb              F#+       Gm
Is this something that I might regret?

Gm       Eb    Bb          F#+                Gm
Come on, come on. Nothing ventured, nothing gained.
Gm    Eb        Bb          F#+                    Gm
You are the one. A lonely heart that can't be tamed.
Gm       Eb    Bb          F#+                Gm
Come on, come on. I'm hoping that you feel the same.
Eb        Bb              F#+       Gm
This is something that I can't forget.
```

**Refrain:**
```
Gm                Eb            Bb
I thought that we would just be friends.
             F#+
Things will never be the same again.
Gm                Eb                   Bb
It's just the beginning, it's not the end.
             F#+         Gm
Things will never be the same again.
             Eb         Bb            F#+           Gm
It's not a secret anymore, now we've opened up the door.
            Eb              Bb
Starting tonight and from now on.
             F#+            Gm   Eb Bb
We'll never, never be the same again.
F#+             Gm    Eb Bb F#+
Never be the same again.

Gm       Eb           Bb           F#+
Now I know that we were close before.
Gm          Eb           Bb              F#+
I'm glad, I realised I need you so much more.
Gm          Eb              Bb        F#+
And I don't care what everyone will say.
Gm                   Eb
It's about you and me.
            Bb           F#+     Gm
And we'll never be the same again.
```

Refrain

```
Rap:   Gm Eb Bb F#+   (repeat)
```

Night and day. Black beach sand to red clay. The US to UK, NYC to LA.
From sidewalks to highways. See it'll never be the same.
What I'm saying my mind frame never changed 'til you came rearranged.
But sometimes it seems completely forbidden.
To discover those feelings that we kept so well hidden.
Where there's no competition. And you render my condition.
Though improbable it's not impossible. For a love that could be
unstoppable.
But wait. A fine line's between fate and destiny.
Do you believe in the things that were just meant to be?
When you tell me the stories of your quest for me.
Picturesque is the picture you paint effortlessly.
And as our energies mix and begin to multiply.
Everyday situations, they start to simplify.
So things will never be the same between you and I.
We intertwined our life forces and now we're unified.

Refrain

```
Gm     Eb          Bb
Come on, come on.
F#+              Gm
Never be the same again.
     Eb       Bb
You are the one.
F#+              Gm
Never be the same again.
              Eb       Bb
It's not a secret anymore.
F#+              Gm
Never be the same again.
              Eb       Bb
It's not a secret anymore.
F#+              Gm    Eb Bb
Never be the same again.
F#+              Gm    Eb Bb
Never be the same again.
F#+              Gm    Eb Bb
Never be the same again.
F#+              Gm    Eb Bb
Never be the same again.
```

M + T: Melanie Chisholm, Rhett Lawrence, Paul F. Cruz, Lisa Nicole Lopes & Lorenzo Martin
© 2000 Rhettryme Music administered by W B Music Corp, Notting Dale Songs Inc, Max Hill Music Publishing, EMI Music Publishing Ltd, London, Warner/Chappell North America Ltd, London, Kobalt Music Publishing Limited. Reproduced by permission of Faber Music Ltd and International Music Publications Ltd (a trading name of Faber Music Ltd). All Rights Reserved.

# THE FINAL COUNTDOWN

(EUROPE)

**Intro:** F#m D Bm E F#m D Bm E F#m E A D C#sus4 C#

```
   F#m                                    Bm
1. We're leaving together but still it's farewell.
F#m                      E/G#            A
And maybe we'll comeback to earth, who can tell.
D            E              A    E/G#      F#m      A/E
I guess there is no one to blame, we're leaving ground.
D                C#m         E
Will things ever be the same again?
```

**Refrain:**
```
E              F#m         D Bm E
It's the final countdown.
               F#m         D Bm E
The final countdown.
```

```
   F#m                                        Bm
2. We're heading for Venus and still we stand tall.
F#m                      E/G#            A
Cause maybe they've seen us and welcome us all.
D          E            A    E/G#         F#m      A/F
With so many lightyears to go and things to be found.
D                C#m         E
I'm sure that we all miss her so.
```

Refrain

```
E          F#m       E A D C#sus4 C#
The final countdown.
           F#m
The final countdown.
```

M + T: Joey Tempest
© Copyright 1986 EMI Music Publishing Limited, London, W8 5SW.
Reproduced by permission of International Music Publications Limited
(a trading name of Faber Music Ltd).
All Rights Reserved.

# JUKE BOX HERO

(FOREIGNER)

```
   E
1. Standing in the rain with his head hung low.
                                 D/E
Couldn't get a ticket, it was a sold out show.
                       E                   D/E
Heard the roar of the crowd, he could picture the scene.
                     E                  D/E
Put his ear to the wall, and like a distant scream.
                 E                 D
He heard one guitar, just blew him away.
                    E                 D
Saw stars in his eyes and the very next day.

                    E                        D/E
2. Bought a beat up six-string in a second hand store.
                   E                  D/E
Didn't know how to play it but he knew for sure.
              E                  D
That that one guitar felt good in his hands.
            E             D
Didn't take long to understand.
              E              D
Just one guitar, slung way down low.
            E                    D
Was a one way ticket, only one way to go.
```

**Bridge:**
```
              B
So he started rocking, ain't never gonna stop.
              B
Gotta keep on rocking, someday he's gonna make it to the top.
```

**Refrain:**
```
        Em      G6       D           Em
And be a juke box hero, got stars in his eyes.
        Em      G6      D        Em
He's a juke box hero. He took one guitar
           G6          D        Em
Juke box hero, saw stars in his eyes.
           G6            D       E
Juke box hero, he'll come alive tonight.
```

3. In a town without a name, in a heavy downpour.
Thought he passed his own shadow by the backstage door.
Like a trip through the past, that day in the rain.
That one guitar made his whole life change.

Bridge
Refrain

M + T: Mick Jones and Lou Gramm
© Copyright 1981 Somerset Songs Publishing, Incorporated.
This arrangement © 2011 Somerset Songs Publishing Incorporated.
International Copyright Secured. All Rights Reserved.
Reprinted by permission of Cherry Lane Music Company..

# (I'VE HAD) THE TIME OF MY LIFE

(BILL MEDLEY & JENNIFER WARNES)

```
  E    C#m7          D                                    E
Now I've had the time of my life and I never felt like this before.
     C#m7           D
Yes I swear it's the truth and I owe it all to you.
    E    C#m7          D                              E
Cause I've had the time of my life and I owe it all to you.


         D/E
1. I've been waiting for so long,
                                      E
now I've finally found someone to stand by me.
         D/E                                               E
We saw the writing on the wall as we felt this magical fantasy.
         D/E
Now with passion in our eyes
                                       E
there is no way we could disguise it secretly.
         D/E                                                     E
So we take each other's hand cause we seem to understand the urgency.

              A                       G
Just remember: You're the one thing I can't get enough of,
A                     B            A/B
so I'll tell you something this could be love because:
```

**Refrain:**
```
E    C#m7          D                                   E
I've had the time of my life and I never felt this way before.
     C#m7          D         Bm7            E
Yes, I swear it's the truth and I owe it all to you.


        D/E                                       E
2. With my body and soul I want you more than you'll ever know.
       D/E                               E
So we'll just let it go, don't be afraid to lose control.
         D/E                                                   E
Yes, I know what's on your mind when you say, "Stay with me tonight."

Stay with me.

              A                       G
Just remember: You're the one thing I can't get enough of,
A                     B
so I'll tell you something this could be love because:
```

Refrain

```
E    C#m7          D                                         E
I've had the time of my life and I've searched through every open door
        C#m7        D          Bm7          E
till I've found the truth and I owe it all to you.
```

Refrain 2x   M + T: Frankie Previte, John De Nicola and Donald Markowitz
© Sony/ATV Tunes LLC, USA / R U Cyrius Publishing / Knockout Music Company / Marcu Music Company Incorporated / Calspen Music. Sony/ATV Music Publishing (UK) Limited / Worldsong Incorporated / Songs of PEN UK / Roba Music Verlag GmbH.
All Rights Reserved. International Copyright Secured.

# LADY D'ARBANVILLE

(CAT STEVENS)

**Refrain:**
```
Em                    D
My Lady d'Arbanville, why do you sleep so still?
Em                    D                  Bm
I'll make you tomorrow and you will be my fill,
                              Em
yes, you would be my fill.
```

```
     Em                    D
1. My Lady d'Arbanville, why do you grieve me so?
Em                         D                  Bm
But your heart seems so silent, why do you breath so low,
                    Em
why do you breath so low?
```

Refrain

```
     Em                    D
2. My Lady d'Arbanville, you look so cold tonight.
Em                    D                      Bm
Your lips feel like water, your skin has turned to white,
                    Em
your skin has turned to white.
```

Refrain

```
     Em                    D
1. My Lady d'Arbanville, why do you grieve me so?
Em                         D                  Bm
But your heart seems so silent, why do you breath so low,
                    Em
why do you breath so low?
```

```
     Em                    D
3. I love you my Lady, though in your grave you lie
Em               G    D                    Bm
I'll always be with you, this rose will never die,
                    Em
this rose will never die.
```

```
     Em                    D
3. I love you my Lady, though in your grave you lie
Em               G    D                    Bm
I'll always be with you, this rose will never die,
                    Em
this rose will never die.
```

M + T: Cat Stevens
© Copyright 1970 Salafa Limited.
All Rights Reserved. International Copyright Secured.

# ICH VERMISS DICH... (WIE DIE HÖLLE)

(ZLATKO)

```
      G                     C              D              G
1. Ich bin nicht Shakespeare oder Einstein, bin nicht Picasso oder Bach.
         C            D                G
Doch eins kannst du mir glauben, ich vermiss dich jede Nacht.
    C                     G
Was hab ich nur mit uns gemacht, warum bist du nicht bei mir?
     C                             D         D7
Hab mich selbst um den Verstand gebracht. Wo bist du?
```

**Refrain:**
```
      Em            G              C                    D
Ich vermiss dich wie die Hölle, hey, du fehlst mir hier total!
      Em            G            C             D
Ich vermiss dich wie die Hölle, jeder Tag ist eine Qual.
    C                     G              Em            D
Ob nun Shakespeare oder Goethe, die sind mir doch scheißegal,
         Em              G              C                G
denn ich vermiss dich wie die Hölle, und du fehlst - mir so total!
```

```
         G                  C              D              G
2. Jetzt sitz ich hier und mein Kopf ist leer, nichts ist mehr homogen.
            C                D                G
Hab die Schnauze voll von dieser Achterbahn, ich muss dich wiedersehn.
    C                     G
Was hab ich nur mit uns gemacht, warum bist du nicht bei mir?
     C                             D         D7
Hab mich selbst um den Verstand gebracht. Wo bist du?
```

Refrain 2x

M + T: Christoph Siemons / Bob Arnz
© EMI Music Publishing Germany GmbH / Endemol Entertainment Publishing
Mit freundlicher Genehmigung der EMI Music Publishing Germany GmbH.

# WE'RE NOT GONNA TAKE IT

(TWISTED SISTER)

**Refrain:**
```
E                B
We're not gonna take it.
E                A
No, we ain't gonna take it.
E                B           E
We're not gonna take it anymore.
```

```
    E                B
1. We've got the right to choose and
E              A
there ain't no way we'll lose it.
E          B              E   B
This is our life; this is our song.
E                  B
We'll fight the powers that be just,
E              A
don't pick our destiny 'cause
E              B            E    B
you don't know us, you don't belong.
```

Refrain

2. Oh, you're so condescending,
you gall is never ending.
We don't want nothin', not a thing, from you.
Your life is trite and jaded,
boring and confiscated.
If that's your best, your best won't do.

Oh...
Oh...
We're right, yeah.
We're free, yeah.
We'll fight, yeah.
You'll see, yeah.

Refrain 2x

M + T: Daniel Snider
© by Universal Tunes. Universal/MCA Music Limited.
All Rights Reserved. International Copyright Secured.

# FALLEN ANGEL

(ALPHAVILLE)

```
      Em                      G
1. I hear those voices on the radio,
C                      B
I switched it off because she told me so.
            Em              G              C     B
She's an investigator, she's like an elevator.
Em                         G
Nobody told me we'd be all alone.
              C
You know somewhere my friend he'd left me in that
B
red light zone, you know.
Em                              G
She said: I've seen your deepest secrets,
               C                           B
son, they're just as lightning in the look of your eyes.
```

**Refrain:**
```
             A                      B
I said: I want you, Baby, I said: I want some more.
             E                   D
I said: I never ever felt it like that moment before.
A/E          B                       C#m
She's an assassin, she's melting steel in my heart,
         A          B
but I beg for more.
               A                       B
She said: I want your body, she said: I want your soul.
               E                       D
She said: A fallen angel takes it but she'll never let go.
A/E          B                   C#m
She's an invader, she's from another world
         A      B      Em G C B  Em G C B
but I beg for more and mooooore
```

```
        Em                              G
2. She's raising feelings cutting like a knife,
C                      B
she's pouring fire into my liquid life.
Em                          G
There's no escaping from her mysteries,
               C                       B
she gives me kisses of the stangest kind.
            Em                          G
She says: I know you'll like it, so come over here.
                  C                              B
She says: Just let that rhythm filter through your body, dear.
                  Em                      G
And then she, she always did it and she always will,
                     C                   B
she'll stay that hunter 'till the end of time.
```

Refrain

M: Gold, Marian / Lloyd, Bernhard / Mertens, Frank
T: Gold, Marian
© 1984 Rolf Budde Musikverlag GmbH, Berlin.

# RETURN TO SENDER

(ELVIS PRESLEY)

```
      C                     Am
1. I gave a letter to the postman,
Dm            G7
he put it in his sack.
C                     Am
Bright and early next morning
    Dm         G7    C
he brought my letter back.

She wrote upon it:
F         G7      F         G7
Return to sender, address unknown.
F       G7      C
No such number, no such zone.
F         G7      F         G7
We had a quarrel, a lovers spat.
D7                                      G7
I write I'm sorry but my letter keeps coming back.


      C                       Am
2. So when I dropped it in the mailbox
Dm            G7
I sent it special D.
C                     Am
Bright and early next morning
    Dm       G7    C
it came right back to me.

She wrote upon it:
F         G7      F         G7
Return to sender, address unknown.
F       G7      C
No such person, no such zone.

F
This time I'm gonna take it by myself
      C
and put it right in her hand.
     D7
And if it comes back the very next day
G7
then I understand.


The writing on it:
F         G7      F         G7
Return to sender, address unknown.
F       G7      C
No such number, no such zone.
```

M + T: Otis Blackwell & Winfield Scott
© Copyright 1962 Elvis Presley Music.
All Rights Reserved. International Copyright Secured.

# SO LONELY

(THE POLICE)

```
     C        G            Am      F
1. Well, someone told me yesterday
   C        G            Am      F
that when you throw your love away
   C        G            Am      F
you act as if you just don't care,
   C        G            Am      F
you look as if you're going somewhere.

     C        G            Am      F
2. But I just can't convince myself,
   C G            Am      F
I couldn't live with noone else
   C        G       Am       F
and I can only play that part
   C        G            Am      F
and sit and nurse my broken heart. So lonely.
```

**Refrain:**
```
C              G          Am       F  C           G          Am       F
So lonely, so lonely, so lonely. So lonely, so lonely, so lonely.
C              G          Am       F  C           G          Am       F
So lonely, so lonely, so lonely. So lonely, so lonely, so lonely.
```

```
     C        G            Am      F
3. Now noone's knocked upon my door
   C        G            Am      F
for a thousand years or maybe more.
   C        G            Am      F
All made up and nowhere to go,
   C G            Am      F
   welcome to this one man show.

     C        G                Am      F
4. Just take a seat, they're always free,
   C G            Am      F
   no surprise, no mystery.
   C        G            Am      F
In this theatre that I call my soul
   C G            Am      F
I always play the starring role. So lonely.
```

Refrain

M + T: Gordon Matthew Sumner
© Copyright 1978 G M Sumner/EMI Music Publishing Limited,
London, WC2H 0QY.
All Rights Reserved. International Copyright Secured.

# MANCHMAL MÖCHTE ICH SCHON MIT DIR
(ROLAND KAISER)

**Intro:** Dm A Dm

```
   Dm              Bb/D            Dm
1. Kühler Abendwind fängt sich in deinen Haaren,
        Bb/D                      Gm
   und du sagst, halt mich ganz fest in deinen Armen!
                                       Dm
   Und im Spiegel deiner sehnsuchtsvollen Augen
   E7                 A        A7
   seh ich die rote Sonne untergehn.

      Dm            Bb/D            Dm
2. Deine Stimme flüstert zärtlich meinen Namen,
            Bb/D                     Gm
   die Berührung deiner Hand setzt mich in Flammen.
                                     Dm
   Und die Tür zu deinem Zimmer lässt du offen.
   E7                  A         A7
   Wie lange kann ich dir noch widerstehn?
```

**Refrain:**
```
D
Manchmal möchte ich schon mit dir
                       G
diesen unerlaubten Weg zu Ende gehen.

Manchmal möcht ich so gern mit dir
                                    D
Hand in Hand ganz nah an einem Abgrund stehen,
          Em          A     A7
wenn ich dich so seh, vor mir seh.
D
Manchmal möchte ich schon mit dir
                                G
eine Nacht das Wort "Begehren" buchstabieren.

Manchmal möchte ich so gern mit dir,
                                      D
doch ich weiß, wir würden viel zu viel riskieren.
            Em      A          Dm
Du verlierst den Mann, ich verlier den Freund.


       Dm           Bb/D           Dm
3. Trotzdem fühle ich mich hin und her gerissen
                 Bb/D                 Gm
   und die Sehnsucht macht sich breit auf meinem Kissen.
                                       Dm
   Du versprichst mir die Erfüllung meiner Träume,
   E7                   A       A7
   da "Nein" zu sagen fällt unendlich schwer.
```

**Refrain**
```
D
Doch manchmal möchte ich schon mit dir.
```

M: Joachim Heider
T: Roland Kaiser / Norbert Hammerschmidt
© 1982 by Edition Intro Meisel GmbH.

# YOUR LATEST TRICK

(DIRE STRAITS)

**Intro:** C#m7 Amaj7 B B/A G#m7 Amaj7 F# F#/A# B B/A G#7 F#m7 G#7 (2x)

```
         E
1. All the late night bargains have been struck
F#m          B              A          B         C#
between the satin beaux and their belles
F#m
and prehistoric garbage trucks
         D9
have the city to themselves.
E
Echoes roar dinosaurs,
F#m         B          A/C#      B/D#  C#/E#
they're all doing the monster mash
     F#m
and most of the taxis, most of the whores
     D9
are only taking calls for cash.
     A                    B           E/G#           A
Mmm, I don't know how it happened, it all took place so quick.
A/B  E/B       E/G#  A     B     A/C# B/D#          C#m7
But all I can do     is hand it to you  and your latest trick.
```

2. My door was standing open,
security was laid back and lax.
But it was only my heart got broken,
you must have had a pass key made out of wax.
You played robbery with insolence and I played blues
in twelve bars down lover's lane.
And you never did have the intelligence to use the
twelve keys hanging off my chain.
Mmm, I don't know how it happened, it all took place so quick.
But all I can do is hand it to you and your latest trick.

3. Now it's past last call for alcohol,
past recall has been here and gone.
The landlord finally paid us all.
The satin jazz-men have put away their horns.
And we're standing outside of this wonderland,
looking so bereaved and so bereft.
Like a bowery bum when he finally understands
the bottle's empty and there's nothing left.
Mmm, I don't know how it happened it was faster than any eye could flick
But now all I can do is hand it to you and your latest trick.

**Outro:** C#m7 A B B/A G#m7 Amaj7 F# F#/A# B B/A G#7 F#m7 G#7 C#m7

M + T: Mark Knopfler
© Copyright 1985 Straitjacket Songs Limited.
Universal Music Publishing Limited.
All rights in Germany administered by Universal Music Publ. GmbH.
All Rights Reserved. International Copyright Secured.

# FROM SARAH WITH LOVE

(SARAH CONNOR)

```
Bm                                    G
For so many years we were friends and yes I always knew what we could do
A                                  G
But so many tears in the rain felt, the night you said
       F#           Bm
that love had come to you.
                                              G
I thought you were not my kind I thought that I could never feel for you
A                                       G                    F#
the passion and love you were feeling and so you left for someone new.
G                                  A
And now that you're far and away I'm sending a letter today.
```

**Refrain:**
```
                Dm                                  Bb
From Sarah with love. She'd got the lover she is dreaming of.
                  C
She never found the words to say but I know that today.
        A
She's gonna send her letter to you.
                Dm                                  Bb
From Sarah with love. She took your picture to the stars above.
                        Gm
And they told her it is true.
A               Dm         Dm/C
She could dare to fall in love with you.
G7/B          Bb                        A              Dm   F#
So don't make her blue when she writes to you "From Sarah with love".

Bm                                    G
Maybe the chance for romance is like a train to catch before it's gone.
A                                       G                       F#
And I'll keep on waiting and dreaming you're strong enough to understand
G                           A
As long as you so far away I'm sending a letter each day.
```

Refrain
Bm G Em F# Bm
```
                F#m                                 D
From Sarah with love. She'd got the lover she is dreaming of.
                  E
She never found the words to say but I know that today.
        C#
She's gonna send her letter to you.
                F#m                                 D
From Sarah with love. She's gotta know what you are thinking of.
                  E
Cause every little now and then and again and again.
        C#
I know her heart cries out for you.
```

Refrain (F#m D E C# F#m D Bm C# F#m)
```
B7/D#         D                        C#              F#m
So don't make me blue when I write to you "From Sarah with love".
B7/D#         D                        C#              F#
So don't make me blue when I write to you "From Sarah with love".
```

M + T: Rob Tyger / Kay Denar
© 2002 by by George Glueck Publishing GmbH / SMPG Publishing (Germany) GmbH. Mit freundlicher Genehmigung von SMPG Publishing (Germany) GmbH.

# KREUZBERGER NÄCHTE SIND LANG

(GEBRÜDER BLATTSCHUSS)

```
     C
1. Ich sitz schon seit 'ner Stunde ziemlich dumm
                            G
allein um einen Kneipentisch herum.

Ich trinke schnell, obwohl ich's nicht vertrag,
                                C
weil ich weder volle noch leere Gläser mag.

Da plötzlich setzen sich 6 Mann zu mir,
                                    G
und bestellen lautstark: Bring' se mal drei Bier!

Ich seh schon doppelt, und das aus gutem Grund,
                           C
denn in Eckkneipen geht es nun mal rund.
```

**Refrain:**
```
C                                              G
Kreuzberger Nächte sind lang, Kreuzberger Nächte sind lang,
                                 C
erst fang' se ganz langsam an, aber dann, aber dann.

         C
2. Jetzt fragt mich doch so'n Typ ob ich studier,
                                    G
ich sag: Ja, Wirtschaftspolitik, drum sitz ich hier!
                                                        C
Da sagt er, dass er von der Zeitung wär und da wär er der Lokalredakteur

Ein Rentner ruft: Ihr solltet Euch was schämen!
                           G
Ein anderer meint, das läge alles am System.

Das ist so krank wie meine Leber! Sag ich barsch,
                              C
die 12 Semester war'n doch nicht so ganz umsonst.
```

Refrain
```
           C
3. Und wie immer erscheint dann diese Frau,
                              G
bei der sind auch nicht nur die Augen blau.

Ich sag: verschwinde, liebe Sünde, rasch von mir,
                                        C
in diesem Lied bleibt's ausnahmsweise mal beim Bier.

Frühmorgens wach' ich auf, sechzehn Uhr zehn,
                              G
die ganze Welt scheint sich um mich zu drehn.

Nur im Magen fühle ich mich nicht so recht,
                                      C
eins von den dreißig Bierchen gestern war wohl schlecht.
```

Refrain 2x

M + T: Beppo Pohlmann
© 1977 by Sinus Musikverlag Hans-Ulrich Weigel GmbH.

# MUSIK NUR WENN SIE LAUT IST

(HERBERT GRÖNEMEYER)

```
       Gm                         F#
1. Sie sitzt den ganzen Tag auf ihrer Fensterbank,
Db/F        F            Eb/Bb      Bb
lässt ihre Beine baumeln zur Musik.
       Gm                        F#
Der Lärm aus ihrem Zimmer macht alle Nachbarn krank,
Db/F        F            Eb/Bb      Bb
sie ist beseelt, lächelt vergnügt.

       Dm              Cm                       Bb
Sie weiß nicht, dass der Schnee lautlos auf die Erde fällt,
Dm              Eb              Fsus4 F
merkt nichts vom Klopfen an der Wand.
```

**Refrain:**
```
            Eb/Bb         Bb
Sie mag Musik nur, wenn sie laut ist,
         Eb/Bb       Bb
das ist alles, was sie hört.
Bb          F/A        Gm
Sie mag Musik nur, wenn sie laut ist,
C                   F
wenn sie ihr in den Magen fährt.
            Eb/Bb         Bb
Sie mag Musik nur, wenn sie laut ist,
            Eb/Bb         Bb
wenn der Boden unter den Füßen bebt,
F/A    Gm         C/E      F        D/F# Gsus4 G
dann vergisst sie, dass sie taub ist.
```

```
       Gm                          F#
2. Der Mann ihrer Träume muss ein Bassmann sein.
Db/F          F             Eb/Bb Bb
Das Kitzeln im Bauch macht sie verrückt.
       Gm                         F#
Ihr Mund scheint vor lauter Glück still zu schrein,
Db/F         F              Eb/Bb Bb
ihr Blick ist der Welt entrückt.

       Dm      Cm                         Bb
Ihre Hände wissen nicht, mit wem sie reden sollen.
         Dm       Eb            Fsus4    F
Es ist niemand da, der mit ihr spricht.
```

Refrain 2x

M + T: Herbert Grönemeyer
© Copyright Grönland Musikverlag
All Rights Reserved. International Copyright Secured.

# TAKE GOOD CARE OF MY BABY

(DICK BRAVE & THE BACKBEATS)

```
G              Em                   C           D7
My tears are falling cause you've taken her away.
     G                G+/B          C            Am7       D7
And though it really hurts me so there's something that I've got to say:

       G         Em       C  D  G         Em           C    D
1. Take good care of my baby. Please don't ever make her blue.
G    -        G7             C                Cm
Just tell her that you love her, make sure you're thinking of her
G          Em           C    D
in everything you say and do. Aah.

       G         Em       C  D  G         Em           C    D
2. Take good care of my baby. Don't you ever make her cry.
G             G7                C                    Cm
Just let your love surround her, paint a rainbow all around her,
G      Em      C    D       G
don't let her see a cloudy sky.
```

**Bridge:**
```
C         D          G           Em
Once upon a time that little girl was mine.
C          D           G         Em    C      D
And if I'd been true, I know she'd never be with you, so:

       G         Em       C  D  G         Em           C    D
3. Take good care of my baby. Be just as kind as you can be.
G           G7              C              Cm
And if you should discover that you don't really love her
G         Em         C    D  G     Eb7
just send my baby back home to me.

       Ab        Fm        Db  Eb   Ab          Fm         Db  Eb
3. Take good care of my baby. Be just as kind as you can be.
Ab          Ab7              Db             Dbm
And if you should discover that you don't really love her
Ab        Fm         Db    Eb Ab  Db Eb
just send my baby back home to me.     Aah.

 Ab         Fm        Db Eb
Take good care of my baby.
 Ab         Fm        Db Eb
Take good care of my baby.
 Ab         Fm        Db Eb
Take good care of my baby.
 Ab         Fm        Db Eb   Ab
Take good care of my baby.
```

M + T: Carole King / Gerry Goffin
© Screen Gems-EMI Music Publishing Limited. Robert Mellin Musikverlag KG
Mit freundlicher Genehmigung von Bosworth Music GmbH.
All Rights Reserved. International Copyright Secured.

**Beat Scherler**
# Best of Pop & Rock for Acoustic Guitar light

Solo Arrangements – Noten + TAB + Leadsheet

**Vol. 1** Applaus, Applaus (Sportfreunde Stiller) · Stay (Rihanna feat. Mikky Ekko) · Hello (Adele) · Thinking Out Loud (Ed Sheeran) · Stay With Me (Sam Smith) · Love Yourself (Justin Bieber) · Wings (Birdy) · Hold Back The River (James Bay)

64 Seiten, D 824/ISBN 978-3-86849-301-6

**Vol. 2** Demons (Imagine Dragons) · Heathens (Twenty One Pilots) · Hero (Family Of The Year) · Million Years Ago (Adele) · There's Nothing Holdin' Me Back (Shawn Mendes) · Renegades (X Ambassadors) · Ist da jemand (Adel Tawil) · The Sound Of Silence (Disturbed)

68 Seiten, D 825/ISBN 978-3-86849-318-4

# Best Of Pop & Rock for Classical Guitar

Solo Arrangements – Noten + TAB + Text

**Vol. 1**
I Don't Want To Miss A Thing · As Long As You Love Me · My Heart Will Go On · You Are Not Alone · All My Life · I Believe I Can Fly · How Deep Is Your Love · Conquest Of Paradise

52 Seiten, D 811/ISBN 978-3-934958-78-4

**Vol. 2**
Always · (Everything I Do) I Do It For You · Stand By Me · Nothing Else Matters · No Woman No Cry · Un-Break My Heart · Without You · You'll Be In My Heart

56 Seiten, D 812/ISBN 978-3-934958-79-1

**Vol. 3**
All You Need Is Love · November Rain · She's The One · Can You Feel The Love Tonight · Californication · Angie · El Farol · Wind Of Change

52 Seiten, D 813/ISBN 978-3-934958-80-7

**Vol. 4**
Eternal Flame · Again · Stairway To Heaven · Fields Of Gold · Imagine · We Are The Champions · Losing My Religion · Stuck In A Moment You Can't Get Out Of It

56 Seiten, D 814/ISBN 978-3-934958-81-4

**Vol. 5**
Bed Of Roses · In My Place · How You Remind Me · Another Day In Paradise · Underneath Your Clothes · To Be With You · Come As You Are · Dreamer

52 Seiten, D 815/ISBN 978-3-934958-82-1

**Vol. 6**
Summer Of '69 · Beautiful · Let It Be · Hotel California · More Than Words · Behind Blue Eyes · Wonderwall · Save The Best For Last

52 Seiten, D 816/ISBN 978-3-934958-83-8

**Vol. 7**
You're Beautiful · Knockin' On Heaven's Door · Speed Of Sound · Boulevard Of Broken Dreams · Everybody's Changing · Here Without You · Every Breath You Take · Whatever You Want

56 Seiten, D 817/ISBN 978-3-934958-58-6

**Vol. 8**
Born To Be Wild · California · Love Hurts · Dear Mr. President · Smoke On The Water · Hey There Delilah · Shadow Of The Day · Dani California

60 Seiten, D 818/ISBN 978-3-934958-99-9

**Vol. 9**
I'm With You · Is This Love · Just Like Heaven · Father And Son · The River · All Apologies · Fallen Leaves · You Know I'm No Good

56 Seiten, D 819/ISBN 978-3-86849-015-2

**Vol. 10**
Bohemian Rhapsody · Hey Joe · I Don't Believe You · Island In The Sun · Oh Me · Secrets · Untitled · Viva la vida

64 Seiten, D 821/ISBN 978-3-86849-168-5

**Vol. 11**
Hells Bells · Mad World · Bitter Sweet Symphony · Over The Rainbow/What A Wonderful World · Hallelujah · Zombie · Make Me Feel My Love · Run

64 Seiten, D 822/ISBN 978-3-86849-189-0

**Vol. 12**
Set Fire To The Rain · The A Team · Times Like These · Lemon Tree · Sweet Child O' Mine · Earth Song · Oye como va · With Or Without You

60 Seiten, D 823/ISBN 978-3-86849-223-1

# Pop & Rock Christmas for Classical Guitar

Christmas Time · Mary's Boy Child · Jingle Bell Rock · Driving Home For Christmas · Happy Xmas (War Is Over) · Rockin' Around The Christmas Tree · Wonderful Christmastime · Mistletoe And Wine · Last Christmas · I Wish It Could Be Christmas Every Day

52 Seiten, D 820/ISBN 978-3-934958-91-3

# Theorie

## 1. Aufbau des Notensystems.

Töne werden im wesentlichen durch vier Faktoren bestimmt:
- das Instrument, mit dem sie gespielt werden / die Klangfarbe
- die Tonhöhe / die Frequenz
- die Lautstärke / die Amplitude
- die Tondauer

Wir betrachten hier nur die Tonhöhe.

Festgelegt ist, dass eine Frequenzverdopplung eine Oktave höher bedeutet, und innerhalb einer Oktave es 12 verschiedene Töne gibt, die alle den gleichen Abstand zu ihrem Vorgängerton haben.
Dieser Abstand ist ein Halbton und immer der gleiche Faktor (12te Wurzel aus 2 = 1.05946). Die Töne heißen unterschiedlich, je nach Tonart, in der sie benutzt werden. Außerdem gibt es länderspezifische Unterschiede.

| Deutsch: | International: | Frequenz: | Abstand | Bezeichnung |
|---|---|---|---|---|
| A | A | 440 Hz | 0 | Prim |
| Ais / B | A# / Bb | 466 Hz | 1 | kl. Sekunde |
| H | B | 494 Hz | 2 | gr. Sekunde |
| C | C | 523 Hz | 3 | kl. Terz |
| Cis / Des | C# / Db | 554 Hz | 4 | gr. Terz |
| D | D | 587 Hz | 5 | Quart |
| Dis / Es | D# / Eb | 622 Hz | 6 | verm. Quinte |
| E | E | 659 Hz | 7 | Quinte |
| F | F | 698 Hz | 8 | überm. Quinte |
| Fis / Ges | F# / Gb | 740 Hz | 9 | Sext |
| G | G | 784 Hz | 10 | Sept |
| Gis / As | G# / Ab | 831 Hz | 11 | gr. Sept |
| A | A | 880 Hz | 12 | Oktave |

Die nächste Oktave nach unten beinhaltet also den Frequenzbereich von 220 Hz bis 440 Hz. Das nächsthöhere A schwingt mit 1760 Hz. Das menschliche Ohr hört Frequenzen von ca. 15 Hz bis 20000 Hz, das sind etwas weniger als 11 Oktaven.

Wir verwenden in diesem Buch die internationale Schreibweise.

## 2. Tonleitern

Die bekanntesten Tonleitern sind die
- chromatische Tonleiter (Halbtonleiter): alle 12 Töne
- Durtonleiter: C D E F G A B C (C-Dur)
  Charakter: melodisch, mitsingbar, fröhlich
- Molltonleiter: A B C D E F G    (A-Moll)
  Charakter: melodisch, traurig / getragen
- Pentatonik (Fünftonleiter): C D E G A
  Charakter: fast jeder Blues ist damit begleitbar
  eignet sich hervorragend für Improvisationen

Kennzeichnend für die jeweilige Tonleiter ist der Abstand zwischen den Tönen - die Stelle des Halbtonschritts. Tonleitern kann man transponieren, indem man jeden Ton um die gleiche Anzahl Halbtonschritte erhöht bzw. erniedrigt. Bsp.: D-Dur: alle Töne zwei Halbtöne höher als in C-Dur: D E F# G A B C# D
Die gleichen Töne findet man in der Molltonleiter eine kleine Terz tiefer. Diese nennt man Mollparallele. Bsp.: B-Moll: B C# D E F# G A B

## 3. Dreiklänge:

Dreiklänge bestehen aus drei verschiedenen Tönen. Maßgebend für die Bezeichnung des Dreiklangs ist der Grundton und dessen Abstand zu den nächsten beiden Tönen.
Durdreiklang: Grundton, große Terz (4 Halbtöne), kleine Terz
(3 Halbtöne) Bsp.: C E G
Molldreiklang: Grundton, kleine Terz (3 Halbtöne), große Terz
(4 Halbtöne) Bsp.: C Eb G

Notation: Durdreiklänge werden mit einem Großbuchstaben des Grundtons abgekürzt.

| Töne | Dur-Akkord | | Töne | Dur-Akkord |
|---|---|---|---|---|
| C E G | = C | | | |
| C# E# G# | = C# | | Db F Ab | = Db |
| D F# A | = D | | | |
| D# G A# | = D# | | Eb G Bb | = Eb |
| E G# B | = E | | | |
| F A C | = F | | | |
| F# A# C# | = F# | | Gb Bb Db | = Gb |
| G B D | = G | | | |
| G# B# D# | = G# | | Ab C Eb | = Ab |
| A C# E | = A | | | |
| A# D E# | = A# | | Bb D F | = Bb |
| B D# F# | = B | | | |

Molldreiklänge werden mit einem Großbuchstaben des Grundtons und einem angehängten m abgekürzt.

| Töne | Moll-Akkord | | Töne | Moll-Akkord |
|---|---|---|---|---|
| C Eb G | = Cm | | | |
| C# E G# | = C#m | | Db Fb Ab | = Dbm |
| D F A | = Dm | | | |
| D# F# A# | = D#m | | Eb Gb Bb | = Ebm |
| E G B | = Em | | | |
| F Ab C | = Fm | | | |
| F# A C# | = F#m | | Gb A Db | = Gbm |
| G Bb D | = Gm | | | |
| G# B D# | = G#m | | Ab Cb Eb | = Abm |
| A C E | = Am | | | |
| A# C# E# | = A#m | | Bb Db F | = Bbm |
| B D F# | = Bm | | | |

# 4. andere Akkorde

Jeder Mehrklang wird Akkord genannt. Je nach den Tönen, die der Akkord beinhaltet ergibt sich der Name des Akkords.

4.1 Sextakkord:
zum Dreiklang kommt die Sexte dazu.
A C E F# = Am6
G B D E  = G6

4.2 Septakkord:
E G B D  = Em7 (beinhaltet die gleichen Töne wie G6, aber anderer Bass)
A C# E G = A7

4.3 großer Septakkord:
E G B D#  = EmMaj7
A C# E G# = Amaj7

4.4 Nonakkord:
der neunte Ton der Tonleiter (None) wird hinzugenommen. Nonakkorde bauen immer auf Septakkorden auf.
D F A C E   = Dm9
C E G Bb D = C9

4.5 suspendierte Akkorde:
Statt der Terz wird entweder die Sekunde (sus2) oder die Quarte (sus4) genommen. Bei suspendierten Akkorden kann nicht mehr zwischen Dur und Moll unterschieden werden, weil die dafür maßgebende Terz ersetzt wird.
G A D    = Gsus2
E A B    = Esus4

4.6 beliebiger Akkord mit zusätzlichen Tönen:
C D E G  = Cadd2
C E G D  = Cadd9
D F G A  = Dmadd4
manchmal sieht man auch eine konkrete Note hinzugefügt:
C E F G  = CaddF

4.7 Verminderte Akkorde
ein verminderter Akkord besitzt immer kleine Terzen als Abstand zwischen zwei benachbarten Tönen.
C Eb Gb A = C°
Eb Gb A C = Eb° (gleiche Töne wie C°)

4.8 Quintakkorde / Power Chords
Ein Quintakkord besteht nur aus zwei Tönen: Dem Grundton und der Quinte. Ein solcher Zweiklang klingt enorm rockig, die Unterscheidung zwischen Dur und Moll entfällt natürlich, da die Terz fehlt.
E B E = E5
A E A = A5

**4.9 Akkorde mit bestimmter Note im Bass:**
Will man sichergehen, dass eine bestimmte Note im Bass ist, schreibt man
diesen Ton hinter den Akkord, mit Schrägstrich getrennt. Der Basston
muss nicht unbedingt im Akkord drin sein.
G C E G = C/G
Eb F A C = F/Eb
C A C E = Am/C
Üblicherweise bleibt der Gitarrengriff gleich, unabhängig von der
Bassnote. Beim Picking empfiehlt es sich aber, die Bassnote zu spielen.

**4.10 Nomenklatur von mehrdeutigen Akkorden**
Bei mehreren Möglichkeiten, einen Akkord zu benennen, geht man zur
Bezeichnung am besten von der Note im Bass aus. Generell spielt es aber
auf der Gitarre keine so große Rolle, welcher Ton an welcher Stelle im
Akkord steht, da die Akkorde beinahe identisch klingen. Dies liegt
daran, dass die Akkorde auch irgendwie gegriffen werden müssen. Auf dem
Klavier macht es aber einen deutlichen Unterschied.
```
F A C D    = F6
D F A C    = Dm7
C Eb Gb A  = C°
Eb Gb A C  = Eb°
A B E      = Asus2
E A B      = Esus4
```

## 5. Umsetzung auf die Gitarre

Eine Gitarre hat 6 Saiten verschiedener Stärke. Diese sind üblicherweise
folgendermaßen gestimmt:

```
E ||---|---|---|--- 6. höchste Saite
B ||---|---|---|--- 5.
G ||---|---|---|--- 4.
D ||---|---|---|--- 3.
A ||---|---|---|--- 2.
E ||---|---|---|--- 1. tiefste Saite
```
          Merkspruch:
          Ein Anfänger Der Gitarre Bleibe Eifrig
          -     -      -    -       -      -

Verkürzt man eine Saite um einen Platz auf dem Griffbrett, erhöht man
deren Ton um einen Halbton.

**5.1 Akkord basteln**
Wenn wir Em greifen wollen, dürfen nur die Töne E G und B beinhaltet
sein. Das bedeutet, die erste, vierte, fünfte und sechste Saite können
leer angeschlagen werden. Die zweite muss um zwei Halbtöne erhöht werden
(auf B) und die dritte Saite auch um zwei Halbtöne (auf E).

```
E  o||---|---|---|---   E
B  o||---|---|---|---   B
G  o||---|---|---|---   G
D   ||---|-o-|---|---   E         E G B = Em
A   ||---|-o-|---|---   B
E  o||---|---|---|---   E
```

abgekürzte Schreibweise: 022000

## 5.2 Barré-Akkorde

Wenn wir den Em-Akkord um einen Halbton als Ganzes erhöhen können, bekommen wir einen Fm-Akkord. Dazu wird der Zeigefinger komplett über den ersten Bund gelegt, Mittel- und Ringfinger verkürzen die A- und D-Saite im dritten Bund.

```
E   ||-o-|---|---|---    F
B   ||-o-|---|---|---    C
G   ||-o-|---|---|---    Ab
D   ||-o-|---|-o-|---    F        F Ab C = Fm
A   ||-o-|---|-o-|---    C
E   ||-o-|---|---|---    F
```

abgekürzte Schreibweise: 133111

## 5.3 Grundakkorde, die leicht barriert werden können

```
022100  E                022000  Em
020100  E7               020000  Em7
022200  Esus4            000000  Em7add4
022400  E5
002220  A                002210  Am
002020  A7               002010  Am7
002200  Asus2
002230  Asus4
002120  Amaj7
```

## 5.4 weitere Akkorde, die ohne Barré gegriffen werden können

```
032010  C
032000  Cmaj7
032310  C7
032030  Cadd9
x00232  D                x00231  Dm
x00212  D7               x00211  Dm7
x00230  Dadd9
x00233  Dadd4
x03211  F
x03210  Fmaj7
320003  G
xx0033  G5
320001  G7
320002  Gmaj7
002222  A6
002223  A7
x01212  A°
201202  B7
```

Stumme Saiten sind mit einem "x" markiert.

# 6.0 Akkorde in einem Lied

Nimmt man die erste, vierte und fünfte Stufe einer Tonleiter als Grundton und baut darauf jeweils einen Dur-Akkord auf, so sind alle Töne der Dur-Tonleiter beinhaltet.
C E G   (C)
F A C   (F)
G B D   (G)
beinhaltet alle Töne der C-Dur-Tonleiter.

Viele Lieder haben ihre Melodie auf den Tönen der Dur-Tonleiter und ihre Akkorde auf diesen (I IV V) Stufen aufgebaut. Die Stufen heißen Tonika (I), Subdominante (IV) und Dominante (V). Oft wird auch der Grundakkord der Mollparallele (VI) zusätzlich verwendet. Im Beispiel eines Liedes in G-Dur finden wir also folgende Akkorde: G C D Em. Man braucht also nur 4 Akkorde lernen, um etliche Lieder spielen zu können. Und glücklicherweise kann man diese Akkorde ohne Barré greifen.

Viele andere Lieder basieren auf den gleichen Akkorden, sind aber in einer anderen Tonart. Warum macht man sich es nicht einfacher und transponiert alle Lieder in die Tonart, von der man diese vier Akkorde kann?
o nicht alle Lieder lassen sich dann noch mitsingen
o die Lieder klingen anders, zusätzlich zur Tonhöhe, da ein G 320003 anders klingt als ein G 355433
o wenn mehrere Musiker zusammen spielen, muss die gleiche (gemeinsame) Tonart gespielt werden
o es gibt genügend Lieder mit mehr als 4 Akkorden, d.h. man spart nur in einigen Fällen das Lernen von zusätzlichen Akkorden.

Will man diese Lieder in Ihrer Tonart spielen können, obwohl man nur die Akkorde von G-Dur verwenden möchte, kann man dies mit Hilfe eines Kapodasters erreichen. Dieser klemmt alle sechs Saiten in einem Bund ab und ermöglicht so, ein Lied in einer anderen Tonart zu spielen ohne Barrégriffe verwenden zu müssen. Beispiel: klemmt man die Saiten im 2. Bund ab, greift dort dann die gelernten Griffe von G-Dur, so spielt man das Lied in A-Dur (zwei Halbtöne höher).

Manche Lieder haben wir in eine andere Tonart transponiert, um sie leichter singen und spielen zu können. Der Hinweis [TRANSP. +2] zeigt an, dass das Lied im Original 2 Töne höher gespielt wird. Um in der Originaltonart zu spielen, setzt man den Kapodaster im 2. Bund. Um ein Lied mit dem Hinweis [TRANSP. -1] in der Originaltonart spielen zu können, muss die Gitarre um einen Halbton tiefer gestimmt werden.

[TRANSP. -5] zeigt an, dass das Originallied fünf Halbtöne tiefer gespielt wird. Um passend zum Original zu spielen, empfiehlt es sich in diesem Fall das Lied zu transponieren. Die Kapodastertabelle kann dazu hilfreich sein.

# Guitar Chords

In dieser Tabelle findet ihr die am häufigsten vorkommenden Akkorde. Die Griffsymbole stellen den Blick auf den Gitarrenhals dar: links liegt die tiefe E-Saite. Über leer angeschlagenen Saiten steht ein Kreis, stumme Saiten sind mit einem „x" markiert.

**XXII**

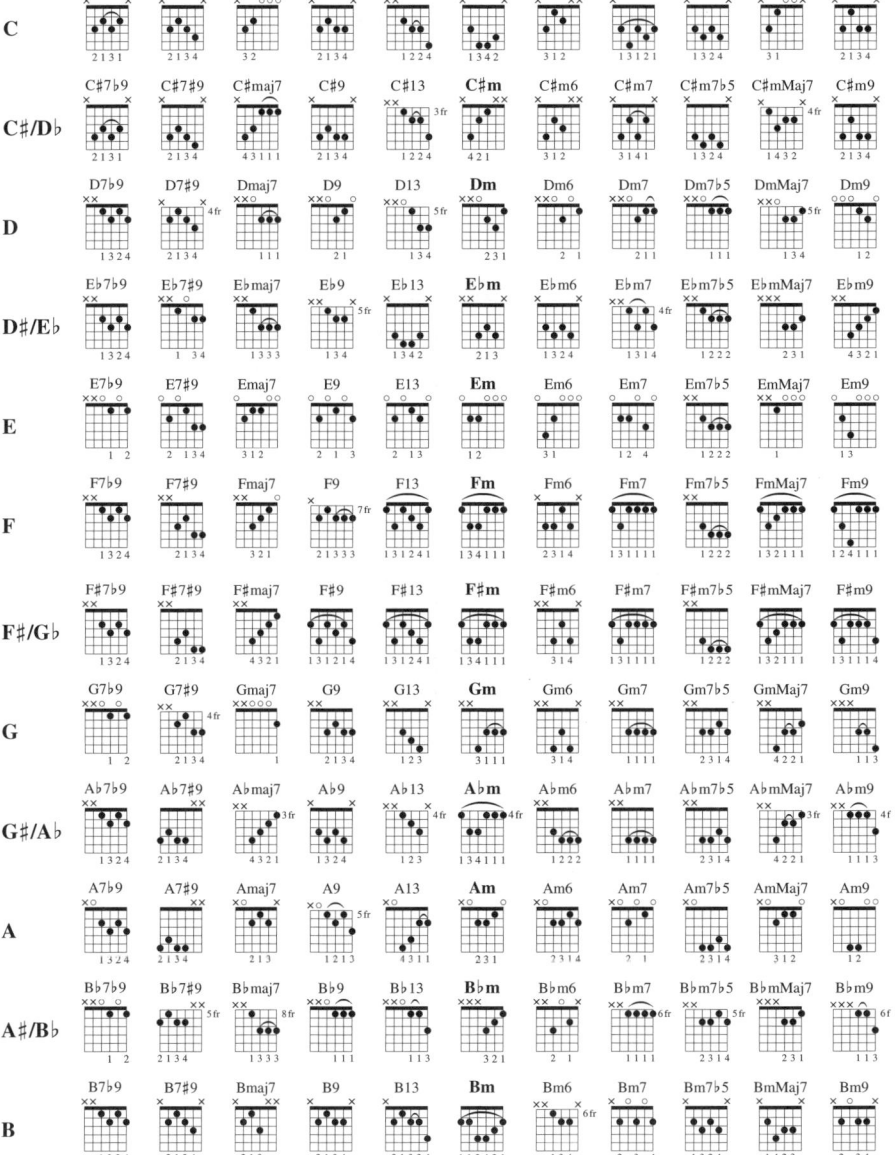

XXIII

# Kapodastertabelle

|     | C     | D     | E     | F     | G     | A     | B     |
|-----|-------|-------|-------|-------|-------|-------|-------|
| 1.  | C#/Db | D#/Eb | F     | F#/Gb | G#/Ab | Bb    | C     |
| 2.  | D     | E     | F#/Gb | G     | A     | B     | C#/Db |
| 3.  | D#/Eb | F     | G     | G#/Ab | Bb    | C     | D     |
| 4.  | E     | F#/Gb | G#/Ab | A     | B     | C#/Db | D#/Eb |
| 5.  | F     | G     | A     | Bb    | C     | D     | E     |
| 6.  | F#/Gb | G#/Ab | Bb    | B     | C#/Db | D#/Eb | F     |
| 7.  | G     | A     | B     | C     | D     | E     | F#/Gb |
| 8.  | G#/Ab | Bb    | C     | C#/Db | D#/Eb | F     | G     |
| 9.  | A     | B     | C#/Db | D     | E     | F#/Gb | G#/Ab |
| 10. | Bb    | C     | D     | D#/Eb | F     | G     | A     |
| 11. | B     | C#/Db | D#/Eb | E     | F#/Gb | G#/Ab | Bb    |
| 12. | C     | D     | E     | F     | G     | A     | B     |

Stephan Schmidt

# ...mit einfachen Gitarrengriffen

## Lieder und Songs

Ob beim Schulausflug, am Lagerfeuer, bei einer Familienfeier oder in der Berghütte – stets wird das gemeinsame Erleben durch den gemeinsamen Gesang gekrönt. Von »Lady In Black« über »Hey Jude« und »Über den Wolken« bis hin zu unverzichtbaren Volksliedern, Schlagern, Oldies, Traditionals und Spirituals – all diese Lieder und Songs können Sie mit allen Strophen direkt vom Blatt spielen und mit passenden Schlag- und Zupfmustern begleiten – und alles ohne Barré-Griffe!

136 Seiten, Spiralbindung mit Rücken,
D 855/ISBN 978-3-934958-40-1

## Kinderlieder

Sie singen gern mit Kindern? Mit Gitarre klingt's noch besser. Drei Griffe reichen völlig aus, um alle 100 Lieder in diesem Buch zu begleiten. Und schon mit zwei Griffen können Sie mehr als 70 Lieder spielen. Ob Geburtstag, Laternenzug oder Weihnachten – zu jeder Gelegenheit finden Sie hier die passenden Lieder.

124 Seiten, Spiralbindung mit Rücken,
D 853/ISBN 978-3-934958-08-1

## Lustige Lieder zur Sprachförderung

Sprachliche Ausdrucksfähigkeit ist die Schlüsselkompetenz für schulische und berufliche Erfolge. Insbesondere das Singen fördert die Sprachentwicklung in Kindergarten und Grundschule auf natürliche Weise. Diese hier enthaltenen Lieder vermitteln Sprachkompetenz mit Bewegung, Echo, Tierstimmen und viel Humor.

52 Seiten, D 856/ISBN 978-3-934958-98-2

## Weihnachtslieder

Endlich können auch weniger Geübte Advents- und Weihnachtslieder begleiten, ohne vor dem F-Griff kapitulieren zu müssen. Alle Lieder sind hier ohne einen einzigen Barré-Griff problemlos spielbar! Neben den Weihnachtslied-Klassikern wie »Stille Nacht« und »O du fröhliche« finden Sie hier auch fröhliche Winterlieder wie »Jingle Bells« und »Rudolf, das kleine Rentier«.

48 Seiten, D 854/ISBN 978-3-934958-17-3

**Michael Langer**
## Acoustic Pop Guitar

**Gitarrenschule mit 18 bekannten Popsongs**

**Band 1: Alle wichtigen Akkorde mit Begleit-Grooves**

Get Back · Wonderful Tonight · Breakfast At Tiffany's · Knockin' On Heaven's Door · What's Up · If Tomorrow Never Comes · Stand By Me · Time After Time · Hijo de la Luna · No Woman, No Cry · Ironic · I Can See Clearly Now · One Of Us · 99 Luftballons · Kiss Me · Fields Of Gold · Lady In Black · Love Is All Around

184 Seiten, Spiralbindung, D 870/ISBN 978-3-934958-12-8  mit CD

**Band 2: Einführung in die Welt des Fingerstyle**

Hey Joe · Let It Be · Angie · Both Sides Now · Hotel California · If You Could Read My Mind · What Can I Do · Teach Your Children · Don't Worry Be Happy · I Still Haven't Found What I'm Looking For · More Than Words · Games People Play · Nobody Knows You When You're Down And Out · Can't Buy Me Love · Talkin' Bout A Revolution · Every Breath You Take · Walking In Memphis · Killing Me Softly With His Song

188 Seiten, Spiralbindung, D 871/ISBN 978-3-934958-43-2  mit CD

## Acoustic Pop Guitar Songbook

**Strumming & Picking**

**Band 1:** Behind Blue Eyes · Bubbly · Wake Me Up When September Ends · Dear Mr. President · Follow Me · Fragile · Your Body Is A Wonderland · To Be With You · Sweet Home Alabama · Viva la Vida · Don't Know Why u. a.

130 Seiten, Spiralbindung, D 873/ISBN 978-3-86849-010-7  mit CD

**Band 2:** Black Velvet · Sitting, Waiting, Wishing · Nur noch kurz die Welt retten · Sunrise · Englishman In New York · You Don't Know · You Give Me Something · Waiting On The World To Change · Someone Like You · Nothing Compares 2 U · Home u. a.

130 Seiten, Spiralbindung, D 874/ISBN 978-3-86849-195-1  mit CD

## Acoustic Pop Guitar Solos

**Noten & TAB**

**Band 1** (easy/medium)
Hallelujah · Knockin' On Heaven's Door · Let It Be · Mighty Quinn · I Kissed A Girl · Smoke On The Water · Streets Of London · Wonderful Tonight · Wake Me Up When September Ends u. a.

130 Seiten, Spiralbindung, D 878/ISBN 978-3-86849-187-6  mit CD

**Band 2** (medium/advanced)
Nothing Else Matters · Wonderwall · Fireflies · You Are The Sunshine Of My Life · Rehab · Nine Million Bicycles · Ain't No Sunshine · One · Stairway To Heaven · Your Song · Always On My Mind u. a.

130 Seiten, Spiralbindung, D 879/ISBN 978-3-86849-188-3  mit CD

**Band 3** (easy/medium)
I Won't Give Up · Let Her Go · Tears In Heaven · Stay · Wrecking Ball · Just Give Me A Reason · Black Or White · Wake Me Up · Get Lucky · New Age · Lifesaver · Hero · One Of Us · Say Something u. a.

130 Seiten, Spiralbindung, D 880/ISBN 978-3-86849-270-5  mit CD